Pet
Behavior
Protocols

What to Say, What to Do, When to Refer

Pet
Behavior
Protocols

What to Say, What to Do, When to Refer

Suzanne Hetts, Ph.D.

AAHA Press
12575 W. Bayaud Avenue
Lakewood, Colorado 80228

ISBN 0-941451-74-7

This book is dedicated to my father, Charles Hetts, to my husband, Dan Estep, and to the four-footed members of my family who are no longer with me but who will live in my heart forever—Brandy, Blaze, Katie, Tipper, and Amos.

Contents

Acknowledgments

No author can take sole credit for a book, as there are always many other people who make it possible. I would first like to thank two women who are now with the Argus Center at Colorado State University: Debby Morehead, the former publications manager at AAHA, and Laurel Lagoni, MS, my friend and cofounder of Changes: The Support for People and Pets Program at the Veterinary Teaching Hospital at Colorado State University. Debby and Laurel first encouraged me to write this book, and without their initial enthusiasm, I might never have decided to undertake the project.

I also thank Anne Serrano, my editor at AAHA Press, who had the difficult task of taking over the book and who was supportive, enthusiastic, patient, encouraging, and appropriately "pushy" to see it to completion. Her suggestions and ideas resulted in a better book. I'd also like to thank Paige Garnett, DVM, and Pia Silvani for their enormously helpful comments and suggestions and for the time they devoted to reading the manuscript.

I must acknowledge all my colleagues, too numerous to mention here, who taught me so much over the years. A few in particular stand out—Peter Borchelt, Ph.D., Dan Estep, Ph.D., Wayne Hunthausen, DVM, Randy Lockwood, Ph.D., Amy Marder, VMD, Pamela Reid, Ph.D., Victoria Voith, DVM, Ph.D., John Wright, Ph.D., and my major professor from graduate school, Philip Lehner, Ph.D. The volunteers who worked with me on the behavior help line I initiated at the Denver Dumb Friends League should also be included in this list. It wouldn't be possible to name all the clients and their animals I have seen over the years from whom I have learned so much and who made me realize how shamefully little we know about the behavior of two species of animals that have been integral parts of human society for thousands of years. I am also indebted to Dr. Marder and Dr. Bergman for the chapter on drug therapy and for their cooperation in meeting some very difficult deadlines.

Lastly, without the support and assistance of my husband, Dan Estep, the book would simply not have been written. He put some of his own projects on hold and shouldered extra responsibilities in both our personal and professional lives so that I could have the time to write. He was also available to offer helpful suggestions, and he was always willing to discuss conceptual issues with me and provide emotional support during my low points. His unselfish contribution to this book is a treasured gift.

Suzanne Hetts

About the Authors

Suzanne Hetts holds a Ph.D. in zoology with a specialization in animal behavior from Colorado State University (CSU), Fort Collins, Colorado. She is certified by the Animal Behavior Society as an applied animal behaviorist. Since 1982, Dr. Hetts has consulted with pet owners, veterinarians, animal care and control professionals, and attorneys regarding animal behavior problems through her private practice, Animal Behavior Associates, Inc., based in suburban Denver and through the Veterinary Teaching Hospital (VTH) at CSU and the Denver Dumb Friends League, a humane society. Dr. Hetts is a frequent speaker at many national humane, animal control, and veterinary conferences. She cofounded the pet loss counseling program at CSU's VTH, is an American Kennel Club obedience judge emeritus, and is a consultant to Delta Society's Service Dog Education System. In addition, Dr. Hetts is past chair of the Animal Behavior Society's Board of Professional Certification, a member of the Association of Pet Dog Trainers board of directors, and the scientific director of the American Humane Association's Humane Dog Training Project.

Amy Marder, VMD, coauthor of chapter 18, is vice president of behavior medicine at the American Society for the Prevention of Cruelty to Animals. She also serves as clinical assistant professor at Tufts University School of Veterinary Medicine, Boston. A published author and frequent lecturer to both veterinary and lay audiences, Dr. Marder is a past president of the American Veterinary Society of Animal Behavior.

Laurie Bergman, VMD, coauthor of chapter 18, worked for five years (until 1998) in private practice attending small animals and exotics. At the time this book was written, she was completing a residency in veterinary behavior with Dr. Marder.

CHAPTER 1

Intervening Effectively and Appropriately in Behavior Cases: Professional Roles, Limits, and Choices

Anyone who works with animals in a professional setting has been asked about resolving problem behaviors. Clients may say:

"I just have a quick question. My cat has started peeing on the carpet, and I want to know what I should do to break her of this habit."

"My dog just doesn't get it. He can come right in from outside and lift his leg on the couch. My husband says if he does it one more time, we'll have to get rid of him. I need to fix this right away!"

"I have tried everything to get my dog to stop destroying my house when I'm gone. I know he's mad at me about something, but I don't know what to do. You're my last resort."

You care about animals and their people, so these kinds of questions have a way of drawing you in. You want to "fix it" so that the animal isn't given away, mistreated, or even euthanized, and you want to help the frustrated and sometimes desperate owner. It also makes good business sense to be able to assist your clients with such problems. Consequently, you may be tempted to jump right in with suggestions. However, don't let your good intentions get the better of you. Wanting to help is not the same thing as being prepared to help.

BEHAVIOR PROBLEMS AND THE SCIENCE OF ANIMAL BEHAVIOR

Many people believe that changing a pet's behavior is just a matter of common sense—that no special scientific knowledge is needed; that no special skills are required; that anybody who is an experienced pet owner or well qualified in another animal-related field automatically knows how to successfully resolve behavior problems. Until the 1970s, this statement might have reflected the state of the art in the field. What was known scientifically about animal behavior was not regularly applied to behavior problems in companion animals prior to that time. Now, however, applied animal behavior is considered a defined field, associated with a growing body of knowledge, scientific literature, research, and techniques. You must be familiar with this information if you are going to help pet owners resolve behavior problems. Attempting to do so without this knowledge can have deleterious side effects, some of which are discussed in later chapters.

Think of it this way: You wouldn't expect someone who is not professionally trained in *your* field to have the specialized knowledge that you possess. You wouldn't expect a nonveterinarian to understand how the liver works, for instance, nor would you expect an adoption counselor in an animal shelter to know how to groom an Irish setter for the showring. In a similar vein, then, if you are not academically trained in the science of animal behavior, you cannot expect to possess the knowledge of someone who is. This doesn't mean that you can't be of help with behavioral questions, anymore than it means I can't give my dog a pill or cut his toenails because I am not a veterinarian. What it does mean is that if behavior is not your primary field, you will need to set some professional limits for yourself, rather than tackling everything a behavior specialist does. This subject is discussed later in the chapter.

Animal behavior as it applies to companion animals is referred to in a variety of ways. In the veterinary world, it is usually referred to as *behavioral medicine* or *clinical animal behavior*. In the behavior world, it is referred to as *applied animal behavior*. The field can be subdivided into different areas based on type of animal (zoo animals, animals in research facilities, food animals, etc.). This book focuses only on two species of companion animals—dogs and cats.

THE IMPORTANCE OF HAVING A PLAN

Taking a scientific approach (veterinarians might prefer the term *diagnostic approach*) to problem solving is much different from offering advice or "tips." With a scientific or diagnostic approach, a plan of action is an intrinsic part of the process. Problems are worked with in stepwise fashion, using a protocol. By contrast, giving advice or tips is a "try this, try that" approach. It is not a scientific approach because the advice isn't based on an understanding of why the animal is doing what he's doing, because the tips may be inconsistent with each other, and because there is no systematic way of knowing how each tip actually affects the animal's behavior.

If you are a veterinarian, you wouldn't begin a surgical procedure or a medical treatment without having a good rationale for doing so. You'd go through your list of "rule-outs" to arrive at a diagnosis, or at least a tentative one, on which your treatment plan would be based. You wouldn't begin a surgical procedure haphazardly ("Let's try cutting here and see what happens!") or randomly devise a medical treatment ("I'm not sure which drug to give, so let's try a combination!").

Even animal-related fields that are much less scientific than animal behavior have plans or protocols. A groomer has a plan or procedure for trimming an Irish setter. An animal shelter has an adoption protocol. Dog trainers have lesson plans for obedience classes. To work with behavior cases, you, too, must have a plan and be armed with the knowledge and experience to implement it.

Having a plan helps you decide what your role should be in behavior cases. It is not realistic to expect that you will have sufficient time, knowledge, interest, or experience to take on every behavior case that comes your way. Even professional behaviorists refer cases to professionals in other fields: A dog who is jumping up on people or won't come when called might be referred to a dog trainer; a dog with a separation anxiety problem might be referred for doggie day care or to a veterinarian for medication; and a cat not using the litterbox reliably might be referred to a veterinarian for a medical evaluation.

This book provides you with a plan, what I've termed a *protocol*, that will allow you to respond to behavior problems and questions in a systematic way. By using this approach, you will aid your client, appear very well informed, and avoid getting in over your head. At each step of the protocol, you will be able to evaluate what role you should play and whether you should continue problem solving, assume a different role, or refer the case. The protocol is a framework from which to work: *It is not a "cookbook" approach to problem solving,* nor will it provide you with all the knowledge needed to resolve every behavior problem.

Your role might not always be that of the problem solver, and by using the protocol, you'll learn ways in which you can be helpful when you are not equipped to solve a given problem yourself. For example, you might assume the role of *educator,* informing owners about what *not* to do (which is sometimes just as important, if not more so). You'll also learn how to serve as a *resource and referral guide,* locating resource people in your community to whom you can refer your clients, as well as how to identify the ones you may want to avoid.

The first three chapters present an overview of problem solving and your roles, communication and "people skills" that are useful in problem solving, and basic animal learning theory. Chapters 4 and 5 focus on problem prevention and contain four principles that you will not find in any other source. Chapter 6 explains the problem-solving protocol that is unique to this book and designed to help you work with behavior problems one step at a time, defining your role as you go. It is used in chapters 7 through 16, each of which covers a specific dog or cat behavior problem. Chapter 17 is a discussion of the difficult topic of euthanasia and behavior problems. Chapter 18, contributed by Amy Marder, VMD, and Laurie Bergman, VMD, covers the fledgling field of psychotropic medication for problem behaviors. It is my hope that the organization of the material and the diversity of topics presented will make this book both an on-the-spot reference guide and a personal development tool for those who want to increase their knowledge of animal behavior.

THE ROLE OF THE BEHAVIOR CONSULTANT—IS IT FOR YOU?

When I went on my first in-home behavior consultation in the early 1980s, I was terrified. A client had invited me into her home, was paying me good money (albeit not much), and was expecting me to have the answers for her dog's behavior problem. I was there as the expert, the one who knew what to do.

Although I had been around dogs all my life, had been active in obedience training for some 6 years at that time, and was enrolled in a doctoral program in animal behavior, I felt completely overwhelmed. I questioned my sanity for ever thinking I had the knowledge and skills to help this woman and her dog. In fact, I was so nervous I couldn't concentrate sufficiently to analyze the information she was giving me. It was very important to me to help this woman and her pet, but I felt I might be in over my head. What if I couldn't succeed? What if I made things worse? What if she'd already tried all the things I was going to suggest?

I suspect that anyone who works with people and their pets in a professional setting has had similar reactions when asked about behavior problems. This is especially true for those whose primary field or training is not in the science of animal behavior. Actually, being nervous about attempting to resolve a pet's behavior problem is a reasonable response because problem behaviors can, quite literally, be killers. Millions of dogs, cats, and other companion animals are euthanized every year in veterinary clinics and animal shelters because of behavior problems. One of the reasons that these problems are killers is that pet owners too often do not receive good information about how to resolve them.

Although some owners just don't make the necessary commitment to their pets, most are earnestly looking for effective help. These owners may say, "We are at the end of our rope,"

"We're at our wit's end," or "We've tried everything." Often, though, they haven't tried the *right* thing because no one they've turned to has properly diagnosed the problem and devised a relevant, humane, and effective behavior modification plan. Owners who are told to try this and try that become increasingly frustrated when things don't improve, and ultimately, they may give up on their pets. You do not want to be yet another person who takes on the role of problem solver without being adequately prepared.

Behavior problems and the process of resolving them must be taken seriously. As with medical problems, the behavior problem must be diagnosed before making treatment recommendations. Furthermore, just as surgical and medical treatments would not be attempted without a basic knowledge of physiology and anatomy, behavior modification should not be undertaken without a knowledge of ethology and animal learning. Offering advice, trying quick fixes, basing recommendations on unscientific or insufficient information, and generally taking on more than you can handle can backfire in a number of ways.

Backfire One: The Owner Becomes Increasingly Frustrated

Behavior problems in and of themselves are frustrating. Excessive barking, elimination outside the litterbox, and other inappropriate animal behaviors can cause an otherwise caring pet owner to develop a very short fuse. If, in good faith, such an owner follows recommendations she's been given and the behavior doesn't improve, the fuse may ignite. Take this example: An owner of a cat who was urinating around the house was advised to confine her pet in a large crate (equipped with litterbox, food, and water) for a month. The cat of course used the box reliably while confined. On being released from confinement, however, he walked over to the other side of the room and urinated on the carpet. The owner was livid at both the veterinarian who made the recommendation and the cat, who was promptly surrendered to an animal shelter. The cat was probably none too happy either, having been in a crate for a month. In the end, nothing positive had been accomplished.

Backfire Two: Your Credibility Is Negatively Affected

If the client discovers from other sources that the information you provided was not accurate, appropriate, or helpful, he or she may well lose faith in you and your business in general. Consider this example: A dog was barking excessively when left home alone. The owner was told by a staff member at an animal shelter to sneak back and throw a can of coins at the dog to reprimand him for the barking. When the behavior was later diagnosed as a separation anxiety problem and the owner learned that the can-throwing approach would probably exacerbate the problem and increase the dog's anxiety, she discontinued her monthly contribution to the animal sheltering agency.

Backfire Three: You Become Liable for Injuries

If you advise a pet owner to handle his or her pet in a way that elicits an aggressive response from the animal, you may be legally liable for injuries that result. For instance, one owner was advised by a dog trainer to give her dog a scruff shake when he did not obey her commands. When her dog failed to get off the bed when told to get down, she grabbed him by the neck as instructed and he promptly bit off her finger. The owner sued the trainer, and the case was settled out of court in the owner's favor.

Backfire Four: The Problem Gets Worse

One example is illustrative: A playful kitten was pouncing on her owner's ankles whenever he sat in a chair. He was told to grab the kitten by the scruff of her neck, throw her into a room by herself, and leave her there for several hours. Unfortunately, the kitten did not learn to stop pouncing on her owner's ankles. Instead, she learned that whenever her owner reached for her, she needed to defend herself, and she began to hiss, scratch, and bite every time he tried to touch her. Thus, the problem escalated from simple play-motivated aggression, which might well have resolved itself over time, to a much more difficult, defensive aggressive behavior problem.

Self-Assessment

Given the preceding examples, you may be thinking that it's simply not worth it to intervene in *any* behavior case. Although that would be an overreaction, the fundamental message here is that trying to problem solve without being prepared to do so often has unpleasant and unfortunate consequences for you, the pet owner, and the animal alike. Working with behavior problems requires a professional, well-planned, and knowledgeable approach. The pet's life and your continued relationship with the owner may both be at stake.

How can you know if you are prepared to problem solve in a particular case? First, check your knowledge of ethology and animal learning. Are you equipped to arrive at a behavioral diagnosis and determine the cause for a specific behavior? Will your recommendations merely be a collection of things you've heard from others or read here and there or a well-reasoned plan whose components are relevant to the problem and to each other? Ask yourself the questions in Box 1.1. If you can't answer yes to most of them, you may want to choose an alternative role for yourself and refer the case to a behavior specialist.

Box 1.1 Self-evaluation questions for choosing a problem-solving role

Question	Case Example
Can I take a behavioral history about this problem? Do I know what questions to ask to determine the type of problem that is causing the behavioral symptom?	Excessive barking can be caused by separation anxiety or territorial behavior (among other things). Can I obtain a behavioral history that will distinguish between these two problems?
If understanding the development and function of a particular behavior is important to resolving a behavior problem, do I have this knowledge?	The procedures used to encourage dogs and cats to eliminate in acceptable locations (usually outdoors and in litterboxes, respectively) are not interchangeable. This is partly due to interspecies differences in behavior development and in the factors that influence location preferences. Do I understand what these differences are and why they are important?

(Box continues)

Will my recommendations for resolving a behavior problem address the specific type of problem rather than merely treat the symptom? If not, is there a rationale that makes the symptomatic approach appropriate?

Constructing a higher fence to resolve an escaping problem is a symptomatic treatment. The reason for escaping is ignored. If the higher fence keeps the dog in the yard without additional problems, this approach may be sufficient. However, if the escaping is motivated by separation anxiety, for instance, other symptoms of the problem are likely to be seen. Can I determine when a symptomatic approach is appropriate and when it is not?

Am I familiar with a variety of problem-resolution methods, only a few of which are based on aversive techniques?

One approach to destructive chewing is to give off-limit items an unpleasant taste. Am I familiar not only with other ways of discouraging unacceptable chewing but also with even more ways to *promote* acceptable chewing behavior?

Do I have the time to complete all the components of a behavior case, including analysis (diagnosis), treatment (devising and explaining a plan), and follow-up?

Obtaining a history and explaining a treatment plan to an owner may require several hours (certainly more than 10 or 15 minutes), and follow-up contacts can occur over several months. Can I realistically expect to have sufficient time to handle the case properly?

ALTERNATIVE ROLES IN BEHAVIOR CASES

Even if you decide that you are not prepared to be involved in problem solving in a particular case, keep in mind that you don't have to bow out of the picture entirely. There are numerous services you can provide and different roles you can play that will be helpful to your client and his or her pet. Everyone will benefit if you choose another role in which you can perform well rather than attempting to muddle through in a role that doesn't take advantage of the skills and knowledge you have to offer.

The Role of Educator

Most likely, you are already comfortable in the role of the educator because you fulfill this role every day in your own area of specialization. Veterinarians educate pet owners about preventative health care. Technicians talk to clients about proper nutrition. Dog trainers teach owners the value of obedience training. Animal care and control professionals educate people about animal ordinances and how to choose a new pet. In sum, even though your primary field may not be animal behavior, you probably already do a good deal of educating on this and other subjects.

The four most common and most critical areas in which you can educate owners are:

- What normal behavior is and what influences it
- Causes of behavior problems
- What *not* to do to resolve a problem
- Responsible pet ownership

Normal behavior. Educating pet owners about animal behavior requires some degree of familiarity with the scientific behavioral literature. Most owners do not have access to this literature, and many are not even aware that it exists. Therefore, one vital role for you is to teach owners about the behavior of their pets using ethological, scientific information as opposed to an anthropomorphic, anecdotal approach. Now is a good time to check your skills in this area. Take the pop quiz in Box 1.2 to assess your ability to recognize some anthropomorphic misinterpretations of animal behavior that are very widespread. Certain questions pertain to fairly technical areas of animal behavior and problem resolution; you'll learn more about some of these topics in this book, and you may also need to do further reading from the references given at the end of each chapter and the additional readings listed at the end of the book. Don't assume that because you've worked with animals for many years you know everything about their behavior. The field of applied animal behavior is advancing rapidly, and all professionals need to keep current by reading the latest literature.

Box 1.2 Common misinterpretations of animal behavior, inappropiate problem-resolution techniques, and chapters in which they are discussed

Statement	Reference Location
Dogs look guilty when they know they've done something wrong.	False, chapters 3, 7, and 8
Pets will misbehave out of spite or to "get back at" their owners.	False, chapters 3, 7, 8, 13, and 14
Pets can be jealous of another pet or human family member.	False, chapters 12 and 15
Confining a dog to a crate or other small area when he can't be watched is the best way to resolve a housesoiling problem.	False, chapter 7
Showing the pet "evidence" of what he did wrong (e.g., a torn pillow, scratched draperies, urine on the floor) is a good way to discipline the animal, even if you don't catch him misbehaving.	False, chapters 3, 7, 8, 13, and 14
A good way to help an animal get over a fear is to take him to the thing that he fears (even if he doesn't want to go) and show him there is nothing to be afraid of.	False, chapters 11 and 16

Causes of problems. Understanding their pets' behaviors from an ethological as opposed to an anthropomorphic perspective helps some owners feel differently about their animals. Consider one example: An ethological interpretation of destructive behavior that occurs only when a dog is left alone might be separation anxiety; an anthropomorphic one might hold that the dog is angry about being left alone and is being destructive out of spite or to "get back" at his owner. These diverse interpretations can have a significant influence on how that owner perceives the pet and the problem and ultimately may affect his decision on keeping the pet and trying to resolve the problem.

What not to do. It is also important to discuss popular problem-solving techniques that should be avoided because of their potential to exacerbate problems. It is surprising how many antiquated ideas about animal behavior are still widely held. For example, rubbing a dog or cat's nose in its feces and other attempts at punishment after the fact are still recommended by some as an acceptable part of housetraining, crates are recommended for separation anxiety problems, and roll-overs and scruff shakes are suggested for aggression problems. If you can prevent an owner from using these and other inappropriate techniques by educating them, you have performed a valuable service.

Responsible pet ownership. It is surprising how many people still think that a female dog or cat needs to have a litter before being spayed or that it is cruel to keep a cat indoors at all times. Workers at animal shelters hear many statements along these lines every day, perhaps even more often than veterinarians do. Helping owners to understand that many of these long-held beliefs have no basis in fact can not only improve and lengthen the lives of their animals but also decrease animal-related problems in the community at large.

The Role of Referral and Resource Guide

Referral guide. Making an appropriate referral is one of the most important services you can provide your clients. Unfortunately, however, the process of referring behavior cases is often not taken seriously. Consider the way in which behavior referrals are made at your facility, and ask yourself the following questions:

1. If you work in a veterinary clinic, who makes the decision to refer a case to a medical or surgical specialist? Which staff members refer clients to behaviorists?
2. What are clients told to expect from their visit with a medical or surgical specialist? What are they told to expect from a behavioral referral?
3. Whatever your field, what would you want prospective clients to expect when they are referred to *you?*
4. How is a particular specialist or referral resource chosen as the one your facility uses?
5. How do you help owners decide between behavior consulting or obedience classes?

The following sections address the issues and concerns underlying each of these questions.

1. *If you work in a veterinary clinic, who makes the decision to refer a case to a medical, surgical, or behavioral specialist?* Obviously, the veterinarian decides when to refer a medical or surgical case to the appropriate specialist, after thoroughly evaluating or treating the animal. In contrast, it is

often a receptionist or technician who refers a pet owner to a behavior specialist. In fact, it is not uncommon for behavior cases to be referred without the animal being seen by a veterinarian at all. This is a potential problem. Some experiences from my own behavior consulting practice are illuminating in this regard:

- A young, intact male Siberian husky was referred to me after he suddenly began snapping when petted on the head. Although this behavior might have indicated dominance aggression, investigation revealed that the aggression was actually caused by pain from an abscessed tooth, which was irritated as the dog's head was jostled when he was petted.
- A cat who had previously been eliminating outside the litterbox because of a litter-aversion problem began to housesoil again, approximately 1 year later. The recurrence of the problem coincided with the birth of the owner's first child. Although we might assume the problem was influenced by the arrival of the new baby, examination by a veterinarian revealed the presence of a urinary tract infection.
- An 8-month-old male cat was referred for a spraying problem. Prior to referring the case, the receptionist at the veterinary clinic had not determined that the kitten was still intact.

Veterinarians must establish some clear guidelines with their staff as to when it is and is not acceptable for an animal to be referred for behavior consulting without first being seen at the clinic. Although it could be debated whether a dog who is barking excessively needs a physical examination, it should not be debatable whether a housesoiling or aggressive pet needs a physical examination (and maybe more).

If you are not in the veterinary field but are in a position to refer owners to behavior specialists, you should try to impress on them the importance of evaluating medical reasons for behavior problems, especially in the cases of housesoiling and aggression. One tactic is to tell owners that if they pursue behavior consulting without first evaluating their pet's medical status, they could be wasting their time and money. Another option is to say that if this were your pet, you would see a veterinarian before assuming the problem did not have a medical cause. In fact, some behavior specialists will only take on a new case on referral from a veterinarian, so if you refer the case without veterinary input, the specialist may send the client and pet back to the veterinarian.

2. *What are clients told to expect from their visit with a medical or surgical specialist? What are they told to expect from a behavioral referral?* If you are a veterinarian, you probably offer your clients some idea of what to expect from an appointment with a medical or surgical specialist. Giving clients a reasonable set of expectations prepares them for the experience, and it may help them to follow through with the appointment. Moreover, it conveys a sense of professional respect for the specialist.

Unfortunately, pet owners looking for a behavior referral are often told something like "Call this number and see if they can help you" or "These people work with behavior problems—they may be able to give you some tips or advice." If you make a behavior referral in this way, you give your clients the unreasonable expectation that their pet's problem may be resolved by a free, brief phone call. Beyond that, you give the impression that you don't take a referral for a behavior problem seriously, and if *you* don't, why should they? Most pet owners have little understanding of what a behavior consultation involves, so the impression you give them will often be their first impression. If they think they are being referred for some informal, free tips, it will be much harder for them to accept that they are consulting with someone who has special knowledge and skills and that resolving their pet's problem will require a formal consulting appointment for which a fee will be charged. In sum, giving owners accurate expectations will result in fewer disappointed or angry clients and communicate your professional respect for the specialist.

3. *Whatever your field, what would you want prospective clients to expect when they are referred to you?* Think about referrals from the reverse perspective. How would you want someone to refer a pet owner to you for the services you provide? Would you be satisfied if the owner was told:

> "Call this veterinarian—he'll give you free medical advice over the phone."
> "Call this animal shelter—you can run in and adopt any pet you want for free, no questions asked."
> "Call this trainer—she'll give you six obedience lessons in one session and won't charge you anything."

If you think that referring a client to a behavior specialist is worthwhile and that the client and the pet can be helped by this referral, then you should make the referral in a way that reflects these attitudes.

4. *How is a particular specialist or referral resource chosen as the one your facility uses?* In your clients' eyes, the people to whom you refer them are extensions of your facility. In making a referral, you are essentially saying, "We're unable to assist you with this problem, but here are the people we trust to help you." Consequently, your clients' experiences with a referral, good and bad, will reflect on you and your facility. In the behavior field particularly, it is up to you to evaluate the credentials and competence of the people to whom you refer clients.

If you are referring a client to a behaviorist, keep in mind that anyone can use the professional titles of animal behaviorist, behavior consultant, dog behaviorist, cat behaviorist, etc., regardless of his or her background and training. The Animal Behavior Society (ABS) professionally certifies applied animal behaviorists who meet its criteria, and the American College of Veterinary Behaviorists certifies veterinarians as specialists in behavior. Interestingly, veterinarians cannot call themselves specialists unless they are board certified, but nonveterinarians are free to use the title "behavior specialist" if they want to. Many people with a wide variety of backgrounds who are not certified offer behavior consulting services, including many dog trainers. Although there are no widely accepted professional certification or training programs for dog trainers, the National Association of Dog Obedience Instructors (NADOI) does endorse its member trainers. In addition, a multidisciplinary project is under way to establish a code, or guidelines, for humane dog training (see Box 1.3).

Box 1.3 Guidelines for humane dog training

Considering the wide variety of sensitive and complex tasks that dogs can be trained to perform, as well as the number of dogs who are taken to obedience classes, it is quite astonishing that there are no widely accepted professional standards, ethical guidelines, training, or certification programs for people interested in becoming dog trainers; nor is there any licensure required for dog trainers. In March 1998, to address these issues and the problem of abusive training techniques, the American Humane Association (AHA) convened a task force composed of dog trainers, veterinarians, veterinary and applied animal behaviorists, and animal care and control professionals. One of the goals identified by the

(Box continues)

task force was to establish guidelines for humane dog training. AHA is continuing to serve as coordinator of this effort, now funded by Delta Society. In November 1998, over 40 professionals in these same fields met to develop a first draft of these guidelines, which will be reviewed and contributed to by many individuals and national organizations. After review and revision, the goal is to have these guidelines accepted, by the year 2000, by all national organizations with a stake in humane dog training. The task force also developed a written definition of humane dog training, which follows:

"Humane dog training enhances the lifelong relationship between people and dogs by:

- Eliciting and/or rewarding desired behaviors,
- Rarely using punishment (always striving toward its elimination), and
- Never causing harm."

The field of dog training and companion animal behavior is currently in a state of transition. Physically forceful procedures such as strong leash and collar corrections, "alpha rolling," and other aversive methods that have been the mainstay of traditional dog training are being replaced by techniques that are better grounded in animal learning and ethology. As a result, methods that are designed to minimize or avoid aversive stimuli, especially those that cause pain, and that focus on the use of pleasant stimuli to both elicit and reinforce behavior are becoming more prevalent. Unfortunately, too many animals (dogs and horses, in particular) are subjected to abuse in the name of training. Here are some examples:

- One dog was blinded by a lack of oxygen to the brain, caused by being strung up (lifted off the floor by a leash and choke chain) and then repeatedly helicoptered (swung around) by a dog trainer; the trainer was later acquitted on charges of cruelty to animals[1].
- An owner whose dog was biting people was told by her veterinarian to hit the dog across the muzzle with a hard rubber hose as forcefully as she could whenever the dog tried to bite (personal communication).
- A trainer was stringing up puppies and then slamming them to the pavement until they almost lost consciousness. When asked to stop by an observer, the trainer assaulted the bystander[2].

How would you feel if you had made a referral to one of these individuals? What effect would such a referral have on your facility's reputation? It is vital that you personally evaluate the trainers or behaviorists to whom you will be referring your clients. Don't start referring clients to people just because they come to your office and give you business cards; instead, sit in on their obedience classes or their behavior consulting sessions. If a trainer or behaviorist won't let you do so, find someone else. Ask if you can drop in unannounced. Ask to see the specialist's résumé and look at the kind of education the individual has in ethology and animal learning. Look for participation (not just membership) in relevant professional organizations, such as the ABS, the American Veterinary Society of Animal Behavior (AVSAB), the NADOI, or the Association of Pet Dog Trainers (APDT doesn't certify its members, but it does promote use of positive reinforcement and minimizing use of aversives in dog training). Ask for references from past clients or referral sources. Interview the trainer or behaviorist regarding his or her methods and philosophies. Just because someone says they use positive reinforcement in training doesn't mean they are not also using aversive procedures inappropriately. A trainer may tell you, "I use positive reinforcement. I hang him up if he tries to bite, and then I'll reward him when I let him down." Use the guidelines in Box 1.4 as a beginning point for finding humane and effective behaviorists and trainers to whom you can refer your clients.

5. *How do you help owners decide between behavior consulting or obedience classes?* Another part of being a referral guide involves helping the owner decide whether her pet needs obedience classes or individual behavior consulting. Because many dog trainers offer behavioral consultations and animal behaviorists may offer obedience classes, it is important to decide what *type* of service the client requires for her pet before choosing the service provider. Good obedience classes and even private lessons are one way for the owner to better control his dog, and a dog who is jumping up, not coming when called, door dashing, etc., is a good candidate for obedience lessons. However, teaching a dog commands through obedience lessons will not solve many behavior problems. Separation anxiety problems, fear-related problems, housesoiling, and similar behaviors will not be helped by obedience classes.

Box 1.4 Guidelines for selecting an obedience trainer or behavior consultant

Finding and Working with an Obedience Trainer*

1. Look for a trainer who relies on positive reinforcement for the right response rather than punishing the wrong response.

2. Observe an obedience class without your dog. Are the dogs and people having a good time? Talk with a few participants to see if they are comfortable with the trainer's methods. If you are not allowed to sit in, don't enroll in that class.

3. Don't allow a trainer to work your dog unless he first tells you exactly what he plans to do.

4. Don't be afraid to tell a trainer to stop if she is doing something to your dog that you don't like.

5. Don't let a trainer (or anyone else, for that matter) intimidate, bully, or shame you into doing something that you believe is not in your dog's best interest.

6. Avoid a trainer who offers guarantees for specific results. Such a trainer either ignores or fails to understand the complexity of animal behavior.

7. Avoid a trainer who objects to using food as a training reward. Food is an acceptable positive reinforcement training tool.

(Box continues)

8. Avoid a trainer who uses *only* choke chains. Head collars are humane alternatives to choke chains and pinch collars.

9. Look for a trainer who treats both people and dogs with respect, rather than with an "I'm the boss" attitude.

Finding and Working with a Behavior Consultant

1. Ask about the consultant's academic training in the science of animal behavior, as well as his hands-on experience.

2. Ask about the consultant's certification—it indicates that the individual has met strict requirements in terms of education, experience, and professional ethics.

3. Look for a consultant who recognizes the importance of *you* working through the problem with your pet rather than sending him somewhere to be "fixed."

4. Ask if the consultant is an active member of any professional organizations. Membership suggests communication with colleagues and an interest in keeping current on new information.

5. Ask for professional references (e.g., from former clients, colleagues, and veterinarians who refer cases).

6. Assess whether the consultant is knowledgeable about positive reinforcement methods, behavior modification techniques such as counterconditioning and desensitization, and how to use food and humane products (such as head collars) in her work.

7. Look for a consultant who will treat you with respect and is not abrupt or abrasive.

8. Avoid a consultant who guarantees problem resolution. Animals are complex beings, and no one knows everything there is to know about them.

9. Avoid quick fixes and any consultant who promotes them. This approach does not do justice to you or your pet.

10. Beware of a consultant who suggests the use of drugs as the first or only solution for a problem. Drug therapy is best used as part of a complete plan. (Only veterinarians can prescribe drugs.)

*Items in this list are modified from those developed by S. Hetts, appearing in C. Rosenthal, 1996, Beware the dog trainer! *Advocate* 14 (2/3):16–7. Reprinted by permission of American Humane Association.

An obedience class can sometimes be used as a setting in which to expose a dog to other people and animals if this is a part of the behavior modification plan. However, this should be done under the direction of the behavior consultant. Most behavior problems are influenced by the characteristics of the dog, the dog's environment, and the owner's behavior, so in-kennel (board and train) services are not recommended: They ignore two of the three factors that are important in causing and resolving problems.

Of course, cats do not benefit from obedience classes (as much as we might wish they would!), so for cat behavior problems, a behavior consultant is the referral of choice (assuming the cat has already been evaluated by a veterinarian).

Resource guide. A plethora of resource materials about companion animals can be found on the shelves of any bookstore, video store, or pet store. New pet-related products, ranging from toys to odor neutralizers, are coming on the market all the time, and owners no doubt ask your opinion about the myriad products available today. Are you prepared to give them accurate feedback? As a resource guide, you can review, test, and critique some of these materials and products for your clients and provide them with accurate information and a list of resources that are effective. Some suppliers are happy to give free samples to animal professionals for just this purpose. Pet owners don't have a way to evaluate all these products or know which to buy for what circumstances. Guiding them in the right direction not only helps them pick "the right tool for the job" but also may save them money (which they might later spend at your business!). Examples of good products are given throughout this book and in the product appendix at the end of the book.

The Role of Facilitator

The facilitator makes it easier for things to happen and goals to be accomplished, and the role of the facilitator overlays all the other roles discussed thus far. In fact, there are facilitator components to any role you fulfill. As a problem solver, you may recommend that a client obtain certain products, such as a head collar; as a facilitator, you can sell head collars at your facility so the client doesn't have to take the time to find one. In your role as an educator, you may need to go into a detailed explanation about why punishing an animal long after a problem behavior has occurred will not work; as a facilitator, you can give the client a handout on the subject to help her gain a better understanding of what you are talking about. As a referral guide, you have decided to whom you will refer a client for behavior consulting and obedience training; as a facilitator, you should have business cards or brochures from these individuals available at your facility (in some cases, you could even make the call to schedule an appointment or reserve a place in a class for your client and his pet). Finally, if you have found a number of helpful products through your role as resource guide, carry those products at your facility or have a list of sources where they can be obtained.

SUMMARY

The goals of this chapter were (1) to help you see the advantages of working with behavior cases in a scientific, systematic way, using a protocol, (2) to help you decide when it is appropriate for you to assume a problem-solving role, (3) to review the disadvantages of choosing a problem-solving role without adequate preparation, and (4) to point out alternative ways in which you can assist clients whose animals are showing problem behavior. As you digest the material in this chapter and as you read the rest of the book, consider the following questions:

- Have you decided when it is and is not appropriate for you to act as a problem solver? What criteria did you use to make these decisions?
- If you want to assume a more active role in problem solving, what steps should you take to prepare yourself?
- Have you talked with your staff members about their role in problem solving and in making referrals?
- Have you identified topic areas in which you need to update your knowledge to better prepare yourself in your role as educator or resource guide? Have you found the reference materials that you will need to review to do so?
- What steps should you take to establish referral resources for behavior cases? Do you need to more thoroughly evaluate the people you are currently using?
- Should you review the pet-related products you are now selling? If you don't carry such products, are there some that you should be offering to clients?
- What procedures can you follow to make it easy for your clients to find and use the best behavior services possible, whether at your facility or elsewhere?

It may be a good idea to discuss these questions with your staff or other people who work at your facility. You may not be able to answer all the questions now. Refer to them repeatedly as you read the book. Addressing these questions is the first step in developing your own plan for working with behavior cases.

REFERENCES

1. Rosenthal, C. 1996. Beware the dog trainer! *Advocate* 14 (2/3):16–7.

2. D'amico, M. 1997. How do you stop abusive dog trainers? *Dog Fancy* 28 (9):6.

CHAPTER 2

Communication Skills

Talking to people about their pets' behavior problems can be challenging. During such a conversation, strong emotions can be triggered for you or the client. If a call about behavior catches you at the wrong moment, you may not have sufficient time to respond to the client's questions without interruption, and you may not be able to meet her expectations for the conversation. In turn, though you want to be helpful, you may become angry, frustrated, or defensive. Over time, if you have enough unpleasant experiences with behavior cases, you may come to dread them rather than look forward to them. Yet whether you now view behavior cases in a positive or a negative light, communication skills and a few basic techniques will help you handle them more effectively and with less stress for both you and the client.

What is your first thought when a pet owner asks you about a behavior problem? Some common negative reactions among animal professionals include:

> "Oh, no, here's another one of those questions I don't know how to answer."
> "Another owner who doesn't know anything!"
> "I don't have time for this right now."
> "Somebody else looking for free advice!"

How you feel about behavior calls will influence your response to them. If an owner gets the impression that you can't be bothered or aren't interested, he will either adopt a similar attitude or become angry and frustrated with you and find someone more willing to help him. If the first attitude prevails, the animal may lose its home or its life; if the second attitude prevails, you may lose a client or customer.

The reactions listed earlier are understandable, and you are certainly entitled to them. However, they aren't very productive in terms of helping pet owners. If that is your goal, as I'm sure it is, certain skills can help you get past those first negative thoughts.

WHY CONVERSATIONS ON BEHAVIOR PROBLEMS ARE STRESSFUL

Talking about behavior problems can be stressful for a number of reasons, some of which apply to other client contacts, as well.

Differing Expectations

The expectations that you and the owner bring to the conversation may differ. An owner often wants a quick fix for her pet's problem. This may be evident when she begins the discussion with a phrase such as, "I just need some tips" or "I just have a quick question." You, however, know that behavior problems rarely have simple solutions and that, sooner or later, the owner is going to need to invest some time (and most likely money) in resolving the problem. Frequently, the owner who wants an easy, immediate, "magic bullet" solution is going to be frustrated or disappointed when it isn't available, and you may well be the recipient of her negative emotions. You, in turn, may become frustrated because the owner isn't open to what you have to say.

Differences in Standards of Care

Your beliefs about what the owner should do may be different from what the owner can or wants to do. Each of us has our own concept of what the standard of care for a pet should be. Usually, those of us in animal-related professions have much higher standards than the average pet owner. Consequently, when an owner seems uninterested in working with a problem or reluctant to do things you feel could easily be done, you may begin to question his commitment to the pet. If your personal standards aren't met, you may become judgmental and angry, which is likely to put the owner on the defensive.

Sometimes, it works the other way around: The owner may be very committed to his pet and to working with the problem, but you feel that efforts to resolve the specific behavior or work with the pet are unlikely to be successful. (A case involving a dangerously aggressive dog would be an apt example.) If you tell this to the owner at the outset, however, he will likely feel that you are trivializing the importance of the animal and his attachment to it.

Emotional Blackmail

The owner may attempt, consciously or unconsciously, to use emotional blackmail to get you to give him what he wants or make you responsible for the pet. When this is going on, the owner will often say something like, "Well, if you can't help me find a way to fix this by tomorrow, I'll just bring him in and have you put him to sleep." In essence, the owner is attempting to make you an accomplice in whatever he decides to do about the pet and its problem behavior. In response to such a comment, you may be tempted to reply with a caustic remark, which, of course, would only make the conversation more difficult. Keep in mind that there may be understandable reasons why an owner would make such a threat. Perhaps he is overwhelmed, frustrated, or even afraid of decisions that must be made in terms of keeping the pet. Certain skills can help you respond to such comments without being ugly or allowing yourself to be manipulated by these kinds of statements. A few of them will be discussed later in this chapter.

Family Conflicts

You may be drawn into family conflicts and disagreements about the pet. Within a family group, opinions may differ about working with a problem behavior and keeping the pet. There also may be differences in what each family member is willing to do and in the degree to which each person is attached to the animal. Family members may get into arguments and power struggles over these emotionally charged matters, children may dissolve into tears or even threaten to leave home, and adults may issue ultimatums ("If he does this one more time, he's gone"), all of which complicate conversations about the problem. In some cases, family members may try to get you to take sides in these disagreements and draw you into their family system.

Being Taken Advantage Of

You may feel the owner is taking advantage of you. This can happen in several ways. If you charge fees for your behavior services, you may feel that the owner is trying to get as much free advice from you as she can. Or if you are the person designated to handle behavior calls at your facility (between all your other duties), you may feel that you never have adequate time to talk to owners and thus that you are not being adequately supported in doing your job. You may also feel defensive if you are asked to help with behavior cases without adequate training, especially if you sense that you are constantly in over your head and required to handle situations you aren't prepared to tackle.

Lengthy Conversations

The owner may monopolize the conversation about the pet's problem. Some owners love to talk about their pets to anyone who will listen. Others are so frustrated with the problem behavior that they simply need an opportunity to vent. An owner of either type may go into great detail about the situation before it is necessary to do so and barely allow you to say a word, making it difficult for you to control the conversation and keep it at a reasonable length and on track. Listening to what seem to be irrelevant details, you may feel pressured by time constraints or become increasingly frustrated yourself.

Opposing Approaches

You may feel awkward or even angry when your diagnosis or treatment recommendations are at odds with information an owner has received from another behavior consultant in your community.

Because of the differences in the qualifications and competency of people who offer behavior consultations, an owner may have been given irrelevant or even harmful treatment recommendations in an attempt to resolve the problem. I sometimes become very angry when I find an owner has received inappropriate information and the pet has been subjected to harmful and, in some cases, even cruel procedures. When you find it necessary to suggest a procedure that is in opposition to what the owner has been doing, it may be difficult to find a tactful way of doing so without demeaning the other consultant and putting him in a bad light. However, it isn't helpful to state your concerns in such a way that the owner is made to feel guilty for implementing techniques from an "expert" she trusted. And "bad-mouthing" another consultant, no matter how incompetent you feel the person is, can come back to haunt you.

As all these examples show, conversations about pet behavior problems can become difficult because they are so emotionally charged. If you are uncomfortable with your client's feelings or if your emotions conflict with hers, it can lead to the type of negative interpretations mentioned earlier. However, by knowing how to respond to the emotional content of the conversation, by reinterpreting the owners' motivations, and by being aware of your own needs, you can respond in these situations without becoming hostile or frustrated. This will allow you to be more helpful to the pet owner and, ultimately, to the pet.

BASIC COMMUNICATION SKILLS

The crisis-intervention model of helping is based on the idea that whenever emotions are high in a conversation, they must be dealt with before anything else can be accomplished. Accordingly, the emotions of angry, frightened, or frustrated owners must be addressed before they are truly able to absorb concrete information about animal behavior. Fortunately, there are several relatively easy techniques you can learn to use in these situations.

Acknowledging

Acknowledging means validating the truth or existence of something. As a communication skill, it can mean validating either your own or the client's emotions: "I know you're upset," you might say, or, "I'm frustrated that I can't spend more time with you right now." To be helpful, these statements must be delivered in a neutral, sincere tone of voice, not in a judgmental or sarcastic fashion. By acknowledging the client's emotions, you let him know that you recognize how important his pet is to him. By acknowledging your own emotions, you are being honest with the client; you are also better able to prevent your feelings from getting in the way, and you will be able to move the conversation forward.

Normalizing

Normalizing puts the client's emotions into context. It lets him know that others, possibly including you, might feel the same way under similar circumstances. "If my dog had chewed up my new shoes, I'd be angry too," you might say, or "I think most anyone would be scared after finding out their dog bit someone." Normalizing tends to have a calming, reassuring effect. It lets the owner know there isn't anything wrong with the way he's feeling.

Self-Disclosing

Self-disclosing means using a personal example to let the client know that behavior problems—and her emotional reactions to them—are common and that she isn't alone. You might, for example, say, "Litterbox problems happen all the time. In fact, my cat was urinating on the bathroom rug for a while, and it made me crazy!" or "My dog used to tear up all kinds of things when I was gone, and I was afraid we weren't going to be able to keep her." If you take this approach, you must be careful not to let the focus of the conversation shift to you and your pet's problem. Keep your personal story brief, and draw the conversation back to the client's animal.

There is one caveat here. Some owners have the unrealistic belief that because you are an animal professional, all of *your* pets should be perfectly behaved—a belief that might lead them to question your competence if your pets have any problems. It has been my experience, however, that it helps most owners to learn that *your* pets aren't perfect. This takes some pressure off them: If you, the professional, don't have perfectly behaved pets, then it's easier for owners not to blame themselves for their pets' problems. If you're still concerned about this or if telling stories about your own pets makes you uncomfortable, then share those stories as though you were talking about someone else's animal.

Using any of these skills may take a few minutes of your valuable time. However, doing so will probably save you time in the end because the client will be less distracted and better able to listen to everything you have to say. You will need to repeat yourself less, and the client will likely comprehend more. These techniques will also help you to feel better about the conversation and to manage your own emotions more effectively.

Controlling the Conversation

At the same time, keep in mind that using these skills may encourage some clients to keep the conversation focused on how they are feeling rather than on the problem at hand. Certain clients, for a variety of reasons, either prefer or actually need to talk about how their pet's problem is affecting them, rather than addressing the problem itself. If you have such a case, remind yourself that it is *not* your role to counsel the client on communicating with her spouse or to give financial advice on repairing damage done by the pet. Instead, your role is to do the best job you can with the pet's behavior problem. When you need to redirect the conversation back to the problem, several phrases can be effective, and how these are delivered can make an enormous difference in the way the client interprets them. You can sound helpful and caring or curt and unpleasant, depending on your tone of voice. Examples of some useful phrases follow:

> "What you are telling me is important information that will be needed during the actual consultation, but for now I need you to tell me X."
> "Perhaps we can come back to that later, but right now I need to let you know that X."
> "I know this is an upsetting situation for you, but I think I can be most helpful to you if we can talk about X."
> "Why don't you discuss this with your family and get back to me?"
> "It sounds as though you might want to think about things for a bit. Why don't you do that and call me when you've decided what you want to do."
> "I'd like to hear more about that later, but now we need to talk about X."
> "I know that's a really important issue for you, but I feel it's more important now that we talk about X."

Initially, you may think you sound stilted or artificial when using such phrases, but, as with any skill, you will get better with practice. So try them for awhile, even if you feel uncomfortable. Most likely, you'll quickly become adept at using them and will be pleased at how helpful they can be.

THE ROLE OF BLAME AND GUILT

One underlying factor that sometimes contributes to the stress of behavior conversations—a factor you may not even be consciously aware of—is a tendency to blame the owner for the problem. The notion that problem pets are caused by problem owners or that there must be something wrong with owners whose pets have behavior problems was popularized in the field of dog training[1]. There has been very little support for this idea in recent years. Surveys have revealed few, if any, differences between how owners of problem versus nonproblem pets interact with their animals[2,3]. These studies found that dogs who had not been to obedience training and who were "spoiled" and anthropomorphized by their owners were *no more likely* to have behavior problems than dogs who had been trained and were neither spoiled nor anthropomorphized. Allowing a dog to sleep on the bed or feeding her snacks from the table, for example, did *not* result in an increased frequency of behavior problems.

In fact, most anyone who works with animal behavior problems can cite examples of knowledgeable, experienced pet owners who have done everything right and still find themselves with a cat who urinates on the floor or a dog who nips at visitors. After all, have you—an experienced animal professional—never had a pet with a behavior problem? Are all your pets perfectly behaved 100 percent of the time? (If you answered yes, you're in denial!) In general, behavior problems are caused by an interaction of factors involving the owner's behavior, the personality of the pet, and the animal's environment[3,4]. It is much too simplistic to attribute the cause of a behavior problem to any one factor alone.

It is also counterproductive to view the owner as the sole cause of the problem. Such an attitude only makes conversations more difficult because the owner will sense your judgmental attitude even if you do not directly voice your opinion. Although blaming the owner might make you feel superior and more knowledgeable, it does nothing to enlist his cooperation in resolving the problem. Therefore, if your goal is to help the pet, aid the owner, and retain a client, you'll need to forsake this attitude.

REINTERPRETING EVENTS

By reconsidering the factors that can make conversations about behavior problems stressful, it is often possible to interpret what is going on in a different light. By reinterpreting events, you can change your emotional reaction to them. Consider the following reinterpretations of the scenarios mentioned earlier.

1. *The expectations that you and the owner bring to the conversation may differ.* It isn't realistic to expect owners to share your understanding of all that is involved in resolving behavior problems. Pet owners rely mostly on advice from friends or other owners who probably aren't any more knowledgeable than they are, or they may turn to the popular literature, which is fraught with inaccurate information.

Recent studies about why animals are surrendered to shelters indicate that many owners know little about animal behavior and that, too often, the pets they acquire turn out to be more work than expected[5,6,7]. Adding to the differences in expectations, many an owner compares the behavior of her current, problem pet to another pet she's owned ("My other dog didn't do this"). In other words, the owner is basing her knowledge about what is normal behavior on her experience with just one, or at best a few, other animals. You, by contrast, have had experience with a great many animals. Obviously, then, you will have different expectations because your experiences are markedly different.

In addition, most people today are socialized into thinking that there is a quick fix for virtually every problem. In human therapy, this has been referred to as the "drive-in syndrome,"[8] referring to the assumption that solving a problem should be as quick and easy as buying dinner at a fast food restaurant. Like the rest of us, owners want their problems resolved in the easiest, least painful way possible.

Sometimes, a naive owner honestly thinks there isn't much involved in changing a pet's behavior. If you can effectively educate this individual about why quick fixes aren't possible, he just may adopt a new view of the problem and prove willing to commit the time and effort required to resolve it. For another kind of owner, however, the expectation of a quick fix reflects the fact that if there isn't an easy solution, she simply won't be interested in working with the pet. Ultimately, you must recognize that this is her decision, not yours. You don't have to buy into the desire for a quick fix by giving superficial advice or, if you are a veterinarian, by using medication as a shortcut or substitute for a behavior modification plan (see chapter 18).

The best you can do in many cases is to give the owner a realistic idea of what he can expect from behavior consulting. Unfortunately, there is a dearth of good follow-up data on the efficacy of behavior modification and the prognoses for different problems. Consequently, although the vast majority of behavior problems can be resolved, it is often not possible to make accurate predictions about outcomes, and the owner must be willing to take the chance if she is going to work with the problem.

2. *Your beliefs about what the owner* should *do may be different from what the owner can or wants to do.* The first thing to consider in reinterpreting this conflict is that you are not fully informed

about what is going on in the client's life or why he feels the way he does. Perhaps his marriage is in trouble or he is on the verge of losing his job, and the added strain of working with a problem pet may be overwhelming. You may not agree with his reasoning, but at least you can understand it. Rather than blaming the owner for not living up to your expectations on standards of care, concentrate instead on what he *can* do. As you talk about options, he may come to feel that it's possible to do more than he thought.

You can also ask a client what he would need in order to follow through with a certain recommendation. If he can't afford to buy a crate, for instance, could your facility rent one to him? In other words, there may be something your clinic, shelter, or training business can do to facilitate problem resolution without overcommitting and bearing too much responsibility for the outcome.

However, there are times when, even though the client wants to do everything possible, you yourself have concerns about working with the pet. In this situation, remember that it is the owner, not you, who must determine whether to live with, work with, or give up on a specific behavior problem. If an owner is willing to tolerate a behavior that you could not, it is not appropriate to impose your standards on him. If you are concerned about a potentially dangerous situation, you may want to talk the owner through the advantages and disadvantages of working with the pet, including the risks and liabilities. It is usually not helpful to tell a client he *should* euthanize an animal. For more help in discussing euthanasia for behavior problems, see chapter 17.

3. *The owner may attempt, consciously or unconsciously, to use emotional blackmail to get you to give him what he wants or make you responsible for the pet.* The owner who uses emotional blackmail in this way is often motivated by frustration and fear. He is probably overwhelmed and looking for an emotional partner to help him cope with the difficult situation he faces. If he is afraid he will not be able to keep the pet, he wants someone to share the responsibility for making the decision to relinquish or euthanize her.

Because fear, frustration, and anger may be involved, try addressing these emotions by using some of the communication skills described earlier. You can clearly state what you can and cannot do. "If you'd like to work with the problem, I'll be happy to help you or refer you to a behavior specialist, but I'm afraid that you'll have to decide for yourself whether it's something you can take on."

You also need to be clear about your responsibilities and your professional limits. Remember that what happens to the pet is up to the owner, not you. You cannot take responsibility for his decision. *Your* responsibility is to be helpful and to provide good service in the role you have chosen. Once you have provided good service, your responsibility ends.

4. *You may be drawn into family conflicts and disagreements about the pet.* Given that a pet's behavior is inextricably linked to the family's behavior, it may be impossible to avoid being drawn into familial conflicts. If that happens, you can view it as a compliment that the family feels comfortable enough in your presence to discuss sensitive issues. But keep in mind that hearing about family dynamics or conflicts does not mean that you have to do anything about them. You are not a family therapist, marriage counselor, or child psychologist. You cannot intervene in complex family relationships. Your job is to stay focused on what changes need to be made to help the pet. How the family members negotiate what it will take to make those changes within their family system is up to them. Use the communication skills already discussed to keep the conversation focused.

5. *You may feel the owner is taking advantage of you.* The old adage that no one can take advantage of you unless you let him applies here. If your sense of being taken advantage of stems from a fee issue, it may be that your client honestly does not realize there is a charge for your behavior

services. Even today, as most veterinarians know, pet owners too often want veterinary services at low or no cost, and if people are reluctant to pay for medical services, it should not be surprising that they are even less willing to pay for "psychological" help. In fact, some owners may even view behavior consulting as a sham service.

Any client who holds these views needs some education about the value of your services, and you may find the information in chapter 1 about making referrals helpful in this regard. Behavior consultations should be handled as a professional service, not as a casual matter of giving tips or advice.

Make sure that you are doing a good job in informing the client about your fees for behavior services, and recognize that if you're sometimes willing to spend an extra 15 minutes talking with her about a problem at no charge, you're sending a mixed message. When you are inclined to do so, it may be better to print out an invoice for your services but discount the entire fee, thereby telling the client that she has been charged and that she can expect to be charged in the future.

You can also use some techniques to control the dialogue so that you don't get trapped into "free advice" conversations. If an owner is pressing you for free advice when you regularly charge for behavior services, try using the following phrases:

> "Without more information, I could inadvertently tell you to do something that could actually make the problem worse because I don't have all the facts I would obtain during a consulting appointment."
>
> "We do work with those kinds of problems—let me describe our services."
>
> "That's the sort of detail we'll get into during a consultation. Would you like to set up an appointment now?"

If you feel you are being taken advantage of because you've been designated to work with behavior cases at your facility without having sufficient time or adequate training to do so, start your reinterpretation of the situation by considering this a compliment. Whoever gave you this assignment believed you were the best person to take on a difficult task. You were seen as a capable individual, one who could be trusted with this extra responsibility. Congratulations! Next, consider talking to your superiors about the information in chapter 1 regarding the dangers of inappropriate problem solving. Chances are they are not aware of the potential problems, and they may do things differently once they are more fully informed.

If you've decided on your own to assume this assignment, then the power to have things differently is under your control. Again, you should refer to a point made in chapter 1: Don't take on cases you don't feel prepared to handle. If your problem primarily involves time management, you may find it helpful to set aside certain hours in the week to answer behavior calls and then decline to do so at any other time. If you find yourself pressed for time while talking with a client, let him know this: You might say, "I need to tell you that I'm running short on time. I have 5 more minutes I can spend with you. Can we finish up during that time, or should we schedule another appointment?" Many of your feelings of being taken advantage of can be dealt with by setting limits or by making others aware of *your* needs.

6. *The owner may monopolize the conversation about their pet's problem.* Rather than viewing a person who talks at length about her pet as bothersome and time-consuming, think about how wonderful it is that she is so invested in her animal. The owner who talks on and on about her pet probably cares enough to have a lifelong relationship with him. In addition, she probably sees you as a fellow animal lover and therefore one of the few people with whom she can comfortably share personal details. To keep discussions with this type of owner on track, use some of the phrases suggested earlier for controlling conversations.

7. You may feel awkward or even angry when your diagnosis or treatment recommendations are at odds with information an owner has received from another behavior consultant in your community. Because you want the best for the animal and his owner, you are entitled to your feelings of frustration and anger about the inappropriate things that were done in the past and the awkwardness of being caught in the middle. Rather than dwelling on previous wrongs, however, be thankful that both the pet and the owner now have the chance to work with you. An owner often needs a thorough but understandable explanation of why you are now asking her to do something totally different from what she has been doing. Be willing to provide as much explanation as is required. Most owners will do things differently if the rationale makes sense to them. Tread lightly when discussing the other consultant's techniques. I often use phrases such as:

> "Well, the field of dog training and behavior is in a state of change right now, and many of the procedures that were popular in the past aren't used as much anymore."
> "You haven't done anything wrong. You did just what you were told to do by the other consultant, but I really think the procedures we've discussed today will be more effective, and here's why."
> "Most people don't like doing unpleasant things to their pets, so I'm glad we've found some procedures that make that unnecessary."

SUMMARY

This chapter has demonstrated that when pet owners contact you about a behavior problem, they may be asking for more than technical assistance. They may need a sympathetic listener—someone who understands what it's like to come home to thousands of dollars of damage to personal belongings or to be awakened in the middle of the night by the sound of cats fighting. They may want reassurance that their problems can be resolved, that their relationships with their pets can be saved, and that the problem behavior is not their fault. They may be looking for a chance to air their feelings of anger, fear, frustration, disappointment, or other emotions. Until people express these emotions, they really aren't ready to adopt a logical approach about what to do. By using the skills discussed in this chapter, you can successfully meet clients' needs without feeling overwhelmed or burdened or that you have to become a therapist in the process.

By using communication skills and reinterpreting events, you will find it easier to transform negative thoughts about behavior cases into more positive ones. Look back to the beginning of the chapter and compare that initial list of negative attitudes with the following positive approaches:

> "This is a great chance for me to learn more about animal behavior."
> "How wonderful! Here's an opportunity to educate another owner."
> "Helping to keep this pet out of the shelter is the best use of my time right now."
> "What a responsible owner—she cared enough to call for help."

These attitudes work better for everyone—you, the pet owner, and the animal.

REFERENCES

1. Woodhouse, B. 1978. *No bad dogs*. Aylesbury, United Kingdom: Hazell Watson and Viney.

2. Voith, V.L., J.C. Wright, and P.J. Dannenman. 1992. Is there a relationship between canine behavior problems and spoiling activities, anthropomorphism and obedience training? *Appl. Anim. Beh. Sci.* 34:263–72.

3. Askew, H.R. 1996. *Treatment of behavior problems in dogs and cats*. Cambridge, Mass.: Blackwell Science.

4. Tortora, D. 1980. Applied animal psychology: The practical implications of comparative analysis. In *Comparative psychology: An evolutionary analysis of animal behavior*, ed. M.R. Denny, 267–94. New York: John Wiley and Sons.

5. Patronek, G.J., L.T. Glickman, A.M. Beck, G.P. McCabe, and C. Ecker. 1996. Risk factors for relinquishment of cats to an animal shelter. *JAVMA* 209:582–8.

6. Patronek, G.J., L.T. Glickman, A.M. Beck, G.P. McCabe, and C. Ecker. 1996. Risk factors for relinquishment of dogs to an animal shelter. *JAVMA* 209:572–81.

7. Salman, M.D., J.G. New, J.M. Scarlett, P.H. Kass, R. Ruch-Gallie, and S. Hetts. 1998. Human and animal factors related to the relinquishment of dogs and cats in 12 selected animal shelters in the United States. *Appl. Anim. Wel. Sci.* 1 (3):207–26.

8. Kohlke, U., and K. Kohlke. 1994. Verhaltenstherapie bei Tieren: Besonderheiten und spezifische Problematik aus psychologischer Sicht [Behavior therapy in animals: Specialties and specific problems from a psychological point of view]. *Kleintierpraxis* 39:175–80.

CHAPTER 3

A Crash Course in Animal
Learning–and Why You Need It

WHY READ THIS CHAPTER?

If you have been in veterinary medicine or a related field for a substantial number of years, do you use the same methods that you did years ago? No doubt, the answer is no. If you did, you might well be out of business, sued for malpractice, or ridiculed by your colleagues. Similarly, you can't be left behind when it comes to animal behavior. You shouldn't work with problems based merely on what you've done or heard in the past. Your recommendations must not only make sense from a diagnostic perspective but also be congruent with what is known about animal learning and the basic ethological principles of dog and cat behavior. That's why at least a rudimentary knowledge of animal learning theory is a prerequisite to working with problem behaviors.

A knowledge of how animals learn is absolutely critical for anyone interested in training an animal, modifying a pet's behavior, or resolving animal behavior problems. Few of us have the skills and experience to train the animals residing in zoos and marine mammal parks: We wouldn't know the first thing about getting a whale to jump into the air on command or making an elephant lift its leg. Yet most of us probably *could* come up with some ideas about training a dog or cat. In part, this is because we are more familiar with the basic behavior patterns of dogs and cats rather than whales and elephants; moreover, we're more comfortable being around them. Beyond that, many of us seem to believe that dogs and cats (and perhaps other domestic or companion animals, such as horses) are somehow exempt from the laws of animal learning. Maybe we think that dogs and cats learn differently and do things for different reasons than other animals because they seem more "humanlike" to us.

Although it's certainly true that domestication has modified the behavior patterns of our companion animals as compared to their wild counterparts, their learning is still based on the principles that apply to the rest of the animal kingdom. The close bonds we have with our pets—and the relationship issues created by those bonds—do not negate the importance of learning when it comes to changing behavior. Granted, the details of a particular training program may differ for a whale and a dog (a dog may not find dead fish very appealing as a food reinforcer, for example!), but the basic concepts still apply.

SHIFTS IN PERSPECTIVE

Away from Aversive Control

Unfortunately, until recent years, many popular techniques used to train dogs and work with behavior problems in companion animals were not congruent with the basic principles of animal learning theory. Indeed, our pets have often learned *in spite* of how we've tried to teach them, not because of it. Dog trainers and others have tended to rely on certain types of aversive control, rather than on eliciting and reinforcing desired behavior (of course, aversive procedures are harder to use with cats because you have to catch them first!). Historically, we have used aversive control on our pets and other domestic animals simply because we could, not because it was the best method available. The aversive control approach is less feasible with larger, nondomesticated animals, so with these animals, the focus necessarily has been on positive reinforcement. If you want to be effective and humane in your approach to behavior problems, you may need to shift your thinking about the best ways to change behavior and about how animals learn.

Anthropomorphism Versus Functional Interpretations

One basic and perhaps obvious perspective is that dogs and cats behave in certain ways because the behavior "works" for them. My experience indicates that most pet owners and too many professionals ignore this fundamental truism in favor of anthropomorphic interpretations of behavior. This latter approach assumes that our pets "misbehave" because they are mad at us, because they are trying to get back at us in revengeful ways, because they are maliciously doing things they know they shouldn't (part of the "he knows he's done wrong" phenomenon), and because they are just willful, rebellious brats who are acting out and thumbing their noses at our authority.

Pets are sometimes viewed as stupid because they aren't learning what we want them to learn. It rarely occurs to us that the fault is ours, not theirs. I once heard a family describe one of their dogs as "not very bright" and asked them why they believed this. They thought hard and stated that this animal wasn't very affectionate and didn't solicit their attention as much as their other dog did. Clearly, of course, that did not mean their dog was stupid. Popular wisdom describes dogs as incessantly trying to boss their owners around and holds that striving to be the "top dog" is what motivates most displays of unacceptable behavior. These examples illustrate the point I made earlier—that our relationships with our pets bias our views of how they learn. This does not, however, change the fact that their behavior is strongly influenced by basic learning principles.

Over the years, I've come to believe that one or more of these misinterpretations is part of virtually every problem behavior case I see. Such misinterpretations color the owners' view of the animal and, in some cases, contribute to their refusal to work with the pet. It's hard to like a pet that you believe is out to get you and purposely annoying or disrespecting you. It's a whole different world when you let go of this "stuff" and say, "Hey—he's just being a dog (or cat)."

Misinterpretations often also result in the use of inappropriate and ineffective techniques to resolve problems. In extreme cases, these include procedures that are at best unfair (such as punishing an animal several minutes or even hours after a misbehavior has occurred) and at worst cruel and abusive (such as disciplining dogs by lifting them off the ground using a leash and choke chain).

So your first assignment is to let go of these interpretations if you are still clinging to them and realize that for an animal, behavior is value-free. Shift your perspective. Instead of thinking, "He's a dastardly devil for coming up with these antics," consider how a specific behavior is working for the animal. You'll find many examples of this perspective shift as you progress through this book.

More Positive Approaches

The second basic shift is from thinking "How can I get him to stop (fill in the blank)" to either "How can I prevent a problem that I know is likely to happen if I'm not proactive?" or "How can I get him to do what I want him to do so I can reinforce that behavior?"

As discussed in chapter 1, if your basic bag of tricks in working with problem behaviors primarily includes aversive control, then you haven't yet made this shift. If you think that your own lack of dominance and the dog's failure to recognize who is the "boss" is at the root of most problems, you haven't yet made this shift. Similarly, if you think that cats can be controlled and dominated in the same way as dogs, well, let me give you my cat for a week!

The principles that will be discussed in this chapter are very basic. They will give you a starting point or a point of reference from which to learn more. If most of this chapter is new territory for you, you might be wise to set some rather stringent professional limits on your involvement with behavior cases (as discussed in chapter 1) until you have expanded your knowledge and experience base. If this chapter is by and large a review for you, it should still serve as a good reference guide, and it will, I hope, give you some new approaches to use in talking to clients about these concepts in ways they can understand. An excellent source for expanding your knowledge is *"Excel-erated Learning: Explaining in Plain English How Dogs Learn and How Best to Teach Them,"* by Pamela Reid, Ph.D. (see the list of additional readings at end of the book). Reid has done a superb job of explaining technical learning theory in an understandable way, using examples that are pertinent to dog behavior. She uses fewer cat examples, but the basic principles are still the same.

TYPES OF LEARNING

There are several types of learning, and this chapter will not cover all of them. The focus will be on the learning that is most relevant to behavior problems typically seen in dogs and cats.

Classical Conditioning

Classical conditioning is also known as respondent conditioning[1] (see Box 3.1). Simply put, classical conditioning involves an animal learning an association between two stimuli. This can be thought of as one stimulus (the conditioned stimulus, or CS) predicting the occurrence of a second stimulus (the unconditioned stimulus, or UCS). Put another way, a previously neutral stimulus (the CS) comes to evoke the same response that another stimulus (the UCS) evokes automatically, without any prior conditioning. This concept was demonstrated in Pavlov's famous experiments with salivation in dogs. Pavlov, a physiologist studying reflexes, presented food to dogs in order to measure their salivation response. He observed the normal response of reflexively salivating when food was seen or smelled. Quite by accident, he also found that after the dogs became familiar with the routine he followed when feeding them, they began to salivate in response to a light that was turned on immediately before the food appeared.

Box 3.1 Useful definitions

Classical conditioning: Process by which a previously neutral stimulus (the CS) predicts the occurrence of the unconditioned stimulus (the UCS) and can elicit the same or a similar response as the UCS

Countercommanding: Instructing an animal to perform an operantly conditioned response that is incompatible with a problem (or undesired) behavior

Counterconditioning: A classical conditioning process by which a UCS becomes a CS for another response. In other words, a stimulus (UCS) that was previously associated with unpleasantness becomes a CS that predicts good things.

Desensitization: Exposing the animal to a low-intensity or weak version of a stimulus, which does not elicit a problem response, and gradually increasing the stimulus intensity. Ideally, the problem response should not be elicited.

Operant conditioning: Based on the principle that behaviors that result in positive outcomes are more likely to be repeated and those that result in negative outcomes will decrease in frequency (Thorndike's Law of Effect)

To the dogs, the light (the CS) predicted that food (the UCS) was coming. The light became associated with the food and evoked salivation by itself.

There are a few important points to be made in regard to Pavlov's study. First, the presentation of the food was not dependent on the dogs' behavior—it would appear regardless of what the dogs did. Second, the response (salivation) was an involuntary reflex, not a controllable behavior. It was not necessary for the dogs to make any kind of voluntary response for the association between the stimuli to be learned. (However, as the examples that follow illustrate, the conditioned response can involve more complex behaviors than involuntary reflexes.) Third, for learning to occur, the CS must *precede* the onset of the UCS by a brief length of time.

Many examples of classical conditioning relevant to dogs and cats illustrate this type of learning. Classical conditioning is important not only in terms of how some behavior problems develop but also as a means of changing problem behavior. Consider these everyday examples:

- Getting out the leash or putting on your tennis shoes (the CS) predicts a walk (the UCS) for your dog—he gets excited (response) over the leash and shoes just as he gets excited about a walk.
- The sound of the can opener (the CS) predicts dinner (the UCS) for your cat—she comes running to the kitchen (probably salivating), ready to eat and expecting food to follow.
- Picking up your keys, briefcase, and lunch (all CSs) predicts you are leaving without your dog (the UCS)—evoking a variety of emotional as well as observ-

able responses in him, perhaps including anxiety, "depression" (lying down and not moving), restlessness, pacing, salivating, whining, or going to a crate or other area where he is confined in your absence. This association is part of what underlies separation anxiety problems. (Cats don't seem to respond to such cues nearly as strongly as dogs do.)

- The ringing of the doorbell (the CS) predicts the arrival of visitors (the UCS) for your pets—your dog begins to bark, growl, or excitedly wag his tail, and your cat runs and hides.
- The sight of another dog in the park (the CS) causes your dog to become aggressive because he has been punished (the UCS) for trying to greet other animals. (Note that there are other reasons why dogs become aggressive in such a situation.)
- The approach of Cat B (the CS) prompts Cat A to run and hide because she has previously been punished (the UCS) for hissing at Cat B.

I see these principles in action almost daily in my home. I'm on the telephone and the computer a good deal of the time, and my dogs and cat have learned that two CSs—first, my voice inflection and the words I use when I end a phone call and, second, the "good-bye" voice of the on-line service provider as I log off the computer—predict that I am then likely to get up from my desk (the UCS). In response to these stimuli, they rise from their lounging positions under my desk because they know I'll be getting up too!

As these examples show, many routine behavior patterns are classically conditioned. In addition, some fears and phobias and other behavior problems are classically conditioned as well. Having an animal learn an association between two stimuli is a much overlooked but extremely useful tool in resolving problems, as we'll see later.

Operant Conditioning

Operant or instrumental conditioning is another type of learning that is very pertinent to applied animal behavior work. With the increasing popularity of "clicker training," there has been some confusion among dog trainers as to what operant conditioning really is. Operant conditioning is based on Thorndike's Law of Effect, which says that the consequences of an animal's behavior will influence the frequency of future behavior[1] (Box 3.1). Specifically, behaviors that result in positive outcomes will be more likely to occur in the future, and those that produce unpleasant outcomes will decrease in frequency. Operant conditioning manipulates consequences to influence the relative frequencies of different behaviors. All dog-training methods attempt to do that, even those using aversive procedures. Clicker training has focused on positive consequences, while historically, most dog-training techniques have used more aversive methods. Thus, clicker training is an example of an application of operant conditioning, but operant conditioning is much more than clicker training. I will discuss five different types of consequences, what they mean, and how they are important in changing behavior as well as in creating behavior problems. These five consequences are:

- Positive reinforcement
- Extinction
- Negative reinforcement
- Positive punishment
- Negative punishment

Positive reinforcement. This outcome can be defined as the occurrence or presentation of something pleasant immediately following a behavior that will make that behavior more likely to occur in the future. Several important ideas influence the effect of positive reinforcement.

Timing. Learning research has shown that a delay of even a few seconds between the response and the reinforcer dramatically decreases the reinforcing effect[1]. Positive reinforcement influences the specific behavior the animal is displaying when the reinforcer is presented. This means that with a delay of several seconds, another behavior could already have occurred. If you have taught obedience classes, you probably know that most pet owners have a difficult time reinforcing the behavior they want. When a novice owner with an excitable dog is trying to reinforce a sit, it is not uncommon for the dog to stand up again while the owner is still praising him as a "good dog." As a result, the dog may be confused about what behavior actually caused the praise—the sitting down or the standing up. Another common example is the new dog owner who is attempting to reinforce elimination outside. She may stand at the back door, watch the dog eliminate, and then praise him as he is walking toward the house; she may even give him a tidbit when he gets to the door. After a few days of this, she wonders why the dog stands at the back door when he is put outside rather than going out in the yard to do his business. If you've read this section carefully, you should understand why.

Primary and secondary reinforcers. A reinforcer is anything an animal will work for. *Primary reinforcers* are things the animal inherently enjoys—food, water, or an opportunity to play or engage in other "life behaviors" (as Ian Dunbar, MRCVS and Ph.D., calls them), such as going for a walk. For some animals (but not all), petting and praise are primary reinforcers. Social stimuli like these are much more likely to be reinforcing for dogs as compared to cats and for well-socialized animals as compared to poorly socialized ones or those with "aloof" or "independent" temperaments.

When attention and social interaction are reinforcing, they can be very powerful and often account for the development of many of the "pestering" behaviors that most pet owners find so annoying. Think of the concept mentioned previously—that is, that animals do what works for them. When animals do annoying things (barking, meowing in the middle of the night, stealing socks, jumping on forbidden places), most owners turn their attention on the pets to make them stop. People may yell, get up and move toward the pet, or do anything the animal wants (pet him, play, get up to feed him) to get him to stop the pestering. From the pet's perspective, receiving attention, even negative attention such as a verbal scolding, is preferable to being ignored. So the annoying behavior continues and usually worsens because it "works" for the pet—it gets the owner's attention.

Being the enlightened, educated behaviorist that I am, I allowed my cat Buffett to trap me into a game of his own making. When I was watching TV, Buffett started jumping up on a shelf near the television and pushing items that were sitting there onto the floor. He continued until I made a move toward him, and then he jumped down and ran into another room. He created this game because it worked—it forced me to pay attention to him rather than the TV. Buffett was not being rebellious, testing my authority, or doing anything that could be similarly anthropomophized. He was simply doing what worked for him. In later sections, I'll discuss how to switch this type of situation around so acceptable behaviors can work for the animal without causing owners to become annoyed enough to consider caticide!

There are several important points here. First, the idea that a reinforcer is anything an animal will work for completely negates the old dog-training adages that "he should work for me, not for food" or that "he should want to please me." Use of the word *should* in such a context implies that if the animal doesn't behave appropriately, something bad will happen, which brings us back to aversive control. The truth is that dogs who "want to please," are simply those for whom social reinforcement works well.

Second, we cannot dictate what will or will not be a primary reinforcer for a given animal. Food is often a good reinforcer, but depending on the animal and the task that is being taught, it also may not be. Food used in training and behavior modification is a very powerful tool, and it does not result in a "cookie-dependent" animal if used properly. If anyone who has used this technique laments, "He'll only behave when he knows I have food," then the proper steps have not been taken. To use food correctly as a reinforcer, (1) the food must be used *only* as a reinforcer, not as a lure or a cue (there's nothing wrong with using food as a lure, but the transition must be made to letting the animal see the food only after the behavior has been performed so that it becomes only a reinforcer), (2) the food must be used on a variable reinforcement schedule, and (3) the cues that tell the animal when food is available and when it isn't must be removed.

If praise and petting are not primary reinforcers for an animal, they can often be made *secondary reinforcers*. A secondary reinforcer is a previously neutral stimulus (or one with weak reinforcing properties) that becomes rewarding because it is paired with a primary reinforcer. For example, if you consistently praise your dog as you give him a treat, after many pairings of food and praise, the praise takes on the power of food. That's what happens with a clicker—a novel sound becomes reinforcing because it has been consistently paired with food. This process of creating a secondary reinforcer (by which one stimulus predicts another) is, once again, classical conditioning. Once the association between the stimuli has been made, the secondary reinforcer can be used for a time without the primary following it, but if this is done too frequently, the association will be lost. Thus, these pairings must continue to occur from time to time in order for the secondary reinforcer to remain potent.

Secondary reinforcers have several advantages. First, they allow you to give the animal a powerful reinforcement without having to have a treat or other primary reinforcer readily available. Second, some secondary reinforcers, such as novel sounds, are much more precise at marking the behavior that is actually being reinforced. A discrete sound is far more accurate than using the phrase "good kitty," which may span several behaviors. This is the basic advantage of a clicker and similar tools.

Miscommunication: Reassurance can result in positive reinforcement. Positive reinforcement can also influence problem behavior when we attempt to reassure an aggressive animal. Most veterinarians have seen a client hold and caress a dog while it was growling at the doctor. Unfortunately, this is an excellent way to encourage dogs to growl at veterinarians. This may be one reason why many dogs are much more easily treated or examined when their owners aren't present—the dogs learn that there is no positive reinforcement for such behavior when their owners are not in the room.

In summary, positive reinforcement is an extremely powerful tool for modifying behavior. It is vastly underutilized in problem resolution, and its significance is often overlooked in the development of behavior problems. For more information about other factors affecting the influence of positive reinforcement, see Reid's book or any of the books listed under chapter 3 at the end of this book.

Extinction. Just as the use of positive reinforcement increases the frequency of a certain behavior, removal of positive reinforcement—also known as extinction—results in a decrease in the behavior. Removing the reinforcement for a behavior is one way to stop undesirable behavior. Extinction is often used for pestering or annoying behaviors that have been positively reinforced (often inadvertently) via attention from the owner. For example, if dog is pawing or barking at you and generally being obnoxious when visitors are around, this is often because he wants the attention of the group focused on him. As I've described, my cat Buffett liked to knock objects off the room divider to get my attention. For him, this attention came in the form of being yelled at, but this was still positive reinforcement. When I ignored Buffett in this situation, I was using extinction because I was removing the reinforcement for the behavior.

There are several important factors to be aware of with extinction. First, the withdrawal of reinforcement usually frustrates the animal. This, in turn, causes him to work harder to obtain the reinforcement. (In the case of my cat, to cite one example, he may begin knocking objects off the divider at a faster pace.) Put another way, owners should be warned that the behavior will get worse before it gets better. Owners must be encouraged not to give in and pay attention to the behavior at this point. If they do, they will reinforce behavior that is even more annoying.

Second, if one behavior doesn't result in the expected reinforcement, the animal is likely to try another behavior. Unless his owners set up a situation to help him choose a desirable behavior, he may pick a behavior that is just as annoying as the one they are trying to extinguish. Buffett, for example, may begin meowing instead of (or in addition to) knocking objects onto the floor. However, if I call Buffett to me and require him to quietly lie next to me, I can reinforce this behavior with the attention that he seeks. In this way, everybody wins.

Third, positive reinforcement may come from internal as well as external sources. Thus, I may have reinforced Buffett's knocking things off by turning my attention from the TV to him (external reinforcement), but the behavior may also be reinforced simply because it is fun for him to watch the objects fall (internal reinforcement). In this case, ignoring Buffett or providing an alternative behavior may not succeed in altering his behavior because watching things fall is more fun.

Fourth, behavior that appears to have been extinguished may show what is called spontaneous recovery. If on Monday, Buffett finally stops knocking things down and lies quietly next to me instead, the annoying behavior may start up again when I sit down to watch TV on Tuesday. Keep in mind that these bursts of annoying behavior should stop more quickly with each succeeding extinction experience.

It is important to explain these characteristics of extinction to owners so they don't become frustrated themselves or, more important, report that they didn't work.

Negative reinforcement. Just as presenting something pleasant can be reinforcing, so can removing something unpleasant. If an animal can "turn off" something aversive through its behavior, then that behavior will increase in frequency because it works for her. Negative reinforcement plays a large role in reinforcing many aggressive and fearful behaviors. For example, if a cat can successfully get a person to leave him alone (in this case, the person is perceived as the "bad thing") by hissing, swatting, growling, and biting, then these behaviors are negatively reinforced because they cause the person, the bad thing, to go away. If a dog can break through a screen door and get inside the house to escape the full effects of a thunderstorm, then his destructive behavior will be negatively reinforced because the storm is less fear producing (has partially "gone away") when the dog is inside.

Traditional dog-training methods have been based largely on negative reinforcement and punishment (which I'll discuss later). One technique used to teach a dog to sit is to tighten a choke chain around his neck as he's standing. When the dog sits, the pressure is released. In this technique, sitting has been negatively reinforced because it has caused the tightness around his neck to go away. This is a stressful way to teach a sit because without additional cues or prompts, the dog has no idea how to get the pressure on his neck released. He has to learn by doing something—anything—until he finally discovers that sitting is what works.

Negative reinforcement is often used to correct annoying cat behaviors. For example, if a cat jumps on the counter and is squirted with water but the squirting stops when he jumps off, then jumping off has been negatively reinforced because it has made the water go away. (In the following pages, I will show that another behavior in this scenario is being punished at the same time.)

For now, the important things to remember about negative reinforcement are: (1) It is *not* the opposite of punishment, (2) it makes behavior *more* likely to occur, (3) it makes use of reinforcement, but it also uses aversive stimuli, and (4) it can play an important role in the development of fears, phobias, and aggression (see Table 3.1).

Table 3.1 Comparing consequences

	Effect on Target Behavior	Aversives Used?	Timing
Positive reinforcement	increases frequency	no	after desired behavior
Extinction	decreases frequency	no (unless removing something positive is considered to be aversive)	withholding of reinforcer after previously reinforced (undesired) behavior
Negative reinforcement	increases frequency	yes	desired behavior "turns off" aversive stimulus
Positive punishment	decreases frequency	yes	after undesirable behavior
Negative punishment	decreases frequency	no (unless removing something positive is considered to be aversive)	undesirable behavior "turns off" pleasant stimulus

Positive punishment. Punishment receives the most focus not only in the way that owners think about resolving problems but also in popular literature about dog training. Punishment alone is usually the least effective or appropriate way to change behavior, and when its use is indicated, it is almost always best used in conjunction with other, nonaversive procedures that elicit and reinforce acceptable behavior. Because of the problems associated with the use of punishment, I will discuss it in some detail.

By definition, punishment decreases the frequency of behavior. Thus, if attempts at punishment have been made and there has been no decrease in the undesirable behavior, then by definition the behavior hasn't been punished. There are two kinds of punishment—positive punishment and negative punishment.

Positive punishment, which is what most people think of when they talk of punishment, is the presentation of something unpleasant immediately following a behavior that makes the behavior less likely to occur in the future. It is important to note that any aversive stimulus can be a positive punisher, not just those that are strongly unpleasant (such as shock or hitting). Thus, a verbal no, a tug on the leash, a swat on the nose, or a shock from an electronic collar can all be positive punishers *if* they decrease the frequency of the behaviors they follow. If they do not, then none of them are punishing stimuli. A stimulus is defined as punishing not by its intensity but by its effect on behavior.

This brings up another point of confusion in the world of dog training, as some trainers claim to use only positive reinforcement. Most trainers are probably using some form of punishment as well, although they call it by another name. Euphemistic words such as *scolding, discipline,* and *correction* all refer to punishment if they mean that something unpleasant follows a behavior that decreases that behavior's frequency. As a client once told me, "Oh, I don't punish him, I just correct him with his leash and collar." Regardless of how the owner phrased it, if this "correction" was decreasing the behavior with the use of an aversive stimulus, then it was punishment.

A number of specific criteria must be met for punishment to be used effectively. These criteria are usually difficult to meet, which is one of the reasons why punishment, especially interactive punishment (see Box 3.2) has limited value in dealing with behavior problems.

First, punishment must be immediate, meaning that it must occur within 3 seconds (preferably less) of the behavior[1]. Just like positive reinforcement, punishment affects the precise behavior the animal is displaying at the time the aversive stimulus is applied. The most common misunderstanding involving this criterion is the notion that the dog "knows he's done wrong," whereby people erroneously conclude that the animal can connect aversive consequences with misbehavior that occurred minutes to hours previously. This is an example of an anthropomorphic interpretation of animal behavior, as opposed to an interpretation based on the principles of animal learning.

> **Box 3.2 Remote versus interactive positive punishment**
>
> **Interactive punishment:** punishment that results from a social interaction with a person
>
> **Remote punishment:** punishment that is either automatically triggered by the animal's own behavior (without human intervention) or surreptitiously triggered by a human observer

Animals do not have a moral sense of right and wrong that keeps them from engaging in certain behaviors. Referring back to the "because it works" model, pets easily learn when punishment will occur and when it will not. Cats learn they can scratch the furniture and dogs learn they can go through the trash when nobody is watching because nothing bad happens as a result. In fact, these activities are probably pretty enjoyable to the animal. When the owner comes home and finds the mess that has resulted, her behavior changes instantaneously. The pet perceives these changes—the scolding voice, the raised eyebrows, the threatening gestures—and feels threatened; he then displays behaviors to "turn off" the threat. In the case of dogs, these are typically submissive behaviors (e.g., ears back, tail down, crouching low), which are misinterpreted as "guilty looks." Cats usually run and hide. If attempts at punishment after the fact have occurred frequently enough, these same behaviors can be elicited when the owner comes home without seeing any mess. In those instances, the dog or cat has learned that if there is a mess when the owner arrives home, bad things will happen. This is not operant conditioning because the outcome (the bad thing) is not contingent on the pet's current behavior. Classical conditioning has occurred instead because one event (the occurrence of the mess and the owner together) predicts the occurrence of another (being scolded). This is very different from what the owner thinks is going on—that the animal is acknowledging the error of his or her ways and connecting the owner's displeasure with past behavior.

Delayed attempts at punishment can also create other problems, as illustrated with the following examples. My cat Buffett is allowed out in the backyard (only under supervision), but sometimes when I'm not watching him closely, he will jump the fence and go into our neighbor's yard. Although I'm irritated at Buffett for doing this, when I go get him I am as nice as I can be. He calmly walks up to me, I pick him up, and we go home until the next time my vigilance lapses and he does it again! If you are familiar with the idea that punishment must be immediate, you will not disagree with my handling of the situation. If you are thinking, "When she got to him, she should have punished him for jumping the fence instead of being nice," then you might want to read these sections again! Had I been angry or rough with Buffett, I would have been punishing him for what he was doing at the time, which was walking up to me. Buffett would have learned to avoid me after he jumped the fence because bad things happen to him *if he is caught on the other side of the fence.* Then I would have a cat who not only jumped the fence but became hard to catch after he was out! In other words, being nice to Buffett when I retrieve him is irrelevant to his fence jumping. To address that, I will need to catch him when he is either on the fence or preparing to jump.

Another common example, which I have seen result in defensive aggressive behavior problems (see chapter 12), occurs when owners attempt to punish dogs for "stealing" a forbidden item, such as food from the counter or tissues from the trash. When the owners find the dog with the forbidden item in his mouth, they chase him, holler at him, and sometimes even hit or scruff shake him, as some people still recommend. As with Buffett and the fence, all this teaches the dog is that *when he is caught with something in his mouth, bad things will happen.* The dog then often begins to respond with defensive threats or aggression (growling, snarling, or even biting) when the owners approach, and the problem behavior that triggered this cycle has not even been addressed.

My Dalmatian Ashley provides an illustration of how things can be handled differently. When Ashley first came to live with us, she liked to forage from the kitchen counters when no one was looking. She once brought me an intact packet of boil-in-the-bag of rice she had snatched from the kitchen sink while I was downstairs. She didn't go somewhere and tear it up, nor did she run around the house and play "keep away" with me. Rather, she brought it right to me and dropped it when I asked her to do so. She did this because whenever I had found her with a stolen item in the past, I called her to me, asked her to drop the item, and praised her when she responded appropriately. Clearly, Ashley had to be taught not to get into things in the first place, but when she did, I had no problem taking them from her. By praising her after she relinquished the object, I was reinforcing relinquishment. The stealing was not being reinforced because that was not the behavior she was displaying when she was being praised.

Second, punishment must be consistent, meaning it must occur *every time* the animal engages in the undesirable behavior. From the preceding examples, together with your own experience, it should be immediately apparent how difficult it is to meet this criterion from a practical standpoint. Most people have better things to do than follow their pets around day and night waiting for them to get into trouble. Furthermore, as I've discussed, when interactive punishment is used, animals quickly learn that punishment only happens in the owners' presence, so they only get into things when their owners aren't around, making it virtually impossible to meet this criterion. The use of remote devices, such as antibark collars that are automatically activated every time the behavior happens is one of the few ways that this criterion can be met easily.

Interactive, inconsistent punishment usually results in the persistence of the behavior; moreover, the behavior will begin to occur more often out of the owner's presence. For example, if the owners consistently punish a cat by squirting her with water when she jumps on the counter, the cat will limit her counter jumping to times when the owners are absent. Owners typically anthropomorphize the animal's response: "He knows he shouldn't do it," they say, "but he does it anyway, especially when he thinks he can get away with it." The "because it works" model tells us, instead, that the pet has either (1) learned to discriminate when punishment will occur and when it won't, or (2) decided it is worth the risk to attempt the behavior because there is a chance (sometimes a better than average one) that nothing bad will happen—in other words, the punishment has been inconsistent. Rather than viewing pets as scheming creatures who are constantly trying to get away with something, it makes much more sense to see them as fairly intelligent beings that are able to learn these discriminations, sometimes with just a few experiences.

Third, punishment must be delivered at the minimum intensity required to stop the behavior. This is a tricky criterion because it is virtually impossible to know in advance what degree of unpleasantness will be required. If we start by using low levels of an aversive stimulus that are ineffective (such as verbal scolding) and gradually escalate the intensity of the stimulus (to yelling or screaming, for example), then we have probably only trained the animal to tolerate a higher level of unpleasantness. Many experiments in animal learning have shown that with gradually increasing intensity, animals can learn to tolerate levels of aversive stimuli that would have actually stopped the behavior if they had been delivered with the first experience. The better approach would be to use something sufficiently aversive at the outset to stop the behavior quickly.

However, if we overshoot the mark and use something that is more intense than necessary, it is very likely that the animal will respond with fear, aggression, or both, thus creating additional problems. This can happen even with punishers that are used at the appropriate intensity to stop the undesirable behavior. Using physically forceful, threatening, or painful interactive punishments (such as hitting, scruff shaking, ear pinching, or strong leash and collar corrections) can cause a dog or cat to react with fear or defensive aggression toward the person instigating these procedures. If the person escalates this treatment, the animal becomes increasingly defensive, and a dangerous cycle is created.

Fourth, the aversive stimulus must occur only briefly. This criterion is related to the stipulation that punishment be immediate. If the aversive event continues long enough for the animal to engage in another behavior, then it is the subsequent behavior, in addition to the problem behavior, that is being affected. Most punishing stimuli should last only momentarily because an animal's behavior changes quickly. Again, my own Ashley and Buffett provide good examples (perhaps like the child psychologist's children who are always the worst behaved).

If I were to catch Ashley with her paws on the kitchen counter or Buffett on top of the dining table, I could yell at them to get off, which they would immediately do. Being the good behaviorist that I am, I would then praise them for complying. However, if I were to continue screaming, then I would actually be punishing the "getting off" behavior. If I kept it up, Ashley would then be likely to show fearful or submissive behavior, and Buffett would likely run and hide. If I then stopped yelling, I would negatively reinforce fear and hiding. Is that what I set out to do? Obviously, the answer is no, but because the "punishment" would have lasted too long, it would have had unintended, adverse consequences.

Unfortunately, this criterion is violated frequently. How many times have you seen a dog jerked around on a leash or a cat being yelled at long after he's stopped doing whatever it was he wasn't supposed to do? I once had a client relate that a trainer had told him to give his dog five jerks on the collar the first time his pet didn't sit when told to. If he disobeyed a second time, ten jerks were required, twenty the third time, and so on. Imagine how long it would take to give twenty jerks on the collar and how many behaviors the dog would show in the meantime to get the owner to stop! This is another example of how punishment is often misused and misunderstood. See Box 3.3 for a summary of the criteria discussed here.

> **Box 3.3 Criteria for effective punishment**
>
> Immediate
>
> Consistent
>
> Delivered at appropriate intensity
> - Minimum intensity sufficient to stop behavior quickly
> - No fear or aggressive responses
>
> Aversive stimulus occurs only briefly

How not to confuse positive punishment and negative reinforcement. If you are confused about what constitutes positive punishment or negative reinforcement in a particular situation, remember what behavior is the target of the consequences. Let's consider the situation in which a dog is taught to sit by tightening his collar when he is standing up and releasing the pressure when he sits. What actually happens in this scenario is that the standing behavior has been terminated because something unpleasant has followed it (that is, the standing has been punished), and *at the same time*, sitting has been negatively reinforced because sitting has caused the aversive tightness around the dog's neck to go away. Similarly, if a cat jumps up on the table and is squirted with water until he jumps off, being on the table has been punished, and jumping off has been negatively reinforced.

Absorbing these concepts will likely take some thought, and you will have to put them into practice before you have a thorough, workable understanding of them. You may need to read the text more than once, refer to the tables summarizing the important points, and perhaps even do some additional reading from the list of references about learning given at the end of the book.

Remote versus interactive positive punishment. Punishment is usually most effective if the punishing stimulus is delivered remotely rather than interactively. (See Box 3.2.) Interactive punishment is delivered by a person (often the owner), and it usually involves some sort of physical force (hitting, leash and collar corrections, etc.), attempts at social dominance (scruff shaking, pinning), or verbal or physical threat (a loud no, raising an arm as if to strike). The characteristics of these procedures make it inherently difficult to meet the effectiveness criteria described earlier. The intensity and duration of these procedures usually vary from one use to the next, and because they require the owner to take action within a few seconds of the animal's misbehavior, consistency and immediacy are problems. If the owner is part of the punishing stimulus, the pet may become fearful of or aggressive to that person in response. This may occur even when the punishment meets the effectiveness criteria, but it is even more likely to happen when the criteria are not met (see later discussion).

Remote punishment, which involves devices that are automatically triggered by the animal's own behavior, separates the aversive stimulus from the owner and is more likely to meet the criteria for effectiveness. Environmental "booby traps" such as Snappy Trainers (a harmless version of a mousetrap that uses a plastic paddle) and products such as the antibark collars are examples of remote punishers. If used correctly, these devices provide immediate and consistent punishment of brief duration whose intensity does not vary. Whether they are of appropriate intensity will depend on the individual animal.

Another type of remote punishment does not involve the owner directly interacting with the animal, although he or she must catch the pet in order to surreptitiously activate a remote device. Squirt guns or bottles, handheld audible products (e.g., an air horn), and ultrasonic noisemakers (e.g., the Pet Agree) fall into this category. Although such devices usually avoid the undesired outcomes that interactive punishment may create, they still must be used immediately and consistently.

Depending on the context of a specific behavior and the desired goal, a combination of interactive procedures and remote devices, such as a verbal no followed by use of an air horn, may be the best technique to use. With this approach, the no is classically conditioned to predict the air-horn noise. The no becomes a conditioned punisher and can be used effectively without the air horn, at least until the association between the two is lost. Examples of how remote devices fit into a complete behavior modification plan will be discussed in the chapters on specific behavior problems.

Problems with positive punishment. Any time aversive stimuli are used, the possibility for abuse exists. *Abuse* is a loaded word that is difficult to define universally. For the purposes of this discussion, we should be concerned about the use of aversive stimuli that fail to meet the criteria for effective punishment. It is inappropriate to use aversive stimuli in violation of these criteria; such an approach may be abusive and must be discouraged. Aversive stimuli that are too intense, that are used inconsistently, that are not contingent on the animal's behavior, and that continue for too long can constitute abusive treatment. Specific forms of punishment are often misused when owners or others working with pets don't have sufficient knowledge about the criteria for using these techniques.

Let's take a worst-case scenario. A dog or cat tears up the drapes when the owner is away. The owner comes home, grabs the animal, hits her, yells at her, throws her in a room, and ignores her for several hours. Because she's frightened, the pet urinates and defecates when she's alone in the room. The owner comes to the door to release the pet, sees the mess, and concludes the animal did it because she was "mad" at the owner for "punishing" her. The owner comes unglued, rubs the pet's nose in its mess, and throws her outside. The pet now refuses to come inside when called because she is afraid, but the owner thinks the animal is just being "disobedient" or "rebellious." If in the preceding scenario the pet is a dog, the owner will then yell at her and drag her inside by the collar. Is it any wonder that a dog treated in this manner later snaps at the owner when he reaches for her collar or that the cat in the previous scenario refuses to come at all and is labeled unsociable? Inadvertently, fears and phobias regarding neutral environmental stimuli can be classically conditioned if the animal associates something in the surroundings, such as the door, with all of this unpleasantness. Sometimes, this can happen after only one experience.

This type of sequence is not uncommon. In fact, I frequently hear similar stories from my clients. From the pet's point of view, the world and the people in it are completely unpredictable and not to be trusted; the safest thing to do is either to take a defensive approach to most interactions or to avoid them altogether.

As you can see, when the criteria for effective punishment are not met, as in the preceding examples, attempts at punishment are at best unfair and at the worst abusive and cruel. If you are going to recommend some sort of punishment procedure, you have an ethical responsibility to understand what is required for its effective use and to do your best to ensure that the owners do as well. I believe that we all should tirelessly work to educate owners, ourselves, and anyone who works with animal behavior to see that these types of scenarios do not persist.

Negative punishment. The other type of punishment is negative punishment. **P**ositive punishment is the **p**resentation (the *p*s are an easy way to remember the definition) of an aversive stimulus following a behavior. Negative punishment, by contrast, is the removal of something pleasant. The most common example of negative punishment is the time-out. For example, when a puppy or kitten becomes too excited and rough while playing, he can be timed-out in one of two ways. He can either be put in a small, quiet area such as a crate or laundry room or the owner can go into another room and shut the door, isolating himself from the pet. In both cases, the animal has lost (has had removed) the opportunity to continue to play (something enjoyable). Time-outs should be brief—probably no longer than a minute. With longer periods, the time-out ceases to be associated with the behavior that caused it, and most young animals can find some way to amuse themselves during the time-out, so that the experience is no longer unpleasant. If you have read in some popular book that owners should ignore their pets for hours or even days at a time as punishment, you can now see why this is an inappropriate approach to a problem.

Negative punishment can replace either positive punishment or negative reinforcement in many dog-training methods and as a behavior modification technique. When attempts at positive punishment seem to exacerbate problems, negative punishment may work better. When my Dalmatian Ashley first came to live with us, she had a terrible problem with jumping up on us, not just lightly putting her paws on our chests but launching herself from several feet away and then hitting us and bouncing back. The first time she did this to me, I unfortunately lost my temper, grabbed her by the scruff of the neck, and screamed, "No! Are you crazy?" Ashley, who apparently thought this was the initiating event of a contest to see who could be the most physical, promptly hit me again at chest level. I knew immediately that what I thought was positive punishment was, in fact, positive reinforcement to Ashley. So I tried the negative punishment approach. When Ashley struck, I folded my arms, turned my back, and walked away from her. She quickly learned that if she wanted my attention, she had to keep her body off mine. We've now refined the interaction: When she sits (instead of jumps up) to be petted, I stop petting her if she puts her paw on my leg, and she, in turn, takes her paw off. I do not need to yell at her, hit her, or jerk her collar. She removes her paw from my leg because she wants me to continue petting her.

To be effective, negative punishment must meet the same criteria as positive punishment, and identical problems are encountered in terms of meeting the consistency, immediacy, and brief duration criteria. It may also be difficult to identify a positive stimulus that can be removed that is more important to the animal than his desire to engage in the problem behavior.

Because negative punishment is the removal of something positive rather than the presentation of something unpleasant, it is less likely to result in abuse. Abuse could potentially happen if the removal of the positive continues for too long or if it involves depriving the animal of something necessary for survival. Clearly, confining a pet for days without food or water as punishment for some misbehavior would not only violate the criteria for effective punishment but would also be considered either neglect or abuse by most people.

Another shift in thinking. The concept of removing something positive to change behavior may require another shift from traditional thinking. Most of us think that if an animal is misbehaving, something must be done to him to suppress the behavior. At times, that is true: If your cat is about to jump on a hot stove or your dog is getting ready to run into traffic, immediate action must be taken. But when you are training new behaviors, incorrect responses can often just be ignored rather than punished. Remember, if the behavior doesn't work for the animal, it will likely not be repeated. So if you are trying to lure a dog into sitting by using a food treat and instead he paws at your hands, rolls over, barks, or the like, nothing unpleasant (such as jerking him by the collar) needs to be done. These undesired behaviors are just ignored and do not result in the dog getting the tidbit. If, however, sitting reliably earns him a treat and the other behaviors do not, then the other behaviors will disappear because they don't work for him. Sitting works, and it will occur with increasing frequency.

Limitations of punishment. In addition to the difficulties involved in the proper application of punishment and the potential for producing undesirable side effects, another important limitation is that punishment cannot teach new behavior. Punishment has an overall negative effect on behavior: It can suppress unwanted behavior, but it cannot teach the animal what to do instead. This is important because the acquisition of acceptable behavior is really the goal in resolving many behavior problems. This will become much clearer in later chapters on individual problems, but let's briefly consider aggression as an example. It really is not sufficient for a dog or cat to learn to inhibit aggressive behavior (which is the best we could hope for with punishment). The real goal is for the animal to learn alternative, friendly behavior. This requires behavior modification techniques that elicit and reinforce desired behavior.

Related to this is the concept that punishment is more effective if the animal is given the opportunity to perform an alternative response that will accomplish the same goal (a response that will work for the animal) as the punished behavior. When animals are left to find an appropriate behavior by trial and error, several things can happen. They may pick another behavior that is just as undesirable, or they may repeat the same unwanted behavior again. This is because punishment creates a "behavioral vacuum" that the animal will try to fill with another behavior that gets him what he wants (we're back to the "because it works" model again). For example, if a dog is barking for attention or a cat is meowing for the same reason and these behaviors are punished with a squirt of water, while a competing behavior, such as being quiet or sitting, results in attention from the owner, then the water is more likely to be effective as a punisher. When alternative behaviors are reinforced in this way, behaviors can often be suppressed with only mild punishers.

Trainers sometimes use the term *correction* to mean administering punishment and then showing the dog what he is supposed to do instead. However, these are really two separate behavioral procedures—punishment combined with whatever procedure is being used to encourage the desired response. It is confusing and not very helpful to invent another term to describe this sequence, especially when *correction* implies something aversive.

CHANGING BEHAVIOR:
"HOW CAN I GET HIM TO DO WHAT I WANT?"

As I noted earlier, the successful resolution of behavior problems often involves not just suppressing undesirable behavior but also teaching and encouraging acceptable behavior. A variety of procedures can be used to teach new behaviors. As discussed, positive and negative reinforcement can be used in operant conditioning to increase the frequency of specified behaviors. However, one form of classical conditioning is also an important tool for changing behavior, especially behaviors that accompany fear and aggression problems.

Counterconditioning and Desensitization

Sometimes, it's not what the animal does or doesn't *do* that is at the root of the problem but how he "*feels*" about certain stimuli that then motivate his behavior. In other words, behavior is difficult to change without changing the underlying motivation, or how he "feels" about the situation. Fears, anxiety, phobias, and aggression involve an emotional reaction or arousal. If we rely on operant conditioning to work with these types of problems, we will probably have only moderate success at best. It has been well documented in the learning literature that if classically conditioned responses are at odds with operantly conditioned behavior, the former will determine what the animal does[2]. Let's look at a few examples.

We can operantly condition a dog or a cat to perform a sit-stay for several minutes (yes, a cat can be taught to do this!). However, if we ask the animal to remain sitting in the presence of something he is truly afraid of—such as the approach of a toddler—the animal will likely get up and leave in order to avoid the feared stimulus. Thus, the emotional response of fear interferes with the animal's ability to perform the operant response of sitting. It might be possible, especially with a dog, to prevent the animal from leaving by punishing him for doing so, but in the example just posed, this would produce a dog who might remain sitting as the toddler approaches but is still fearful (and perhaps even more so because of the added threat of punishment). Imagine what might happen if the toddler then reaches out to pet the dog. If the dog is afraid and can't escape the situation, he may snap or bite. If the animal in question is a cat, she will run away to avoid the child, and the response of running away will be negatively reinforced. The bottom line is that neither animal has learned to be less afraid of the child (and in fact may have become more afraid). This illustrates the limitations of operant conditioning in working with problem behaviors that involve emotional arousal.

In these situations, which are extremely common in behavior work, the techniques of counterconditioning and desensitization are invaluable. Counterconditioning means teaching (conditioning) the animal to associate something good with a stimulus that previously predicted something bad. Using the preceding example, if the dog is appropriately conditioned by receiving treats when the toddler appears, then the child's presence (which previously evoked fear) will instead trigger a "warm fuzzy" for the pet—a pleasant reaction because to the animal, "child means food." The child is no longer an unconditioned stimulus that evokes fear but a conditioned one that predicts food. If the dog or cat is no longer afraid when the child approaches, it will be able to successfully perform the sit-stay (which may actually be irrelevant to problem resolution) and not be motivated to run, hide, or bite (which *is* relevant to problem resolution). It is important to note that what operantly conditioned behavior the animal is doing (sitting, standing) when the pairing of child and food occurs doesn't matter.

Desensitization is often used in conjunction with counterconditioning because it may be difficult for new associations to be made if the emotional reaction is intense. Desensitization involves exposing the animal to a weak version of the stimulus (in the preceding example, keeping the child far away) and gradually increasing the stimulus intensity (slowly bringing the child closer). There are a variety of ways to modify stimulus intensity in the common contexts in which these techniques are used (see Box 3.4).

Box 3.4 Ways to decrease stimulus intensity during desensitization

- Increase the distance between animal and stimulus
- Decrease the volume (loudness)
- Make the stimulus move more slowly
- Make the stimulus smaller in size
- Change the characteristics of the person to ones the animal finds least threatening
  - Age, gender, height, clothing, facial hair, glasses, etc.
- Change the behavior of people the animal finds threatening
  - Avoiding eye contact, not reaching for the animal, not moving toward animal

Counterconditioning and desensitization will be explained in more detail in chapters 11 and 16 on fears and phobias and chapters 12 and 15 on aggression.

Countercommanding

Counterconditioning is often misrepresented in the popular literature. It is important to remember that it involves classical conditioning, not operant conditioning. Its operant analog is countercommanding. Countercommanding means operantly conditioning another behavior for the animal to perform instead of the problem behavior[3]. For example, a dog could be taught to look at his owner rather than lunging for people when on walks or sit when a toddler approaches, as in the previous example. Keep in mind, however, that if the presence of another person triggers a strong emotional response (which it probably does if aggression is involved), the desire to lunge may override the operantly conditioned "look-at-the-owner" response. Counter-commanding probably works best if the animal reliably responds to commands, if he is not highly motivated to perform the undesired behavior, and in situations in which he is easily controlled, such as on leash or with the owner in close proximity[3]. However, when a problem behavior with an emotional component to it occurs in a "real-life" setting and the dog has more opportunity to choose how to respond, countercommanding is less likely to be effective.

SUMMARY

This chapter has outlined some of the complexities involved in animal learning and suggested that learning principles are often ignored or violated when popular techniques for resolving problems are used. Yet the information presented here has only scratched the surface of topics that are essential knowledge for anyone working with behavior problems. Other relevant topics include flooding, shaping, prompting, differential schedules of reinforcement, and stimulus control. Although these topics are beyond the scope of this reference guide (flooding is discussed briefly in chapter 11), it is vitally important for you to be well acquainted with them if you are to succeed with behavioral consulting. Learn more about these topics by reading from the list of additional readings at the end of the book.

REFERENCES

1. Schwartz, Barry. 1978. *Psychology of learning and behavior.* New York: W.W. Norton.

2. Breland, K., and M. Breland. 1961. The misbehavior of organisms. *Amer. Psych.* 61:681–4.

3. Reid, P.J., and P.L. Borchelt. 1996. Learning. In *Readings in companion animal behavior,* eds. V.L. Voith and P.L. Borchelt, 62–71. Trenton, N.J.: Veterinary Learning Systems.

CHAPTER 4

Problem Prevention
for Puppies and New Adult Dogs

This chapter deals with problem prevention with puppies or adult dogs that are new to the household. For information on dogs with preexisting problems, refer to the chapter specific to that problem.

HELPING OWNERS SET REALISTIC EXPECTATIONS

We all know that puppies require training and supervision, but many owners mistakenly assume that if they acquire an adult dog, they will avoid all the work a puppy entails. Even the best adult dog, however, will need a transition period to adapt to a new environment and learn the rules of the house. After working at an animal shelter for almost 4 years, I am firmly convinced that an adult dog coming into a new home should be treated just like a puppy for the first few weeks. If the dog adapts well and things go smoothly, then she can be given the freedom of a well-trained adult soon thereafter. However, if owners do this too quickly, bad habits can be established that are much more difficult to change than to prevent. If new owners of adult dogs anticipate having to deal with puppylike behavior for a while, they will be prepared for occasional mishaps, rather than being disappointed when they think they are going to have clear sailing because they obtained an adult dog. It's much better to have owners who are pleasantly surprised at how well things go than to have them be angry and disappointed because their expectations were too high. Every pet owner should be prepared for some degree of household damage from having an animal share his or her home (see chapter 8).

TALKING TO OWNERS—ELICITING INFORMATION

When you talk to owners during appointments soon after they've acquired a new animal, simply asking them if they are having any problems or if they have any questions may not be sufficient. Their new animal may be showing signs of developing behavior problems, but they may think such behaviors are of no concern. First, a negative response might, in fact, signal the owners' lack of awareness of problems in the making rather than the fact that all is truly going well. Second, just asking if they have questions won't give you any information on the sort of house-training or other basic training procedures they are using. They may be rubbing their dog's nose in his waste, but if they think that's the appropriate way to discourage accidents in the home, they won't have any questions for you. So, instead, you need to solicit information from owners rather than expecting they will provide you with what you need to know to help them prevent problems. Ask open-ended questions such as the following:

> "What kinds of housetraining procedures are you using?"
>
> "How are you dealing with normal puppy chewing and mouthing behavior?"
>
> "What are you doing to socialize your puppy, to encourage friendly behavior to everyone he meets, both in public and at home, and to teach him to be at ease in new surroundings?"
>
> "What kinds of games do you play with your puppy?"
>
> "What kinds of toys does your puppy have?"
>
> "How are you introducing your children and their friends to your new dog?"
>
> "How are you introducing your new dog to the rest of your family pets?"

PRINCIPLES OF PROBLEM PREVENTION

I have identified four important principles in problem-prevention programs:

1. Eliciting and reinforcing appropriate behavior
2. Preventing or minimizing inappropriate behavior
3. Minimizing the use of punishment and using punishment correctly when necessary
4. Providing for the pet's behavioral needs or meeting the puppy's or kitten's developmental needs

I'll discuss each of the principles prior to applying them to specific behaviors.

1. *Eliciting and reinforcing appropriate behavior.* There is no better example of the "how can I get him to do what I want so I can reinforce him for it?" approach than problem prevention. Problem prevention requires teaching appropriate behavior or making it likely to happen. Prevention of a problem implies there is no preexisting problem, so why would a focus on aversive control even make any sense?

2. *Preventing or minimizing inappropriate behavior ("mistakes").* Preventing problems also means not allowing inappropriate patterns to develop. Allowing inappropriate behavior will interfere with the pet's ability to learn the desired habits. If inappropriate behavior occurs more often than desired behavior, it will become a pattern that is difficult to change.

3. *Minimizing the use of punishment and using punishment correctly when necessary.* Minimizing the use of punishment is actually accomplished by adhering to the other three principles mentioned in the preceding list. If punishment is required, it must be used based on the criteria for effective punishment discussed in chapter 3.

4. *Providing for the pet's behavioral needs or meeting the puppy's or kitten's developmental needs.* Remember that animals behave in the ways they do because the behavior works for them. Most problematic behavior in both dogs and cats is normal behavior for them but becomes a concern because of where, when, or how often it occurs. Thus, it is not realistic to expect dogs not to chew, cats not to claw, or any pet not to eliminate or play. Problem prevention is not about trying to inhibit these behaviors; rather, it is about helping to channel their expression in ways that the owner considers appropriate. We need to help the owner provide for the pets' behavioral needs instead of focusing on suppressing perfectly normal behaviors.

In this chapter, I will suggest what to tell clients about these principles as they apply to each of the following behaviors or training situations:

- Housetraining
- Chewing and other destructive behaviors
- Socialization—creating friendly dogs
- Mouthing and nipping
- Establishing a leadership position
- Preventing problems during play
- Introducing a new dog to resident dogs
- Introducing a new dog to children

Housetraining

I believe it is important to refer to the process of teaching appropriate elimination behavior as "housetraining," not "housebreaking". House*training* implies that owners are teaching the dog what is acceptable; house*breaking* implies that there is some bad habit that needs to be changed, and it has the connotation of aversive control. It's a good idea to tell owners why you use the term *housetraining*—it sets the stage for how they should be thinking of this process.

For dogs, the process of housetraining makes use of the dog's normal pattern of elimination. If given the chance, dogs tend to move to other areas to eliminate, rather than soil their den or resting areas. Thus, housetraining dogs means giving them time to realize that the entire house is their den and establishing an area (the yard, the park) for elimination. Notice that the developmental literature says that dogs won't eliminate in their den *if given the chance to do so elsewhere*[1]. This does *not* mean that a crate, if one is used, has some magical property so that as long as the dog is crated, he won't eliminate (see the section on crate training). If he is crated too long or if he becomes anxious, a dog will indeed soil his crate.

Housetraining requires a major time and energy commitment. When our Dalmatian Ashley came to us at about 5 months of age, I had not had a puppy in almost 15 years. I had forgotten what it takes to housetrain a dog. We had baby gates at the entrance to almost every room, and we carried one around with us and set it up across the doorway of whatever room we were in. I found myself jumping up from my desk every few minutes if Ashley was not in full view. "Where's Ashley?" became a constant query in our household, and we soon found that going outside to reinforce elimination was no fun when it was 2 A.M. or snowing. However, all these inconveniences paid off when Ashley was well housetrained in a few weeks.

1. *Eliciting and reinforcing appropriate behavior.*
   - Consistently use a "do you want to go outside?" phrase and head for the door.
   - Consistently use a "go do your business" phrase while the dog is preparing to eliminate (sniffing, circling, etc.) and also when he does so.
   - Go outside with the dog and provide quiet, verbal praise during elimination.
   - Walk to the dog, give her a tidbit, or throw a toy as soon as possible after elimination is finished. (Remember, reinforcement pertains to what the dog is doing at that moment, so waiting until the dog walks back to you or the door won't do!)
   - If the dog enjoys being outside, don't make her come in as soon as she eliminates. She may begin to delay elimination in order to stay outside.

2. *Preventing or minimizing inappropriate behavior ("mistakes").*
   - Be aware of and don't ignore the variety of behaviors a dog can show that indicates he needs to eliminate, including pacing, whining, circling, sniffing, or even moving off to a distant part of the room. When you notice such behavior, respond with, "Do you want to go outside?" and head for the door.
   - Know where the dog is at all times. Use a leash to tether him to you; use baby gates to keep him in the room with you; close doors to unoccupied rooms.
   - Confine the dog when he cannot be supervised or watched. Use a small room (e.g., laundry room or mudroom), a playpen, an exercise pen, or a crate (see section on crate training).
   - Have a consistent feeding time.
   - Have a consistent schedule for taking him outside—every few hours for puppies; two to four times a day for adults; first thing in the morning and last thing at night; before being confined; and after meals, naps, or playtime for dogs of any age.
   - To clean soiled areas indoors, use enzymatic cleaners, which break up the organic material that produces the odor (see product appendix).
   - Do not clean soiled areas with ammonia products.
   - Make the transition to less confinement or supervision gradually. The transition to allowing the dog free run of the house for a full workday cannot be made in one step; it may take several weeks or a month.
   - Consistent routines and at least intermittent reinforcement for proper elimination are good procedures to follow throughout the dog's lifetime.

3. *Minimizing the use of punishment and using punishment correctly when necessary.*
   - Punishment is not necessary in housetraining.
   - If you find a mess, clean it up and do nothing to the dog.
   - If you see your dog eliminating in the house, get her to quickly follow you outside by using your "go outside" phrase in an encouraging tone of voice, followed by the "do your business" phrase once you are outside.
   - Remember that accidents happen because you fail to adequately supervise your dog, you do not take him outside frequently enough, or you are unaware of or ignore signs that he needs to eliminate (not all dogs will go to the door or bark, especially in the early stages of housetraining).

4. *Providing for the dog's behavioral needs or meeting the puppy's developmental needs.*
   - If the dog will likely need to eliminate during a confinement period, the area must be large enough to provide an elimination area away from the resting area.
   - A small crate is not appropriate for a young puppy who will be unsupervised or alone longer than she can control herself because it does not provide a space for elimination away from the resting area.
   - Overnight, young puppies must be crated within hearing range, as they will likely need to be taken outside. Alternatively, owners can set an alarm to wake them up every 2 to 4 hours, depending on the age of the puppy.
   - Provide an acceptable elimination area outside—the area should be soft in texture (grass) or whatever type of surface the dog prefers, protected from weather extremes (shady in summer heat, shoveled in winter), and free from any stimuli the dog fears.

- Because dogs do develop preferences for certain types of substrates on which to eliminate, it may be a good idea to accustom puppies to eliminating on different types of surfaces (grass, gravel, etc.) to prevent problems when the preferred surface is not available, as when traveling or on walks. However, this should be done cautiously so that housetraining won't be disrupted; problems could ensue if you only give the dog access to surfaces he is reluctant to use.
- Do not rely on consistent, daily crating or other types of close confinement for extended periods over the dog's lifetime or to the detriment of his need for exercise, play, and social interaction.

Chewing and Other Destructive Behaviors

In my work at an animal shelter, as well as my behavior consulting practice, I have found that most new owners have more tolerance for destructive behavior from puppies than from adult dogs. However, many do not realize that dogs can be expected to show puppylike destructive behavior until they are over a year old. I often get calls from owners of 8- or 9-month-old puppies who can't understand why their dogs are still chewing everything in sight. The answer is simple: That's what 8- and 9-month-old puppies do when they aren't well supervised! Similar to mouthing and nipping, much of this normal, puppytype behavior often begins to decrease on its own when the puppy is 12 to 18 months of age. The many other reasons for destructive behavior in adult dogs will be addressed in chapter 8. This section pertains only to destructive chewing motivated by investigative and playful behavior in young dogs.

1. *Eliciting and reinforcing appropriate behavior.*
    - Provide a variety of interesting toys and items for chewing. Select them based on the dog's preferences and the veterinarian's advice regarding safe chewing objects.
    - Rotate toys so the dog has different ones every few days.
    - Some toys should provide for self-play. Among these are toys that deliver a tidbit when they are manipulated, such as the Buster Cube, Activity Ball, Goodie Ship, or Roll-a-Treat (see product appendix).
    - Positively reinforce the dog when he is playing with or chewing on his own toys, using praise, petting, or a treat. This can be done when the dog on his own begins to chew on or play with appropriate toys.

2. *Preventing or minimizing inappropriate behavior ("mistakes").*
    - Know where the dog is at all times. Use a leash to "tether" him to you; use baby gates to keep him in the room with you; close doors to unoccupied rooms.
    - Confine the dog when he cannot be supervised or watched. Use a small room (e.g., the laundry room or mudroom), a playpen, an exercise pen, or a crate.
    - Puppy-proof the home by putting enticing items out of reach, so that the dog's opportunity to chew on them is minimized.
    - Don't confuse the dog by providing "old" versions of off-limit items to be used as toys (e.g., old socks, shoes, towels).
    - If the dog returns to certain off-limit items repeatedly, either prevent his access to them or booby-trap them (a remote punisher can be used).
    - Make the transition to less confinement or supervision gradually. The transition to having free run of the house for a full workday cannot be done in one step; it may take several weeks or a month.

3. *Minimizing the use of punishment and using punishment correctly when necessary.*
  - Use remote punishment so that there is an immediate, unpleasant consequence for chewing unacceptable items. Snappy Trainers, Bitter Apple, and motion detectors that emit a loud noise or trigger other devices when disturbed (for example, turning on a hair dryer) can all be effective remote punishers (see product appendix).
  - Interactive punishment should be avoided.
  - If the dog is caught chewing on an unacceptable object that hasn't been booby-trapped, remove it and give the dog one of his own toys instead.
  - The need for punishment can be minimized by providing proper supervision, limiting access to off-limit items, reinforcing appropriate behavior, and satisfying the dog's chewing, social, and exercise needs.

4. *Providing for the dog's behavioral needs or meeting the puppy's developmental needs.*
  - Provide consistent opportunities for physical exercise, such as walks, fetching games, etc.
  - Pay attention to what types of toys the dog prefers and provide a variety that meet his preferences. Dogs need an assortment of toys—things to chew, things to shake and treat as pretend prey, and things to fetch.
  - Remember that teething can be uncomfortable, causing some puppies to want to chew almost constantly. Toys cooled in the refrigerator or freezer may feel particularly good on sore gums. Wetting a rag and then freezing it or freezing whole carrots are other alternatives.
  - The need to chew is a lifelong trait, so don't neglect chew toys (chewies) for the adult dog, too.
  - Dogs who like to dig can be given their own digging area and encouraged to use it by burying tidbits or chewies there.
  - Do not confine or crate the dog for excessive periods (e.g., 10 hours a day, 6 days a week) or rely on confinement as a lifelong procedure. When confinement is necessary, it is crucial that dogs also have the opportunity for adequate play and exercise.

Socialization: Creating Friendly Dogs

The term *socialization* is used to describe a concept, a process, and an outcome. As a concept, it means the forming of social bonds or attachments. As a process, it means providing an animal with opportunities to have pleasant experiences with a variety of people, places, and things. As an outcome, it refers to an animal who is at ease (friendly and not aggressive or fearful) with most people, in unfamiliar environments, and with novel stimuli; such a dog will adjust well to change.

The sensitive period. A sensitive period for socialization in puppies occurs between about 6 and 12 weeks of age[1]. During this time, puppies are not afraid of much, and it is relatively easy for them to enjoy new people, places, and things. This period is referred to as a sensitive period because socialization occurs extremely readily during this time—puppies are sensitive, or primed, for it to happen. The socialization period is limited by the puppy's increasing fear of the unfamiliar. There are two normal developmental fear periods—one at 8 weeks, which ends the peak time for socialization that started at 6 weeks, and another between 12 and 16 weeks, which marks the end of the sensitive period for socialization[1].

The importance of socialization. What happens or doesn't happen during the sensitive period can have dramatic effects on a dog's adult behavior. Puppies who lead backyard lives and only interact with a few people may grow up to be fearful or aggressive when meeting new folks. They also may have a difficult time when encountering anything new. Poorly socialized dogs can be afraid of many harmless things; they tend to startle easily and react with fear to unpredictable events. Many people assume such dogs have been abused, but it is more likely they have not been well socialized. An inadequately socialized dog also doesn't generalize well. This means that although he becomes comfortable with one stimulus—such as Aunt Sara visiting—he may still react fearfully to Aunt Jane; moreover, the fact that he is comfortable with Aunt Sara during her summer visit may not carry over to her visit at Christmas.

1. *Eliciting and reinforcing appropriate behavior.* In the context of socialization, this means providing good socialization experiences. Remember that socializing a normal puppy is a different task than attempting to resocialize a poorly socialized adult who is already fearful or aggressive, which requires more of a problem-resolution approach (see chapters 11 and 12).

- Create pleasant, enjoyable experiences for the puppy with a variety of people with different characteristics—tall and short; male and female; young and old; people with glasses; men with facial hair; women wearing hats, gloves, or coats; people of different ethnic groups.
- Create pleasant, enjoyable experiences for the puppy in a variety of places—parks, other people's homes, veterinary clinics, the grooming shop, pet stores with slick floors, water, etc. (Make sure the puppy is current on his vaccinations, and avoid areas that have had recent outbreaks of contagious diseases such as distemper.)
- Create pleasant, enjoyable experiences for the puppy with a variety of environmental experiences—showing them umbrellas, canes, baby strollers, vacuum cleaners, or brooms or taking them on rides in the car, walks downtown, etc.
- Create pleasant consequences from people who approach or reach into your car—gas station attendants, toll booth attendants, fast food personnel, etc.
- Create pleasant experiences with other dogs—small ones and large ones, males and females, and dogs with different physical characteristics.
- Introduce the puppy to other species of animals he is likely to encounter, based on his lifestyle—cats, horses, birds, livestock, etc.
- Make sure the puppy has a good time with each of these experiences by using food, toys, or petting as part of these encounters.

2. *Preventing or minimizing inappropriate behavior ("mistakes").* In this case, inappropriate behavior would be fear or aggressive behavior during socialization experiences.

- Do not force a dog to experience something he fears. Dragging a fearful puppy around the neighborhood or forcing a cringing dog to accept petting from a stranger is not socialization.
- Allow the puppy to take his time in approaching a new stimulus if he is reluctant to do so, and encourage him to make small advances by laying a trail of treats or throwing a toy.
- If problems occur, make the experience easier for the puppy. For instance, if he is reluctant to approach a tall man, have the man sit down so he appears less threatening.
- Don't overwhelm the puppy with situations he can't tolerate.
- Take particular care to socialize the puppy to children.

3. *Minimizing the use of punishment and using punishment correctly when necessary.*
   - Punishment is never indicated for fearful behaviors, including aggression motivated by fear. Punishment is not part of socialization.
   - Rather than punishing a fearful, threatening, or aggressive response that is triggered by a socialization experience, immediately make the situation easier for the puppy so that friendly behavior can be elicited.
   - If an interaction doesn't go well, it should not be repeated in the same manner; instead, it should be made easier for the puppy. If the puppy is repeatedly exposed to situations that produce a problem response, the goal of socialization is not being accomplished.
   - A mild verbal no in reaction to a problem response may indicate to the puppy the response was not acceptable, but it does nothing to help him learn to be friendly.
   - If the dog continues to display problem reactions such as fear or aggression, this is no longer a problem-prevention situation but one that requires behavior modification.

4. *Providing for the dog's behavioral needs or meeting the puppy's developmental needs.*
   - Do not neglect socialization during the sensitive period. Doing so may result in a dog who is not at ease and who therefore may become fearful or aggressive in any new situation or with unfamiliar people. You owe it to your puppy to socialize him well, so that he can develop to his fullest potential.
   - Continue to provide socialization experiences past the sensitive period. Dogs will likely regress if they are relegated to the backyard for the rest of their lives.
   - Adult dogs who are fearful or aggressive require a problem-resolution approach rather than basic socialization.

Mouthing and Nipping

These normal puppy behaviors are among the most frustrating ones for owners, especially if there are children in the family. They are also often misinterpreted as signs that the puppy is becoming an aggressive dog. Contrary to what many popular books state, these behaviors tend to disappear naturally as the puppy matures, even if little is done to discourage them. They become more of an issue when inappropriate aversive procedures are applied, which only aggravate the behaviors or cause fearful or aggressive problems.

1. *Eliciting and reinforcing appropriate behavior.*
   - When the puppy tries to chew on a hand or other body part, substitute something else to chew on—a rawhide treat, a Booda bone, etc. (see product appendix).
   - When reaching out to pet the puppy, offer a tidbit with the other hand. This keeps the puppy's mouth occupied during petting (and is also a good socialization tool).
   - Engage the puppy in an alternative behavior by throwing a ball, having him sit, etc.
   - If the puppy starts to mouth or nip and then inhibits himself and stops, praise him lavishly, offer a treat, or bring out a special toy to play with (unless these reinforcements are presented immediately, the puppy will not associate them with the inhibition of the mouthing).

2. Preventing or minimizing inappropriate behavior ("mistakes").
- Avoid enticing the dog to play with fingers, feet, or other body parts.
- Avoid teasing the puppy with the hands (slapping the sides of his face, etc.).
- Pet the puppy under the chin rather than over the head.
- Do not quickly the jerk hands away if the puppy starts to mouth them (children especially have a tendency to do this). The puppy is likely to jump after the hands in play.
- Until the puppy has been taught some self-control, avoid rough wrestling games that agitate him into nipping.

3. Minimizing the use of punishment and using punishment correctly when necessary.
- The use of positive punishment methods, which are interactive and physical, are likely to evoke fearful or aggressive responses or cause an escalation of the nipping behavior if the dog perceives the interaction as a game.
- Avoid scruff shaking, grabbing the collar, hitting on the nose, stuffing fingers down the mouth, holding the mouth closed, etc.
- Sometimes, giving a high-pitched "yipe," as if you are in pain, may startle the dog enough to interrupt the behavior. This technique can be followed by negative punishment.
- Two potentially effective negative punishments for mouthing are (1) giving the puppy a brief time-out (putting him in small, quiet, confined area for a few minutes), and (2) walking away from the puppy. In both situations, the puppy's mouthing causes the removal of something enjoyable, namely, interaction with the owner. Either of these techniques may be preceded by a verbal no (or the "yipe") that *immediately* follows the nipping to alert the dog to his unacceptable behavior.

4. Providing for the dog's behavioral needs or meeting the puppy's developmental needs.
- Provide plenty of opportunities for interactive play, such as fetching.
- Provide plenty of appropriate objects for chewing.
- Be patient! Let the puppy grow up.

Establishing a Leadership Position

Dominance is perhaps the most misunderstood and overused concept in the popular dog literature. Virtually every possible behavior problem has been attributed to the owner's lack of dominance over the dog. (The most ridiculous one I've heard was that coprophagia [stool eating] was a dominant behavior.) Consequently, a mythology has developed regarding all the things that must be avoided to prevent the dog from becoming a controlling monster. These include not letting him go through doors ahead of the owner, not feeding him until after the owner has eaten, not letting him on the bed or furniture, and not playing tug-of-war. So-called dominance exercises[2] have also been recommended in which the puppy or dog is held or forced into submissive positions, sometimes very roughly, to the point of creating fearful responses. There is no evidence that any of these procedures prevent aggression or any other kind of behavior problem. In fact, one study found no correlation between playing tug-of-war or allowing a dog on the bed and the occurrence of dominance aggression[3].

Part of the problem is that the definition of *dominance* has often been broadened to explain any type of disobedience or misbehavior. In my experience, relatively few dogs develop dominance aggression problems that result in bites to family members. Many more dogs are generally unruly: They are unresponsive to basic commands; engage in annoying, attention-getting behaviors; and are "pushy," or continually testing the owner to determine what behavior will be allowed. For our purposes, if we think of dominance as being about control of resources and social status, it is clear that these behaviors are not dominance problems at all. In fact, dominance aggression problems are probably caused by interactions between many genetic and environmental factors. Consequently, it is not realistic to think that dominance aggression can be prevented with a few simple exercises, especially since the etiology (cause) of such problems is not even well understood[4]. One study found that different types of early intervention and client education did not change the frequency of problem puppies[5].

Accordingly, this section on leadership does not refer to the prevention of dominance aggression. Instead, leadership should be thought of as establishing interactional patterns between the dog and owner in which the dog learns to (1) willingly give up control in social interactions and control of possessions, (2) acquiesce to the owner's requests, (3) accept dominant gestures and postures (see later section) from the owner that are commonly part of many interactions, and (4) willingly assume a submissive posture when asked. All of these responses can be taught using positive techniques rather than confrontational procedures and aversive control.

1. *Eliciting and reinforcing appropriate behavior.* Remember, these are problem *prevention* techniques. Some of them can be dangerous if a dog has an existing aggression problem. There are countless ways that dogs can be reinforced for giving up control and responding to the owner's requests; only a few examples are included here.

- Use a "nothing in life is free" approach. The dog must obey an easy command (e.g., "sit") before receiving anything he wants, including attention, food, and praise. Tidbits can be used to teach commands, as well as provide an additional reinforcement (the other reinforcement is what the dog wants).
- Teach the dog to enjoy getting off the bed or furniture when asked by tossing a treat on the floor.
- Teach the dog to enjoy receiving dominant gestures such as hugs and reaching for his collar by offering a tidbit or showing him a favorite toy at the same time.
- Make assuming subordinate postures, such as rolling over, enjoyable because they result in pleasant handling and petting.
- Teach the dog to enjoy having someone near his food dish by dropping a special treat in it as you walk by.
- Teach the dog to like having objects taken away by removing an important possession (such as a rawhide or favorite toy) and replacing it with something equally enjoyable or better (such as a tidbit).

2. *Preventing or minimizing inappropriate behavior ("mistakes").*

- Don't allow pestering or controlling behavior to work for the dog. For example, don't respond to barking for attention.
- Avoid playing keep-away or chasing games, in which the dog is encouraged to grab or lunge for a toy or other object.
- Don't avoid doing innocuous things to the dog (brushing, toweling off his feet, etc.) because you perceive he doesn't like it. Use positive techniques and gradual exposure to teach him to enjoy these interactions.

- Follow through to see that the dog responds to commands when they are given. Don't allow noncompliance. This doesn't mean positive punishment is necessary, but be persistent until the desired response is performed.

3. *Minimizing the use of punishment and using punishment correctly when necessary.*
   - Physical, interactive punishment (hitting, scruff shaking, etc.) should be avoided because it can trigger either offensive or defensive aggressive behavior.
   - Negative punishment may be best. Don't give the dog access to what he wants until he obeys a command or walk away and ignore him to discourage attention-getting behavior. If the dog won't relinquish a toy, end the game by walking away and ignoring him.
   - By properly applying the rest of the principles, the need for punishment should decrease.
   - If the dog consistently reacts with threats (growling, showing teeth, snapping) or aggression (biting), then this is no longer a problem-prevention situation but one that requires behavior modification.

4. *Providing for the dog's behavioral needs or meeting the puppy's developmental needs.*
   - Puppies and adult dogs require consistent rules regarding acceptable and unacceptable behavior. If, for example, pestering behavior works for a dog one day but she is punished for it the next day, she will not learn not to pester and may mistrust her owner.
   - Physical confrontations, physical force, and other aversive procedures are not necessary to establish a leadership position over a dog.
   - Puppies and dogs need to be encouraged and reinforced, not physically coerced, to acknowledge the owner as leader.

Preventing Problems during Play

One of the ways in which domestic dogs differ from their wild counterparts is that their play behavior persists at a higher frequency during adulthood. Play helps fill the needs for social interaction, physical activity, and environmental enrichment. Typically, problems in play patterns develop because the dog is getting too excited and out of control or because he won't relinquish his toys. These two issues are partially addressed using the techniques described in the sections on mouthing and nipping and on establishing a leadership position. Terry Ryan's and Jean Donaldson's books[6,7] have good sections on innovative games to play with dogs.

A lot of mythology has developed over the inadvisability of playing "tug-of-war" games with dogs. Playing tug-of-war with a dog who already has a possessiveness problem and challenges people over relinquishment of toys and other items is probably not a good idea. However, this is not the same thing as saying that playing tug-of-war *causes* the problem in the first place. There are no data to support such a statement, and in fact, one study showed no correlation between tug-of-war and the development of aggressive behavior problems[3]. Because my Dalmatians, Ashley and Mocha, play tug-of-war constantly, I have had ample opportunity to observe this doggie game. I am completely convinced that playing tug-of-war is not about possessing the toy; it is about the game. I have repeatedly seen one dog or the other gain control over the toy and immediately thrust it back at the other dog, as if to say, "Here, let's play some more." One trainer interprets tug-of-war not as competition over the toy but as two dogs or a dog and owner cooperating to "kill" or destroy the toy[7]. Suggested rules for tug-of-war are that (1) anytime the dog's mouth touches the person, the game ends, and (2) the owner always possesses the toy at the end of the game. I think the first rule is important, but I'm not sure the second one is relevant. In summary, there is no reason to make a general statement that tug-of-war games should be avoided with all dogs. Many dogs can be played with in this manner and do just fine. For those who don't, such games can be avoided or highly controlled.

1. Eliciting and reinforcing appropriate behavior.
- Focusing on fetching games has many advantages. Fetching forces the dog to give up control of the toy and also is a good way to teach relinquishment of objects.
- Provide plenty of interactive toys that the dog can use to entertain himself. Examples were given in a previous section.
- Play also involves chewing and manipulation of objects, which when directed at inappropriate items results in destructive behavior problems. Refer to the section on chewing.

2. Preventing or minimizing inappropriate behavior.
- Don't allow children to play unsupervised with puppies or new adult dogs until each has learned appropriate behaviors. Young children need continued supervision around the dog (see section on children and dogs).
- Don't play chase games initially, with either the dog chasing the children or vice versa. Later, when the owner is more knowledgeable about the dog's temperament, allowing the dog to chase the owner can be an exercise to teaching coming when called.
- As mentioned previously, don't provide old socks, shoes, etc., for play toys.
- Don't allow "teasing" games, in which people slap the dog's face with their hands.

3. Minimizing the use of punishment and using punishment correctly when necessary.
- Use negative punishment to deal with play that gets out of control. End the game and walk away.
- Do the same if the dog refuses to relinquish a toy. This will only be effective if playing with the owner is more fun than possessing the toy.
- Interactive, physical positive punishment is often perceived by the dog as rough play and should be avoided.

4. Providing for the dog's behavioral needs or meeting the puppy's developmental needs.
- Provide safe toys for chewing, based on veterinary recommendations.
- Provide toys that allow for different kinds of play—chasing, chewing, and manipulation.
- Provide sufficient opportunities for play. Play periods should be scheduled frequently for young or very active dogs. Owners often don't realize how much play time these types of dogs need.

Introducing a New Dog to a Resident Dog

The goals when introducing a new dog to another family dog are (1) to prevent fear or aggressive reactions; (2) to allow normal canine greeting behaviors, such as sniffing; (3) to allow some agonistic behaviors (defined in chapter 12), such as low-level growls and threatening postures (which are normal during initial meetings as the dogs assess each other); (4) to keep these behaviors from escalating into aggression; (5) to have the dogs associate good things with each other's presence; and (6) to avoid interactive or physical punishment.

1. *Eliciting and reinforcing appropriate behavior.*
   - Introduce the dogs in a neutral location to minimize the chances of the resident dog viewing the newcomer as a territorial intruder.
   - Design interactions to help both dogs expect good things to happen in each other's presence. When they greet and sniff each other, talk to them in a happy, friendly tone of voice, offering both a few tidbits (resident dog first).
   - Allow only brief interactions initially, as prolonged ones sometimes escalate to provoke fear or aggression.
   - If one dog reacts appropriately submissive to challenges from the other dog, reinforce the submissive behavior even if it is from the resident dog.
   - If there is more than one resident dog, introduce each to the new dog individually to prevent them from ganging up on the newcomer.

2. *Preventing or minimizing inappropriate behavior ("mistakes").*
   - Watch carefully for body postures that indicate increasing tenseness (raised hackles [piloerection], the baring of teeth, deep growls, a stiff-legged gait, or a prolonged stare), and interrupt the interaction by calling the dogs away from each other or engaging them in alternative behaviors.
   - Also watch for dominant body postures that probably indicate one dog is attempting to establish social dominance over the other (direct eye contact, chin or neck of one dog over shoulders of the other, or one dog placing front feet over shoulders of the other). If the other dog accepts these postures, there may be no problem, but if not, threatening behavior or aggression can result. Consider interrupting the interaction by calling the dogs away from each other or engaging them in alternative behaviors.
   - Avoid tight restraint, such as holding one dog in your arms or pulling tightly on leashes during initial interactions, as this sometimes makes threatening behavior or aggression more likely. If dogs are on leash, try to keep the leashes loose or let the dogs drag them.
   - Avoid having the dogs together in a small space, such as a car or hallway, until they have become comfortable with each other.
   - Supervise interactions at home, and do not allow dogs to be alone together until they consistently demonstrate friendly behaviors with each other for at least a week.
   - Allow a natural dominance hierarchy to develop if one dog is able to control important resources such as food, toys, or space. Support the dominant dog's status by allowing this to occur even if the resident dog is not dominant.
   - For a while, start a "Jolly Routine" (à la Bill Campbell[8]—happy, encouraging talk) whenever the dogs approach each other, even if no aggressive or threatening postures are exhibited. This classically conditions the association of good things with each other's appearance.
   - Go slow with introductions. Don't expect that the dogs can be together continuously from the first day. If they don't do well at first, separate them except during managed interactions. Taking things slowly is worth it if fighting problems can be prevented.

3. *Minimizing the use of punishment and using punishment correctly when necessary.*
- The goal in introductions is to establish a positive relationship, so punishment should be minimized.
- If interactions turn threatening or a fight breaks out, remote punishment is better than interactive punishment. Try a loud noise, such as an air horn, an ultrasonic device, or a water gun. This should be used only to interrupt the current interaction; it should not used repeatedly.
- If supervised interactions consistently result in fearful, threatening, or aggressive behavior, either the introduction was too abrupt or this is not a problem-prevention situation but one that requires problem resolution.

4. *Providing for the dog's behavioral needs or meeting the puppy's developmental needs.*
- Maintain the routine of the resident dog(s) as much as possible. Keep the time and location of feeding, exercise, play, and sleep the same as before the new dog arrived.
- Give each dog individual play and social time.
- Make sure the new dog has sufficient opportunity to bond to the owner, without having to compete with the resident dog for attention.
- Support whatever dominance hierarchy the dogs establish for themselves.
- Don't undermine this hierarchy by preventing the dominant dog from asserting her position or by taking a resource (such as a toy) away from the dog who was able to gain possession and returning it to the other dog.

Introducing a New Dog to Children

Kids and dogs are not automatically going to start off with a wonderful relationship. They are two different species, and neither really understands the behavior and the needs of the other. Active participation from adults will be necessary in order to teach the dog and the children acceptable behavior and to set limits on both. This section is about introductions, and it pertains to a dog's *initial meeting* with children in the family, their friends, or other children he encounters on walks or elsewhere. Even if the dog does well with children in the family, you should not assume he will be fine with all other children. As their relationship develops, other problems may occur between kids and dogs, such as play patterns, mouthing, and nipping; steps to prevent such problems are covered in previous sections in the chapter.

The general goals in introducing dogs to children are similar to those encountered in introducing dogs to other dogs—preventing fearful or aggressive responses, teaching the dog to associate good things with the child's presence, and keeping both the dog and the child from getting out of control.

1. *Eliciting and reinforcing appropriate behavior.*
- The child should be standing still or, preferably, sitting when the dog is first introduced.
- The dog will usually feel more at ease if he is allowed to approach the child rather than vice versa.
- The child should toss tidbits on the ground as the dog approaches, starting when the dog is 3 to 4 feet away.
- The child should avoid body postures that the dog might perceive as threatening. These include eye contact, reaching toward the dog, leaning over him, hugging or kissing him, or approaching him front to front.

- After the dog is at ease (showing no fearful, threatening, or aggressive behavior) when picking up treats from the ground at the child's feet, have the child hold her hand at her side with a tidbit in her fist. This may require that she squat down or sit on a chair. She should not move her hand toward the dog.
- As the dog sniffs her hand, she should slowly open her fist, allowing the dog to take the tidbit from her open palm (do not let her try to feed it to the dog). Repeat this several times.
- If the dog is comfortable taking the treat, the child can then gently scratch him under the chin with her fingers as he does so.
- The child can then ask the dog to obey a command that the dog responds to reliably in return for the tidbit.
- More interaction can gradually be allowed, such as looking at the dog more directly and petting or stroking him, if the dog is doing well.
- Alternatively, if the dog knows how to fetch (returning the toy and relinquishing it without a struggle), the child can throw a toy for the dog.

2. *Preventing or minimizing inappropriate behavior ("mistakes").*
- Do not allow children to rush up to a dog they haven't met before.
- Do not allow quick movements, loud talking or screaming, hugging, or reaching toward the dog during initial interactions.
- If the dog is fearful, do not tighten up on his leash or require him to sit-stay. This may make a fearful dog snap as the child approaches because he cannot back away.
- Allow the dog to avoid the interaction if he is not comfortable with it. Do not force a fearful or anxious dog to accept petting.
- If the dog is boisterous and jumping up rather than fearful, require him from the beginning to sit as he receives the treat.
- For boisterous dogs, use a head halter, such as a Gentle Leader (see product appendix).
- Dogs and children must be supervised every minute during the introductory period to prevent problems that could endanger one or both of them.

3. *Minimizing the use of punishment and using punishment correctly when necessary.*
- For overly friendly dogs who are jumping up on people, negative punishment is best. The child should move away when the jumping occurs and approach when the dog is sitting or standing quietly.
- Punishment is never indicated for fearful responses, including fear-motivated aggression.
- If the dog consistently shows fear or aggressive behavior when meeting children, problem resolution techniques are necessary.

4. *Providing for the dog's behavioral needs or meeting the puppy's developmental needs.*
- Puppies should be socialized to children, beginning during the sensitive socialization period (see previous section).
- Dogs need to be protected from mistreatment by children. That the child "doesn't know any better" is not an excuse; the child needs to be taught appropriate behavior around dogs.

CRATE TRAINING

Crate training can be an effective management tool in problem prevention, particularly with housetraining and preventing certain types of destructive behavior. It is not always an appropriate problem-resolution tool (see later chapters). Crating should be a relatively short-term management procedure, rather than a life-long routine in which the dog is always crated when the owner is away from home. Crating or other means of confinement should not be a way to avoid resolving behavior problems. One study found that dogs who were crated or confined in the basement or a garage most of the day were at increased risk of relinquishment to a shelter[9]. When a crate is used, the dog should be properly introduced to it, using the following procedures.

Crate training can take days or weeks to accomplish, depending on the dog's age, temperament, and past experiences. Remember that training should take place gradually and that being in the crate should always be a pleasant experience for the dog.

Introducing the Dog to the Crate

Locate the crate in an area of the house where the family spends much of its time and add some soft bedding to it. Lead the dog to the crate while talking to him in a happy, pleasant tone of voice. Be sure the crate door is securely fastened in the open position so it won't hit the dog and frighten him. Encourage him to approach and enter the crate by dropping tidbits of food in and around it or tossing several favorite toys inside. Don't force the dog to enter if he is reluctant or frightened. Repeat this experience until the dog will enter the crate willingly. If after several days he still refuses, use a plastic crate and try completely or partially removing the top half of the crate to create a more open space.

Feeding the Dog in the Crate

To create pleasant associations with the crate, the dog can be fed there temporarily. Put his food dish inside the crate (or at the door of the crate if he is still somewhat reluctant to enter), and at first allow the dog to eat with the door open. After several feedings, close the door, and with each feeding leave the dog in the crate for a few minutes longer after he's finished eating. Make sure there is room for him to comfortably lie down, even when the food dish is in the crate. Be sure to let the dog out of the crate before he begins whining or barking to get out to eliminate.

Accustoming the Dog to the Crate for Longer Periods

After the dog is relaxed while eating in the crate and remaining there for 10 or 15 minutes after eating, begin confining him for short periods while someone is home. Encourage the dog to enter the crate using a consistent phrase (e.g., "crate up") and a tidbit or toy. Move in and out of the room where the crate is—the dog should be able to see someone frequently at first. Gradually increase the length of time the dog is crated and the amount of time when no one is in the room with him. Work up to about an hour. At this point, the dog can be crated when alone or overnight.

Troubleshooting

If problems arise and the dog becomes fearful, eliminates in the crate, or barks, howls, or whines, the first step is to repeat some of the basic training by crating him for short periods, providing pleasant experiences with the crate, etc. If difficulties in crating persist, a separation anxiety problem or some other fear-related problem should be considered, and appropriate steps should be taken to resolve the underlying problem, rather than attempting to make the crate escape-proof or punishing the dog.

Continue to crate the dog for short periods from time to time when someone is home so that for the dog, crating does not become synonymous with being left alone. Crating is invaluable for keeping puppies out of trouble, providing a safe place for dogs during travel, or giving dogs a sanctuary away from pestering children or too many visitors. However, crating should be viewed as a relatively short-term management tool, not as a lifetime pattern of housing. The goal should be to work on any problems and to train the dog so that it will not be necessary to crate him 8 to 10 hours of every workday throughout his life.

SUMMARY

In this chapter, I have addressed some of the common situations that most pet owners encounter when they bring a new dog into the home, particularly a young one. A problem-prevention program could be outlined for every potential problem behavior—barking, escaping, territorial aggression, etc. In a few situations, there may be some overlap between problem prevention and problem resolution.

One of the important research needs in the field of applied animal behavior is a better understanding of why specific behavior problems develop and how they can be prevented more effectively. We've all seen cases in which owners seem to have done everything right and yet problems still occur. The problem-prevention approaches offered here are not guaranteed to be effective, but they are based on ethological principles, animal learning, and a focus on humane approaches to problem behavior.

REFERENCES

1. Scott, J.P., and J.L. Fuller. 1965. *Genetics and the social behavior of the dog*. Chicago: University of Chicago Press.

2. Riegger, M.H., and J. Guntzelman. 1990. Prevention and amelioration of stress and consequences of interaction between children and dogs. *JAVMA* 196:1781–5.

3. Goodloe, L.P. 1996. Issues in description and measurement of temperament in companion dogs. In *Readings in companion animal behavior*, ed. V.L. Voith and P.L. Borchelt, 32–42. Trenton, N.J.: Veterinary Learning Systems.

4. Serpell, J., and J.A. Jagoe. 1995. Early experience and development of behaviour. In *The domestic dog: Its evolution, behaviour and interactions with people*, ed. J. Serpell, 79–102. New York: Cambridge University Press.

5. Overall, K. 1994. Prevention of aggressive disorders. *Canine Pract.* 19:19–22.

6. Ryan, T. 1998. *The toolbox for remodeling your problem dog*. New York: Howell Book House.

7. Donaldson, J. 1996. *The culture clash*. Berkeley, Calif.: James and Kenneth Publishers.

8. Campbell, W.E. 1975. *Behavior problems in dogs*. Santa Barbara, Calif.: American Veterinary Publications.

9. Patronek, G.J., L.T. Glickman, A.M. Beck, G.P. McCabe, and C. Ecker. 1996. Risk factors for relinquishment of dogs to an animal shelter. *JAVMA* 209:572–81.

CHAPTER 5

Problem Prevention for Kittens and New Adult Cats

As in the last chapter, the focus in this chapter is on preventing problems, not resolving them. For information on cats with preexisting problems, refer to the chapter specific to the problem of concern.

HELPING OWNERS SET REALISTIC EXPECTATIONS

There is more popular literature on raising puppies than kittens. In fact, entire books are devoted to the procedures to follow when a new dog comes into the family, but what to do with a new cat has received much less attention. In my experience, the most common mistake new cat owners make is to think they really need do next to nothing—just set up a litterbox in an out-of-the-way place, pour some litter in (the generic, least expensive kind, of course), maybe buy a cute scratching post, then bring the cat home, and she'll be fine. Some people acquire cats because they think they will be less work than dogs. To some degree, this is true. However, introducing a new cat to the home requires more effort than is suggested in the preceding example, and the introduction period is a crucial one because first impressions are so important to cats. A little extra time invested now can go a long way toward making the new cat the relatively trouble-free companion owners expect.

TALKING TO OWNERS—ELICITING INFORMATION

When veterinarians and animal shelter staffers talk to a new owner, they often ask the usual questions: "Do you have a litterbox?" "Have you bought a scratching post?" Unfortunately, the yes or no answers they receive tell them virtually nothing about whether the owner is on a good problem-prevention path. Consider asking the following questions instead:

"Why don't you tell me how you've set up your litterbox(es)?"
"What kind of scratching post(s) have you provided for your new cat?"
"What are you doing to socialize your kitten?"
"How do you play with your cat?"
"What kinds of toys does your cat have?"
"How are you introducing your cat to the family, children, and other people?"
"How are you introducing your new cat to the rest of your family pets?"

PRINCIPLES OF PROBLEM PREVENTION

In the remaining sections of this chapter, I will suggest what to tell clients about the principles of problem prevention that were introduced in chapter 4 as they apply to the following topics:

- Preventing elimination problems: Creating the perfect litterbox
- Preventing scratching problems: Creating the perfect scratching post
- Play and play-motivated aggression
- Creating friendly cats: Socialization, handling, and introduction to the family
- Introducing cats to other family cats
- Introducing cats to dogs

Preventing Elimination Problems: Creating the Perfect Litterbox

The best way to prevent elimination problems is to provide a cat with litterboxes that meet his behavioral needs. If there are no existing problems and the cat's preferences are typical, usually this is quite easy to do, provided you are aware of what those behavioral needs are when it comes to elimination.

This does not mean that cats have to be trained to use a litterbox as you would train a dog to eliminate outside. Cats choose their elimination areas for different reasons than dogs. As soon as a kitten can move around, she has a tendency to play, investigate, and dig in any loose particulate matter that is available to her[1]. At about 4 weeks of age, when the kitten matures enough to eliminate on her own (without being licked by the queen), she will seek out this loose material to use. The cat does not have to be trained to do this—it is a normal developmental occurrence. Thus, it is not necessary to take a young kitten to a litterbox and move her paws back and forth in an effort to teach her to scratch. She already knows how to do this much better than we do, and such experiences may actually create anxiety and contribute to a litterbox aversion. Furthermore, a kitten does not have to observe the queen or siblings use a litterbox in order to do so herself[1]. There are many reports of orphaned kittens using litter material without having any role models to observe.

What may be important is the type of litter material the kitten becomes accustomed to when she is young. Some evidence indicates that early experiences go a long way toward determining a cat's initial preferences for where and on what to eliminate. Thus, a kitten born to a stray queen who lives outside may develop different preferences than one born in a home and exposed to litter as soon as she is mobile. Although there are no data to indicate that kittens not exposed to litter material when young are more prone to elimination problems than those who are (my Tipper-Cat started life as a farm cat but never had any litterbox problems), based on what we know of the development of normal elimination behavior, it makes sense to start a kitten out on the type of litter material that we want her to use as an adult.

1. *Eliciting and reinforcing appropriate behavior.* Providing for the cat's behavioral needs is so much a part of preventing litterbox problems that operant conditioning (reinforcements and punishments) has little effect in the process. Refer to the section on meeting the cat's behavioral needs.

2. *Preventing or minimizing inappropriate behavior ("mistakes").*
- It may be helpful to confine a newly acquired cat to one or two rooms for a few days (or to allow her in the rest of the house only under supervision) so she learns where her litterbox is and does not have a chance to establish bad habits.
- Do your best to meet the cat's behavioral needs, as described in the following passages. If you find her needs differ from the average, by all means change the litterbox to suit her individual preferences. A cat will demonstrate her preferences through her behavior.

3. *Minimizing the use of punishment and using punishment correctly when necessary.*
- If, during the introduction period, the cat is caught eliminating somewhere other than the litterbox, a mild remote punisher can be used (a loud noise or a squirt of water) with the goal of startling the cat. The first time this happens, immediately reassess the litterbox characteristics and make whatever changes seem necessary.
- If the cat is repeatedly not using the box, punishment is not going to be helpful for preventing or resolving the elimination problem. Switch to the problem-resolution mode instead (see chapter 13).
- Whether you catch the cat eliminating outside the box or just find the mess later, it is not a good idea to take the cat to the litterbox. This would be an unpleasant experience for her: She will probably be frightened or anxious because of your angry behavior, which could then contribute to the development of a litterbox aversion.

4. *Providing for the cat's behavioral needs or meeting the kitten's developmental needs.* Designing the perfect litterbox requires knowing what that is from the cat's point of view. Characteristics to consider are grouped in different categories, followed by specific information you can share with the owner.
- Litter
  - Studies show that when given the choice, most cats prefer fine-grained material that feels soft[2]. A clumping litter is usually finer than clay.
  - My experience indicates that most cats do not like deep litter. I find 1 and a half to 2 inches of litter is usually best. Some cats like it even shallower; a few may prefer more. Some owners have the mistaken idea that the more litter they put in the box, the less often they will have to clean it.
  - Use unscented litter. Some cats do fine with scents, but in general, it's a safer bet to keep the litterbox free of scent. One study found that cats with litterbox problems were more likely to have scented litter[3].
- Type of box
  - Use a box that suits the cat's physical characteristics. Large cats may need bigger than average boxes (one type is shaped something like a boat). Kittens and elderly or ill animals may need a box with lower sides for easier access.
  - I recommend not using a cover initially unless there is a compelling reason to do so. Covers sometimes make it more difficult for a cat to adjust herself to her liking, and some cats may be reticent about entering a dark area; the cover also prevents the cat from monitoring her surroundings while she is in a vulnerable position.
  - Provide at least as many boxes as there are cats in the family.

- Location, location, location
    — Cats need privacy, so placing the litterbox in a high-traffic area is usually not a good idea.
    — At the other extreme, locating the box in an out-of-the-way corner of the basement poses two possible problems: It may be so out of the way that the cat is reluctant to go there because she doesn't spend much time in that area, and the owner may neglect cleaning routines (out of sight, out of mind).
    — Cats need to be able to see in as many directions as possible while they are in the box or to be protected on some sides by walls or other barriers. Don't locate the box so that the cat's view is blocked, allowing a person or animal to startle or "ambush" her.
    — Avoid locating the box near appliances whose noises may startle the cat (a washer, dryer, furnace, etc.).
    — Do not place multiple boxes next to one another. This may make all boxes inaccessible to other cats if one box is being used. Some cats don't feel comfortable eliminating with another cat nearby.
    — Try to position the box so there is more than one exit route from it. This prevents a cat from being trapped in the box by another pet.
    — It may be wise to locate boxes in different areas of the house, for example, upstairs as well as on the main floor.
- Cleanliness
    — Feces and clumps should be scooped daily. A computerized litterbox that activates 10 minutes after the cat leaves the box and rakes the waste into a container below the box is now available (see product appendix).
    — There is great variability in how clean cats needs their boxes to be. To prevent problems, however, assume that the cleaner the box is the better. (It is sometimes helpful to leave one stool or clump in the box to serve as an odor cue to draw the cat to the box.)
    — The litter should be changed often enough so that it always looks dry and clean. Frequency will depend on the number of boxes used in the house, the type of litter used, and the number of cats in the home.
    — There should be no dried urine or stool on the box, and no odor should be detectable from the box itself. If there is, the box needs washing. Washing frequency will vary from once a week to rarely (if liners are used). Use a mild, unscented cleaning product for this task.
    — Liners may be used to make upkeep easier. There is a huge amount of variability in terms of cats' tolerance for liners. I have found that if the liner's open end is rolled closed and clamped to the box with a bag clip, the liner is less likely to develop loose folds that cats may catch while scratching.

Preventing Scratching Problems: Creating the Perfect Scratching Post

The first step in preventing scratching problems is to understand why cats scratch. Then you must identify the individual cat's scratching preferences. (For simplicity, the term *scratching post* as used in this section is intended to encompass any object used for scratching, post or otherwise.) There are at least four reasons why cats scratch. Scratching is, first and foremost, a marking behavior. In scratching, both a visual mark and an olfactory mark are produced. Other motivations for scratching include claw maintenance and stretching. Scratching has also been reported to be a social behavior that occurs during play, in contexts involving arousal (such as greeting[4]), and as a threat display when other cats are present[5,6]. Given that scratching can serve such a variety of functions, cats will want to scratch in different areas depending on their motivation. For example, a cat scratching to stretch after napping will need a post near her resting areas, but she may also require one near entrances to the house, where her marking behavior may more likely be triggered. It is not known whether cats prefer different textures or substrates for scratching, depending on the function motivating it.

The myth that cats don't need scratching posts if they are allowed outside reflects a lack of understanding about the behavioral needs for scratching. Cats should have scratching objects available in behaviorally relevant locations. Cats also do not scratch objects to make their owners mad. They scratch objects that feel good to them and that will accomplish the behavioral goals of scratching.

Individual cats have different scratching preferences. Some may prefer horizontal objects over vertical ones; others may like to rake their claws down an object in long strokes; and still others may prefer to dig their claws in and repeatedly "pick" in the same spot. To prevent scratching on inappropriate objects, an owner may need to (1) provide objects with these different characteristics, (2) observe the new cat to determine her preferences, and then (3) provide additional posts and other objects that suit those preferences.

Some behaviorists believe that cats prefer shredded, torn, and unsightly scratching objects that are almost falling apart from repeated use[7]. This is because such material is easy for the cat to sink his claws into, because his scent is heavily implanted in the object, and because the shredded appearance reflects the visual marks. Unfortunately, owners often decide it's time to replace the post when it reaches this condition. With his favorite scratching post gone, the cat may seek undesirable places to scratch.

1. *Eliciting and reinforcing appropriate behavior.*
   - Satisfying the cat's behavioral needs is the most important factor in eliciting appropriate behavior (refer to later section).
   - Use things that will motivate the cat to approach and investigate the post. Try scenting it with catnip or attaching a toy that protrudes from the top of the post to encourage the cat to jump up and perhaps scratch on her way down.
   - Try scratching the post with your fingers as the cat watches. (This recommendation is based on my own anecdotal observation, for I can often get my cat Buffett to scratch his post by doing this. It is not a fool-proof technique, and it may not be effective with every cat, but I do think it encourages a pattern of using the post, which may be helpful in establishing the habit of scratching there at other times.)

2. *Preventing or minimizing inappropriate behavior ("mistakes").*
   - Initially, "cat-proof" the house as much as possible. Put objects that the cat will likely enjoy scratching out of reach (e.g., turn stereo speakers toward the wall).
   - If an enticing item can't be removed, change its texture so it is less appealing. Cover it with plastic, sandpaper, double-sided sticky tape, or a vinyl carpet runner with its pointy side facing outward. A section of carpet runner or sandpaper can also be put on the floor where the cat would need to stand to scratch the object (e.g., on the floor in front of the drapes).
   - If objects can't be removed or made less attractive, you may need to limit the cat's access to them when you can't watch her until good scratching habits are established.

- Mistakes can be minimized by providing for the cat's behavioral needs (see later section).
- Damage to household items caused by scratching can be minimized by clipping the cat's nails on a regular basis.

3. *Minimizing the use of punishment and using punishment correctly when necessary.*
   - If the cat is caught in the act of scratching something she shouldn't, a remote punisher can be tried (a loud noise delivered by an ultrasonic device or an air horn or, alternatively, a squirt of water). However, keep in mind that the effectiveness of the remote punisher will depend on whether the attempt at punishment meets the criteria of consistency, immediacy, intensity, duration, and the provision of alternatives (as discussed in chapter 3).
   - Interactive punishment is not recommended for the usual reasons: It can result in fearful and aggressive reactions, and the cat will only learn not to scratch forbidden objects when the owner is around.
   - Making the object less appealing, as described earlier, can be thought of as remote punishment because when the cat tries to scratch, she has an unpleasant experience.
   - Use the occurrence of inappropriate scratching to learn more about the cat's preferences. What is it about her preferred object (location, texture, size, etc.) that her scratching posts are not providing?

4. *Providing for the cat's behavioral needs or meeting the kitten's developmental needs.*
   - Provide scratching posts in areas where the cat will likely need them, based on the various behavioral reasons for scratching:
     — Near favorite resting places for stretching
     — In easily accessible areas for play and claw maintenance
     — Near doors to the house for greeting and marking
     — Near off-limit objects the cat has tried to scratch in order to provide an acceptable alternative
   - After identifying how the cat likes to scratch (picking, raking, or both depending on the motivation), provide textures that will allow this:
     — Horizontally wrapped sisal will not allow a cat to rake in long strokes but is superb for picking.
     — Objects covered with carpet are better for raking, as are loosely woven upholstery materials with longitudinal threads[7].
     — Cut cardboard can be used to satisfy both the picking and raking preferences.
   - Some of the scratching objects should be tall enough to allow the cat to extend to her full reach (which is probably why many cats like drapes). Few commercially available objects (except the tall cat condos) allow cats to reach that high.
   - Determine what angle the cat likes to scratch—horizontal, vertical, something in between, or all of the above. (For example, my cat Buffett usually prefers vertical objects, but my three-legged Tipper-Cat preferred horizontal ones because she found it difficult to balance on her back legs if she tried to scratch vertically.)
   - Make sure the scratching post is sturdy and will not collapse, move, or fall over when the cat uses it.

Play and Play-Motivated Aggression

Kittens are some of the most playful creatures on earth. Although playful kittens are fun and appealing to watch, they can also be aggravating if their play includes aggressive behavior directed toward people or if it becomes so rambunctious that household items are damaged. Cats display different kinds of play behavior[8, 9]. Solitary play includes object play and self-play. In object play, the play behaviors are directed toward inanimate objects. This category includes behaviors that would be seen in predation, including chasing; pouncing and leaping on objects; and prey manipulation behaviors such as batting, grasping, sniffing, licking, or tossing objects in the air. When engaged in self-play, cats chase their tails or pounce on invisible objects. Locomotor play involves not only running, tumbling, and similar behaviors but also climbing over, under, in, around, or through any large object. Social play involves behaviors directed toward another cat or kitten or to people and other animals, as well. These play patterns can include elements of sexual, predatory, and agonistic behavior (see chapter 12 for a definition). Social and object play can present problems for owners when they themselves become the target.

Cat owners must learn to distinguish play behavior from more serious aggression. In other species, such as dogs, clear communicative signals indicate that the behaviors that follow are playful and not to be taken seriously; the familiar "play bow" displayed by dogs serves this function. Play signals in cats, however, have not been so clearly identified and may not be as easily recognizable, most likely because cats are not as social as dogs. A half-open mouth, described as a kitten's "play face," seems to be one play signal, as may a modified version of "the pounce." It has also been suggested that particular rates of tail movement can signal play. In social play with other cats, pouncing, rolling over on the back with paws in the air, and the "play face," combined with pawing or lunging, were the most common play solicitation signals[9]. Because some similar postures can also be seen in aggressive displays, it may be difficult for you to know whether a cat or kitten has a play problem or an aggression problem without seeing the behavior yourself, so you should ask the owners about the context in which the behavior occurs. Is the cat ambushing them at the bottom of stairs, around corners, when they get out of bed or the shower, etc., and using an attack-and-run pattern? In these contexts and if the cat is under one year of age and the only cat in the family, chances are that the behavior is play. Another clue is that cats are usually quiet during playful attacks but may growl, hiss, or spit when being aggressive[10]. Playful aggression can result in bites and scratches that break the skin, so the intensity of the behavior is not a good guideline.

As with most problems, prevention does not mean inhibiting the expression of the behavior but rather directing it onto appropriate objects. Most cat owners don't realize how much playtime kittens and young cats need. The prevention of problems should focus on providing sufficient outlets for play.

1. *Eliciting and reinforcing appropriate behavior.*
   - Provide appropriate play objects for different types of play and sufficient opportunities for play (as will be described). As appropriate play behaviors become more established, they are self-reinforcing because they are enjoyable.
   - Meeting the cat's behavioral needs for play is the most important factor in eliciting appropriate behavior.

2. *Preventing or minimizing inappropriate behavior ("mistakes").*
   - Avoid playing with the cat with your hands, feet, or any other body part. Kittens chasing and pouncing on hands and feet are cute, but this is an inappropriate pattern of behavior.
   - Avoid toys designed as gloves with dangling balls on the fingertips, worn while playing with your pet. Using these makes hands part of the toy from the cat's perspective.

- Anticipate when the inappropriate behavior is likely to occur, and be prepared to redirect it onto appropriate objects. For example, toss a toy down the stairs prior to descending to redirect attacks to feet.
- Don't neglect playtimes. Provide them frequently, especially for young or very active cats.

3. *Minimizing the use of punishment and using punishment correctly when necessary.*
- Never use interactive punishment such as hitting, slapping, or pinning. Such punishment either creates a cat who is hand-shy and fearful or exacerbates the initial problem if the cat views these responses as play and escalates his attacks.
- Remote punishment (a loud noise from an air horn or an ultrasonic device or a squirt of water) may be used if the cat attacks before the behavior can be redirected. After punishment, engage the cat in appropriate play.
- If a kitten becomes overly excited during play and begins biting, end the game by walking away. Attempting to pick her up and put her in a room for a time-out may prompt additional bites.

4. *Providing for the cat's behavioral needs or meeting the kitten's developmental needs.*
- Provide a variety of toys that allow the cat to express the behaviors involved in different types of play:
    — Toys to chase and pounce on
    — Toys to manipulate, bat, swat, and carry around (yes, some cats will play fetch!)
    — Toys to hide in, crawl under, etc.
- Rotate the availability of the cat's collection of toys so that she has different ones every few days.
- Provide adequate time for social play by using a cat dancer or other toy that involves interaction with you. Many cats who are displaying playful aggression are not receiving enough interactive playtime. Schedule playtimes around the times when playful attacks are likely to occur.

Creating Friendly Cats: Socialization, Handling, and Introduction to Family

In the last chapter, I discussed the sensitive period and the different connotations of the term *socialization*. Most of what we know about behavioral development and socialization in the dog was the result of a 20-year study, initiated in the 1950s[11]. No comparable study has been done on cats, and there were no reported data-based studies on the cat's socialization to people until the 1980s.

Based on the work of Eileen Karsh[12], the sensitive period for socialization in cats begins, peaks, and ends much earlier than in dogs, in fact, before kittens are taken from the litter. The socialization period begins at about 2 weeks of age, peaks at about 4 to 5 weeks, and ends at about 7 weeks with the kitten's increasing fear of the unfamiliar. The importance of socializing dogs is well recognized, but little has been written about the effects of gentle handling and exposure to people in regard to the social behavior of cats. Karsh's work demonstrated that cats who were handled before the age of 7 weeks more readily approached and stayed near people when tested. Cats who were handled 40 minutes a day were more social than those handled only 15 minutes a day. Finally, cats who were handled by only one person displayed the greatest amount of social behavior toward their individual handlers, but those handled by five different people showed less fear of strangers than those handled by just one individual.

Recommendations for socialization and early handling up to 8 weeks of age. Karsh's findings have practical applications. Despite the early onset of the socialization period, researchers do not recommend adopting kittens prior to the age of 8 weeks because separation from the queen and littermates too early may have detrimental effects[12]. This means that breeders, shelters' staff members, and others who care for litters of kittens must handle them in order to socialize them to people. For our purposes, handling means gently holding the kitten, touching her, and petting her but not forcibly restraining her. Kitten-handling programs should be started early, even as soon as 2 weeks of age, and kittens should be handled by more than one person in order to decrease their fear of strangers. Finally, the amount of handling seems to be important, with up to 40 minutes a day known to be beneficial, as mentioned earlier; however, the kitten should not become overwhelmed, tired, subjected to communicable diseases, or denied sufficient contact with the queen and siblings.

Later handling: Introducing kittens and older cats to the family and others. How an older kitten or adult cat new to the household responds to additional socialization attempts will depend on her personality and her previous experiences. Cats who were not well socialized when very young may never accept unfamiliar people or new surroundings, and it may take them a long time to become comfortable with family members and their new home. How cats react to new experiences also depends on personality type. Several different researchers[12, 13, 14] have identified three personality types in cats: sociable and confident, timid and shy, and active and aggressive (see Box 5.1 for descriptions). Thus, there is enormous individual variation among cats as to how friendly, confident, and sociable they will be. Even with lots of socialization experiences, a shy, timid cat may never be confident around visitors or be a "lap cat" with the family. Although new cat owners should give their cat positive socialization experiences as will be outlined, it is also important that they understand the personality differences among cats and appreciate the unique personality of the cat that has joined their family.

Box 5.1 Cat personality types

Sociable and confident
Approaches people readily, curious about surroundings, easygoing, trusting

Timid and shy
More reluctant to approach people and explore new environments, nervous, can be unfriendly

Active and aggressive
Tense, less friendly, may be "hostile," curious, physically active, easily excited

Source: Based on work reported in E.B. Karsh and D.C. Turner, 1988, The human-cat relationship, in *The domestic cat: The biology of its behavior*, ed. D.C. Turner and P. Bateson, 159–78, New York: Cambridge University Press.

When I was working at an animal shelter, I encountered a new cat adopter who ultimately returned the pet because she was upset that he wanted to sit in her lap too much, which disrupted her needlepoint work. At the opposite extreme, one family returned a cat because he wasn't friendly enough and wouldn't sit in the childrens' laps while they were watching TV. These experiences are supported by the results of a recent study[15]. The study found that cats who were obtained unexpectedly and whose owners did not have specific expectations about the cat's role in the family were at less risk of surrender to a shelter than those whose acquisition had been carefully planned and whose new owners had specific expectations about the cat's personality and behavior. The message here is that we should educate new cat owners not only about socializing them but also about the normal variation in sociability among cats.

1. *Eliciting and reinforcing appropriate behavior.* These procedures pertain to socializing kittens and helping well-socialized adult cats adjust to a new household. Cats who have existing aggression or fear-related problems will require more of a problem-resolution approach (see chapters 15 and 16).

- Try to introduce the new cat to family members one or two people at a time, rather than having a pack of people surround him.
- Let the cat approach you; don't rush up to him. Sit or kneel down, hold your hand out, let the cat sniff your finger, and then gently scratch him under the chin, on top of his head, on the cheeks, or behind the ears. If he won't approach, don't force him. Try using toys or treats to lure him to you, or just sit quietly and let him take his time. Young children may need adult assistance to stay quiet and calm.
- After the cat is comfortable with the family, create pleasant, enjoyable experiences for him with a variety of people—men, women, children, tall people, short people, etc. (Use the procedures just outlined in introducing the cat to these new people.)
- Cats should be gradually exposed to normal, environmental stimuli—vacuum cleaners, the TV, stairs, different surfaces (carpet, tile), etc. These stimuli should never be intense enough to frighten the cat. Adult cats who have already had these experiences may be just fine, but kittens may be somewhat overwhelmed.
- Make sure the cat enjoys each of these experiences by incorporating food, toys, or petting as part of these encounters.

2. *Preventing or minimizing inappropriate behavior ("mistakes").* In this case, inappropriate behavior would be the expression of fear or aggressive behavior during the socialization or introduction experience.

- In the early stages, avoid petting the cat for long periods or with long strokes down his body or belly. Unlike dogs, many cats do not liked to be petted in this way, and such petting can trigger the "don't-pet-me-anymore" syndrome (see chapter 15 on feline aggression).
- Do not restrain the cat if he wants to walk away, and don't rush in to pick him up. Children especially should be prevented from doing this.
- Do not force a cat to experience a situation that elicits fear.
- If problems occur, remove the cat from the situation immediately and make the experience easier for her the next time. For example, if a noise frightens her, muffle the sound.
- Don't overwhelm the cat with situations he can't tolerate because they are too intense.
- Take particular care to socialize the cat to children. Start with older children who will follow directions about what to do and what not do with the cat (as described earlier).
- Don't overwhelm the cat with too many new experiences at once. Give him plenty of time to adjust to each new experience, especially if he appears to be the timid or shy type or not well socialized previously.

3. *Minimizing the use of punishment and using punishment correctly when necessary.*
   - Punishment has no place in socializing cats.
   - If the cat shows any aggressive, threatening, or fearful behavior, remove her from the situation and make the situation easier for her the next time. If these responses continue, a problem resolution approach will be necessary (refer to chapters 15 and 16 on feline aggression and fears and anxiety).

4. *Providing for the cat's behavioral needs or meeting the kitten's developmental needs.*
   - Provide both kitten socialization in the early weeks and extended socialization experiences later on. Keep in mind how early the socialization period begins in kittens.
   - Kittens older than 7 weeks can still be socialized, but it will require more effort.
   - Feral cats, who have received no human contact into young adulthood, may never be able to become companion animals.
   - Don't neglect the cat's need for pleasant experiences with a wide variety of people and things into adulthood.
   - Provide the cat with some private places to escape to (such as a cat pole with a high perch), especially if there are children or other pets in the family.
   - If fearful or aggressive behavior seems to be the cat's typical reaction, a problem-resolution approach will be required.

Other aspects to socialization. Although much has been written about the importance of socializing puppies to different environments, the same is not true for kittens. Neither popular books on cats nor the scientific literature says much about taking kittens in the car or on short trips to help them become comfortable in places other than the house or yard. Yet cats *can* learn to enjoy family excursions. Some friends of mine took their cats on camping and fishing trips; they would tie the cats on long lines while they were fishing and at the campsite, and the cats would have a great time exploring the outdoors. I've also known cats who have been trained to go for leash walks around the neighborhood.

Typically, however, cats don't like to ride in a car, don't like harnesses and leashes, and are very nervous when taken to unfamiliar places, although there seems to be no inherent characteristic in the cat to account for this. Perhaps only the rare cat who is socialized as a kitten to different environments can successfully adjust to new places and experiences outside the home environment.

One example of an environmentally socialized cat is the show cat. Cats that participate in shows are usually first taken to such events at a very young age, and they seem to tolerate new environments quite well. Thus, owners of kittens should consider socializing their pets to different environments by taking them on brief car rides, to the park (on leash, of course, which in itself is another socializing experience), to visit friends, and to the veterinarian or groomer (just for petting and treats at first). Initially, these experiences should be brief and very easy for the kitten (perhaps just sitting in the car), until he is calm enough to become curious. Cats are very difficult to socialize to new locations as they get older.

Introducing Cats to Other Family Cats

There is great variation among cats regarding how well they tolerate living with other felines. Some cats are very gregarious and can tolerate several peers; others are forever meant to be the sole cat in the household. In addition, a resident cat may do well with certain other cats but not *all* other cats. The problem for cat owners is that it is very difficult, if not impossible, to predict what kind of relationship any two cats will develop.

Owner expectations. Owners often obtain a second cat because they think their first cat needs a companion if she is left alone all day. Rather than basing their decision about obtaining another cat on their own anthropomorphic view of the situation (which is often based on guilt), owners should be cautioned to assess the behavioral characteristics and history of their resident cat to decide whether an additional cat is appropriate. The social system of dogs suggests that providing a companion is usually a good idea for them, but the same cannot be said for cats. Although cats can live in groups and form close social bonds with other individuals, they do not have the group structure that dogs do, and they are capable of a mostly solitary existence. Owners should be encouraged to think about the following questions:

What is the cat's history of living with another cat? If he has lived with other cats most of his life and done well, acquiring a new cat may be appropriate (although this does not guarantee that the relationship with the new cat will be equally companionable). If, however, he has no experience living with other cats, he may do best if he remains a singleton, for cats who have had little inter-action with others of their species may not be well socialized to them. The number of cats in the household should also be considered. A high density of cats in a small space is almost guaranteed to produce problems.

How does the cat react when he sees other cats in the neighborhood? If the sight of another cat turns the owners' cat into a yowling devil, they may want to think twice before acquiring a new one. The cat is probably very territorial, and he may not take to a new cat that he sees as an intruder. It is possible that he could come to accept another cat in time, but the introductory period will be critical.

Owners need to be educated about how crucial first impressions are for cats. When I take on a cat-to-cat aggression case, one of the first things I ask the owner is how the cats were initially introduced. If the owner gives me a blank look and says, "Well, we just brought the new one in and put her down in the living room," I've probably identified at least one source of the problem. If the first encounter between a new cat and a resident cat is a frightful experience filled with hissing, growling, and spitting, this sets the tone of their relationship for a long time, if not permanently.

Owners also must be aware of how long it may take cats to completely accept one another. One study of cats housed communally for a long period in a shelter found that they displayed few affiliative, friendly behaviors until they had lived together for over a year[9].

Finally, owners need help to develop a realistic set of expectations about the cats' ultimate relationship. Most owners want their cats to be best friends and may be disappointed if this doesn't happen. They should be prepared for anything from close friendship to mutual avoidance and, in the worst case, ongoing conflict. To give cats the best chance of hitting if off, consider offering the following recommendations on preventing problems.

The goals in introducing a new cat to a resident cat are much the same as those in intro-ducing dogs to one another: (1) to prevent fear or aggressive reactions, (2) to keep low-intensity threats (hissing, swatting) from escalating into aggression, (3) to have the cats associate good things with each other's presence, and (4) to avoid the use of interactive or physical punishment.

1. *Eliciting and reinforcing appropriate behavior.* (Starred items [*] also pertain to cat-to-dog intro-ductions, see next section.)

- At first, the cats should only be allowed to smell and hear each other, *not* see or touch each other.*
- This can be done by confining the new cat to a small section or one room of the house, equipped with all the necessities (litterbox, food, water, scratching post, toys, bed, etc.).*

- After she is comfortable there (which will take anywhere from several hours to several days), confine the resident cat in this area and allow the new animal to explore the house, under supervision. This allows each cat to become familiar with the other's scent.*

- Feed or offer both cats treats close to the door to this room (with one cat on each side). This helps them learn to associate good things with the other's presence. Use "to die for" treats, such as small pieces of tuna, chicken, or salmon.*

- Try slipping one end of a toy underneath the door to encourage the cats to paw at it or each other in a playful way.

- When both are comfortable with the other's presence on either side of the door, use doorstops to wedge the door open about an inch from both sides. This allows the cats to peek at and paw each other if they want to, but it prevents them from having complete access to one another too quickly, which could cause trouble. Do not progress past this step until the cats can see each other without displaying fearful or aggressive responses; ideally, they should show some friendly behaviors. Continue to use toys, food, and petting as long as the cats aren't threatening each other. Touching an agitated cat may result in a bite.*

- Next, wedge the door open a little farther but not so much that the cats can get to one another. Repeat the previous step.*

- An ideal next step is to give the cats a full view of one another behind a screen or glass door before they are brought together. If this isn't possible, one or both cats can be put in individual crates to which they have previously been acclimated. Keep the crates far enough apart at first so the cats remain calm and then gradually move them closer together. If the cats are trained to wear a leash and harness, these could also be used.*

- When the cats are first together while loose, keep the session brief, and continue to offer enjoyable things (food, toys, petting).*

2. *Preventing or minimizing inappropriate behavior ("mistakes").* (Starred [*] items also pertain to cat-to-dog introductions, see next section.)

- If the cats are threatening or fearful when close to either side of the door to the confinement room, offer the tidbits at a greater distance from the door, where both cats can be calm.*

- Do not move the introduction along too quickly—rushing the process is the most common mistake made during introductions. The cats should be tolerating each other well at each step before progressing to the next. One bout of fighting may set the introduction back for months.*

- During their initial time together, if any hissing or conflicts occur, try to distract the cats into another activity—dangle a toy, get the resident cat into the kitchen with the sound of food preparations, etc. If these reactions continue, back up a few steps in the introduction process.

- Avoid having the cats together in a small space, such as a car, until they have become comfortable with each other.*

- Supervise interactions at home, and do not allow the cats to be alone together until they are consistently demonstrating friendly behaviors with each other for at least a week.*

3. *Minimizing the use of punishment and using punishment correctly when necessary.*
- Punishment is rarely helpful in cat introductions because it fails to teach the cats to associate good things with each other's presence.
- If aggressive or threatening responses occur, distract the cats as indicated earlier, move back a step or two in the introduction process, or do both. Perhaps things moved too quickly.
- If a fight does occur, try making a loud noise (e.g., using an air horn or an ultrasonic device) or use a water gun to break it up before either cat is injured. Don't try to pull the cats apart or use interactive punishment. These techniques should be used to interrupt the current interaction, not as a repeated procedure.
- If interactions consistently result in fearful, threatening, or aggressive behavior, either the introduction was too abrupt or this is not a problem-prevention situation but one that requires problem resolution.

4. *Providing for the cat's behavioral needs or meeting the kitten's developmental needs.*
- Maintain the routine of the resident cat(s) as far as possible by keeping feeding, play, and sleeping times and locations the same as before the new cat arrived.
- Socialize kittens to other cats. Kittens who don't see other cats after they are taken from the litter at 7 to 8 weeks of age may not get along well with others as adults.
- Understand that some adult cats will be better as only cats.
- Recognize that cats may establish individual territories within the house (see chapter 15). Make sure that all the necessities (food, water, litterbox, scratching post, etc.) are provided in each territory.
- Keep realistic expectations about the length of time it will take for cats to adjust to each other. Forcing an introduction can result in cats who do not get along, which, of course, is not good for either of them.

Introducing Cats to Dogs

The ideal and easiest situation is to only have cats who have been socialized to dogs and dogs who have been socialized to cats! One study found that kittens who were raised with dogs from the age of 4 weeks did not react defensively when tested with other dogs at 12 weeks[18]. Another found that kittens raised only with puppies became very attached to them and exhibited signs of separation distress when they were parted[19]. My cat Buffett is certainly attached to "his" dogs. Having grown up with dogs from the age of 4 months, he meows plaintively when they leave the house. He can usually be found sleeping somewhere close to them.

Unfortunately, people owning both dogs and cats usually aren't as lucky in having animals that have been socialized to the other species from a young age. In most cat-to-dog introductions, the cat reacts defensively and the dog wants to chase the cat. I had one case, however, in which a very confident, large, long-haired calico cat successfully chased a year-old fearful and unsocialized chow-mix dog out of the house during an attempted introduction. Sometimes, it can be hard to determine whether the dog wants to play or whether he is displaying serious predatory behavior, so strict supervision and controlled introductions are important to ensure the cat's safety (or, in the case of the aforementioned calico, the dog's!).

1. *Eliciting and reinforcing appropriate behavior.*
- The introduction process will be easier if the dog knows some basic obedience commands, such as sit, down, come, and stay. If not, teach the dog these commands, using tidbits to elicit a reliable, willing performance.

- Use some of the procedures that work for cat-to-cat introductions (starred [*] items in preceding section).
- When the time comes for a full face-to-face meeting, the dog can be on leash. Alternatively, the dog or cat or both can be crated (assuming they have previously been exposed to a crate). If the cat is crated while the dog is loose, be sure to cover the crate initially so that only one side is exposed.
- Work with the dog so that she can be reinforced for sitting or lying down at a distance from the cat without chasing him or, if the cat is crated, without charging the crate. Work with the cat, using treats and petting, so that he is not fearful. If the dog is crated, encourage the cat to approach the crate as long as the dog is quiet and calm. Keep a sufficient distance between the animals so that neither is fearful, aggressive, or overly excited.
- Progress with one or both animals confined, leashed, or held until both animals can be calm in close proximity to one another. Allow each to investigate and sniff the other. If there are concerns about the dog's behavior, she can be muzzled. Be careful about holding a cat during the introduction. If he becomes frightened, he is likely to scratch or bite.
- Usually, the most critical time is when the cat begins to move around, rather than lying still as he would in a crate. Put the dog on a down-stay (use a leash) while she watches the cat walk around the room. Lavishly reinforce the dog with tidbits, attention, and petting to calm and relax her, rather than being poised to spring.
- Allow a little more interaction—e.g., open the door to the crate or let the dog drag the leash.

2. *Preventing or minimizing inappropriate behavior ("mistakes").*
   - Use some of the procedures that work for cat-to-cat introductions (starred [*] items in the preceding section).
   - Do not progress too rapidly with the introduction. Both animals should be relaxed in each other's presence at each step before progressing.
   - Do not rely on the use of punishment for inappropriate behavior. If used more than occasionally, punishment can cause either animal to associate bad things with the other's presence, creating problems with fearful or aggressive behavior.

3. *Minimizing the use of punishment and using punishment correctly when necessary.*
   - If the cat swats at the dog if she becomes too curious, don't scold him. If the dog backs off, great; if she does not, do not allow her to escalate her behavior. Have her sit or lie down instead.
   - If the dog chases the cat, a remote punishment such as a squirt from a water gun may be used. This approach will work best if the dog is squirted the instant the chase begins, rather than many seconds into it. This timing difficulty may limit the effectiveness of this approach. If used, however, the punishment *must* be followed by an easier interaction in which the dog can be reinforced for not chasing the cat.
   - If chasing or other problem reactions continue to occur, either back up a few steps in the introduction process or consider a problem-resolution approach rather than a problem-prevention one (see the appropriate chapter based on what behavior is occurring).

4. *Providing for the cat's behavioral needs or meeting the kitten's developmental needs.*
- Some cats are quite capable of quickly putting a dog in her place with hissing, growling, swatting, or even biting. How successful the cat will be depends, in part, on the dog's motivation. If the dog is showing predatory reactions (not playful ones), any threat or aggression from the cat may cause the dog to attack. A playful dog will likely either back off or consider the cat's response an invitation to continue the game.
- Even a declawed cat can successfully set limits with a dog because the dog responds more to the cat's threatening behavior and body postures than to the sting of a sharp claw.
- Do not allow the dog to harass the cat so that he hides and is afraid to move around (or vice versa, although this is less likely). Try one or more of the following techniques: Supervise the animals more effectively, reintroduce them, implement problem-resolution procedures, or separate them.

DECLAWING

Declawing is a very controversial procedure. Some veterinarians refuse to do it; others offer it routinely at the time the cat is spayed or neutered; some will perform it only after behavior modification techniques for scratching problems have proven unsuccessful; and still others offer alternatives (e.g., cutting the tendons, which is a less invasive procedure). I will divide this subject into two separate issues: (1) whether the procedure is humane and should be performed at all, from an ethical or moral standpoint, and (2) the behavioral effects of declawing.

The issue of humaneness will not be addressed here, for it is likely that neither those who believe declawing is inhumane nor those who believe it is a reasonable option will be persuaded otherwise. Furthermore, I believe it is not my place to make a judgment one way or the other. Everyone is entitled to his or her personal opinion about this issue, and veterinarians have the choice to perform declawings or not as they see fit. Similarly, the many animal shelters that protest declawing are entitled to do so, as well.

However, the second issue regarding what is known about the behavioral effects of declawing can appropriately be addressed here. Although it has long been believed that declawing *causes* cats to become aggressive (to bite), to have litterbox problems, and to undergo other less defined "personality changes," the results of several studies do not support these beliefs. One study found that declawed cats bite people no more often than clawed cats[10], and another found that declawing neither increased the risk of cats developing behavior problems nor decreased desirable behaviors[16]. A survey of owners who had their cats declawed revealed a very low frequency of litterbox problems after the surgery[17]. Finally, in a survey of cats surrendered to an animal shelter, declawing was not correlated with reports of inappropriate elimination or any other behavior problem[15]. No studies to date report an increased incidence in behavior problems in declawed cats. However, no prospective studies, in which the frequency of problem behaviors are measured before as well as after declawing, have been done. The bottom line, then, is that currently available data do not indicate that declawing routinely causes behavior problems or personality changes. An objection to the procedure on ethical or humane grounds is, of course, a separate issue.

SUMMARY

Litterbox troubles, fighting between family cats, and other problems can develop at any time in the life of a cat for reasons not involving factors associated with problem prevention. Though more data are needed in this regard, I believe that many common cat problems are preventable. Don't neglect helping our feline friends get off to a good start.

REFERENCES

1. Borchelt, P.L., and V.L. Voith. 1996. Elimination behavior in cats. In *Readings in companion animal behavior*, ed. V.L. Voith and P.L. Borchelt, 179–90. Trenton, N.J.: Veterinary Learning Systems.

2. Borchelt, P.L. 1991. Cat elimination behavior problems. *Vet. Clinics of North Amer. [Small Anim. Pract.]* 21 (2):257–64.

3. Horwitz, D.F. 1997. Behavioral and environmental factors associated with elimination problems in cats: A retrospective study. *Appl. Anim. Beh. Sci.* 52:129–37.

4. Mertens, C., and R. Schar. 1988. Practical aspects of research on cats. In *The domestic cat: The biology of its behaviour*, ed. D.C. Turner and P. Bateson, 179–92. New York: Cambridge University Press.

5. Leyhausen, P. 1979. *Cat behavior: The predatory and social behavior of domestic and wild cats.* New York: Garland STPM Press.

6. Bateson, P., and D.C. Turner. 1988. Questions about cats. In *The domestic cat: The biology of its behaviour*, ed. D.C. Turner and P. Bateson, 193–201. New York: Cambridge University Press.

7. Hart, B.L., and L.A. Hart. 1985. *Canine and feline behavioral therapy.* Philadelphia: Lea and Febiger.

8. Beaver, B.V. 1992. *Feline behavior: A guide for veterinarians.* Philadelphia: W.B. Saunders.

9. Bradshaw, J.W.S. 1992. *The behaviour of the domestic cat.* Wallingford, Oxon, United Kingdom: CAB International.

10. Borchelt, P.L., and V.L. Voith. 1996. Aggressive behavior in cats. In *Readings in companion animal behavior*, ed. V.L. Voith and P.L. Borchelt, 208–16. Trenton, N.J.: Veterinary Learning Systems.

11. Scott, J.P., and J.L. Fuller. 1965. *Dog behavior: The genetic basis.* Chicago: University of Chicago Press.

12. Karsh, E.B., and D.C. Turner. 1988. The human-cat relationship. In *The domestic cat: The biology of its behaviour,* ed. D.C. Turner and P. Bateson, 159–78. New York: Cambridge University Press.

13. Feaver, J.M., M.T. Mendl, and P. Bateson. 1986. A method for rating the individual distinctiveness of domestic cats. *Anim. Beh.* 34:1016–25.

14. Meir, M., and D.C. Turner. 1985. Reactions of home cats during encounters with a strange person: Evidence for two personality types. *J. of Delta Society* 2:45–53.

15. Patronek, G.J., L.T. Glickman, A.M. Beck, G.P. McCabe, and C. Ecker. 1996. Risk factors for relinquishment of cats to an animal shelter. *JAVMA* 209:582–8.

16. Bennett, M., K.A. Houpt, and H.N. Erb. 1988. Effects of declawing on feline behavior. *Comp. Anim. Pract.* 2:7–12.

17. Landsberg, G.M. 1991. Feline scratching and destruction and the effects of declawing. *Vet. Clinics of North Amer. [Small Anim. Pract.]* 21 (2):165–79.

18. Fox, M.W. 1969. Behavioral effects of rearing dogs with cats during the "critical period of socialization." *Behaviour* 35:273–80.

19. Kuo, Z.Y. 1960. Studies on the basic factors in animal fighting. Part 7: Interspecies coexistence in mammals. *J. of Genetic Psych.* 97:211–25.

CHAPTER 6

Response Protocol
for Behavior Problems

This chapter explains the format that will be used for the next ten chapters, each of which focuses on a specific behavior problem. Therefore, it is essential that you read this chapter first. Also, keep in mind that no part of the response protocol described here should be mistaken for a "cookbook" approach to problem solving. Rather, the purpose of this protocol is to give you a framework within which you can assess the role you might choose in any behavior cases. It suggests a way to organize your approach and take things one step at a time. The protocol is a tool to help you approach behavior cases in a systematic way, rather than taking a "try this, try that" approach, but it is *not* a "recipe" for what to do in any specific case.

When I take on an unusual case or encounter a behavior problem I don't have much experience with, I consult several references to see what they say about the problem in question. These detailed resources are invaluable, and there is no substitute for in-depth reading, consulting colleagues, and learning as much as you can about a particular problem prior to consulting on it. The sources at the end of each chapter and the additional readings list at the end of the book are both provided for this purpose.

Sometimes, however, a different type of resource is needed. I may want to refresh my memory about potential causes of problems (rule-outs, from a diagnostic perspective), about questions I want to ask my client during the behavioral interview, about what treatment options other professionals recommend, and about any cautions others have offered in regard to specific techniques. At other times, I may just need some help in organizing my thoughts about a case. The purpose of the rest of this book is to provide that kind of resource for you. The chapters on specific problems are organized on the basis of a response protocol, and they are meant to be used as a reference guide.

If you are more experienced in working with behavior cases, the response protocol will serve as a refresher, a double check on your approach, and possibly a source of some new ideas. If you are a novice at behavior consulting, the protocol will help you approach a case in a systematic fashion, rather than diving in haphazardly. Organizing a behavior case into a series of steps allows you to periodically assess whether it is appropriate for you to continue with the case or whether it's time to refer your client to a specialist (see Box 6.1). Perhaps most important, the protocol can help you identify what you don't know, as well as what you need to know before you decide to take on a problem-solving role. If you read through the protocol steps on a given problem and find yourself asking, "What does she mean by that?" or thinking, "I never heard of that before," consider this an indication that you need to consult some additional resources and get more information before you proceed.

> **Box 6.1 The value of this behavior reference guide**
>
> - To provide concise, accurate information in an easy-to-use format
> - To help you work with behavior cases systematically
> - To break a behavior case into a series of steps to help you determine at what point you may have reached your professional limits and should refer the case
> - To provide a framework that helps you identify the areas in which you need to increase your knowledge

THE IMPORTANCE OF HAVING A PLAN

In the first chapter of this book, I discussed the importance of taking a scientific approach to behavior problems and having a plan or protocol from which to operate. Experience has taught me that in their well-meaning attempts to help pet owners, many novice behavior consultants jump in with recommendations without truly knowing the nature of the problem (arriving at a behavioral diagnosis), without understanding what the recommendations are designed to accomplish (determining how and on what basis the problem can be resolved), or without taking a systematic approach to resolution (deciding what should be done first, seeing how the recommendations relate to one another and to the diagnosis, and knowing what happens if things don't work as planned).

With their medical background, veterinarians and veterinary technicians are familiar with the importance of diagnoses and rule-outs and having a treatment plan. Academically trained scientists with research backgrounds know the importance of organizing an approach to a problem in a slightly different way—the scientific method or hypothesis testing, which involves formulating a hypothesis about a problem, devising ways to test its accuracy, gathering data, and then reevaluating the hypothesis based on test results. A protocol similar to these diagnostic and research methods can and should be applied to behavior cases.

For those of you without a medical or scientific background, it may at first be difficult to organize a behavior case into a step-by-step plan. The protocol introduced in this chapter will help you do that. The terms and steps that will be described are somewhat different from those used in either a diagnostic or a research approach, but if you are familiar with those methods, you will easily see the parallels. Following the protocol and taking a behavior case a step at a time will also make it easier for you to know when you are getting in over your head and when it might be wise to assume a role other than that of the problem solver.

DIAGNOSIS AND THE BEHAVIORAL HISTORY

Included in each response protocol is a list of common causes for the specific problem behavior, followed by a series of questions about the behavior; the answers to those questions will help you categorize the cause of a particular problem. For example, housesoiling and destructive behavior in either dogs or cats can have a variety of causes. In order to determine *why* either of these behaviors is occurring, you will need to ask the owner questions on a variety of topics, including when, where, and how frequently the behavior occurs (after you have the behavioral description of the problem). The list of questions in each chapter represents a partial or minimum behavioral history. *These questions should not be viewed as a replacement for or an equivalent to a complete behavioral history.* A complete behavioral history relies on feedback from the owner; the answers an owner gives influence what other questions need to be asked. Thus, it isn't possible to develop a standard or "cookbook" behavioral history.

Many good references provide examples of behavior history forms, the types of questions to include, and how to conduct a behavioral interview or history-taking session[1,2,3,4]. If you are completely unfamiliar with behavioral history taking, you should read one or more of these excellent references.

Many novice behavior consultants (and even some more experienced ones) often have trouble making the link between (1) posing the appropriate questions and evaluating the answers in the behavioral history, (2) assessing how a particular problem "looks" at presentation (e.g., what are the characteristics or behavioral manifestations of a destructive dog with separation anxiety?), and (3) making the diagnosis. For instance, even if you read up on separation anxiety and history taking, you still may not know what specific questions to ask and what answers to look for or how to distinguish a separation anxiety problem from one in which the dog is misbehaving when alone because he's learned he won't get caught. Put another way, you need to know how to use the answers to the questions you ask to arrive at a behavioral diagnosis. As you become more experienced with history taking, you'll discover that you are formulating a hypothesis about the cause of the problem or creating your list of rule-outs as you are asking questions.

If you do not have time to ask questions, refer the case to someone who does. This is far better than trying to help owners manage or resolve a problem without having some sense of why their animal is doing what he's doing. Alternatively, make time to get the information you need by scheduling a separate appointment for that purpose with the owners. Whether you have time to obtain at least this minimum amount of information is one of the decision points you can use when you weigh continuing to work with the case yourself or referring it to a behavior specialist.

RESPONSE PROTOCOL FOR BEHAVIOR PROBLEMS

In the following section, I'll explain the steps of the response protocol. I will discuss why each step is important, what is required to complete each step, and how, at each step, you can assess your role in the case or choose what role you wish to play (educator, facilitator, referral and rescue guide, or problem solver, as covered in chapter 1).

1. Obtain a Description of the Problem Behavior

The following descriptions of behavior problems will sound familiar to anyone who works with pet owners:

"He goes crazy during thunderstorms."
"He's going all over the house."
"He doesn't get along with my kids."
"He's just neurotic."
"He doesn't like visitors."
"He's out of control when the doorbell rings."
"He isn't adjusting well to living with our family."
"He's aggressive to other animals."

Based on any of these descriptions, do you know anything about what the pet in question is actually doing? If you were asked to draw a picture of his behavior, could you do it? The answer is clearly no. All of the preceding statements are either interpretations of behavior, anthropomorphic descriptions, or simply too vague to be of any value. So, the first step in any behavior case is to *obtain a behavioral description of the problem behavior.*

Remember that descriptions are not interpretations. Don't be fooled by statements like the last one cited earlier—calling an animal aggressive is an interpretation, not a description. Does the word *aggressive* tell you what the animal is doing? The answer is no. The dog or cat could be biting, scratching, barking, growling, hissing, or exhibiting a number of other behaviors that may or may not fall under a behavioral definition of aggression (see chapter 12). Examples of descriptions of behavior are:

> "During a thunderstorm, he quivers, drools, and tries to crawl in my lap."
> "He's urinating on all the beds in the house."
> "Whenever my kids walk up to him, he growls at them."
> "He's pulling his hair out."
> "When someone new comes to the house, he runs into the other room and hides."
> "When the doorbell rings, he runs to the door barking and growling, and I can't get him to stop."
> "He's jumping up on my kids and barking at us when we sit down to eat dinner."
> "He's chasing the cat."

The words that owners use to describe behavior may reveal little about what the pet is actually doing. I was once called by an owner concerned about a housesoiling problem. She stated that her dogs were "going to the bathroom" in the house overnight. When I asked her to describe what they were doing, she said that when her husband walked past the dogs' beds at night on his way to the bathroom, they would growl at him, he would kick them, and then they would urinate. Obviously, this was not a problem about going to the bathroom, unless one is referring to the husband!

You may need to use a variety of communication and interviewing skills to elicit behavioral descriptions. If I'm having difficulty getting owners to describe a behavior, I often ask them to draw me a verbal picture of what their pet is doing or tell me what he looks like when he's showing the problem behavior. Details about the pet's body postures are critical for most problems. Never assume that you know what behavior clients are referring to ("he's going in the house") until they have provided you with a verbal description so that you can actually picture the pet in your mind as he exhibits the behavior in question. If you take even a partial behavioral history, you'll add many details to this basic behavioral description.

In many cases, a behavioral description of a problem can also be thought of as a symptom: It is not a diagnosis or a cause of the problem. Too often, people start to treat symptoms rather than treating causes. For example, if a cat is not using the litterbox, they may confine her; or if a dog is being destructive when alone, they may crate him. Treating symptoms before you know the cause can result in inappropriate and ineffective recommendations. Obtaining a behavioral description simply allows you to know exactly what the pet is doing so that you can formulate meaningful questions about the problem.

2. Evaluate Potential Medical Causes for the Problem Behavior

If you are a veterinarian, it is your job to perform whatever physical examinations, laboratory testing, or other diagnostic procedures you think necessary in order to be reasonably confident that the behavior change or problem described by an owner is not due to disease or some other physical cause. As a nonveterinarian behaviorist, I work almost exclusively by veterinary referral. If a client who has not been referred by her veterinarian contacts me, I usually ask that she speak with the veterinarian first to see whether he or she feels the animal should be examined prior to a behavior consultation. I may not be as adamant about this if the problem is, say, a barking dog, but I am quite insistent when either housesoiling or aggression is involved. In fact, one of my major frustrations is when either the veterinarian or a clinic staff person, having heard an owner's brief description or even his or her *interpretation* of an aggressive or housesoiling problem in a telephone call, decides that the animal's problem has a behavioral cause without examining the animal or doing any laboratory testing. (This relates to the issue discussed in chapter 1 regarding which staff members in a clinic have the authority to refer a behavior case.) Keep in mind the medical model: Veterinarians usually don't refer cases to other specialists without doing a preliminary workup themselves.

I also find that too many dog trainers and shelter personnel are ready to assume that a problem is behavioral without suggesting the owner contact a veterinarian first. It is in everyone's best interest—the pet owner's, the animal's, the behaviorist's, and the veterinarian's—to evaluate and rule out or treat medical causes for behavioral problems. Behavior consultants and veterinarians should continue to work closely together throughout the course of a case.

I've had cases involving both dogs and cats in which a medical problem wasn't discovered until a second visit to the veterinarian. A West Highland white terrier puppy is a case in point. The family was having trouble housetraining this 4-month-old puppy. After doing a urinalysis that proved normal, the veterinarian referred the case to me. We seemed to be making progress with some very strict housetraining procedures when the puppy relapsed. The frequency of his urination didn't sound right to me, so I referred the owners back to their veterinarian, another urinalysis was done, and a urinary tract infection was revealed.

In subsequent chapters on individual problems, the sections on evaluating medical problems will not provide specific recommendations about what medical workups or diagnostic procedures should be done; that will be left to the veterinarian. However, examples of conditions that can affect behavior will be given when appropriate. For a good review of this topic, see the references listed at the end of the chapter[5, 6].

3. Educate Owners About the Problem Behavior

Chapter 1 discussed the many ways in which owners can be educated about behavior and behavior problems. In the context of the response protocol, owners must be educated about:

- What the cause of a behavior problem might be, in order to replace their own anthropomorphic interpretation of the situation ("Our cat urinated on the bed because he's mad at us")
- Myths about problem solving ("I've always heard that once dogs taste blood, there's nothing you can do to stop them from biting")
- Techniques to avoid ("Uncle Joe told me to confine my cat in the bathroom for two weeks; he said that would teach her not to poop on the carpet")
- Realistic expectations about normal behavior, the process of problem resolution, and prognosis ("We've scolded him repeatedly for chewing on the furniture. He's 8 months old—shouldn't he know better by now?")

Use some of the communication skills discussed in chapter 2 when you talk to owners about these issues. Changing their perceptions should be done gently and with respect, not by mocking them or talking down to them. Even if you decide not to become involved in recommending a problem-resolution plan, you can still educate owners about these topics. They need to understand the cause of the problem, as well as what *not* to do, so that they will be better informed if they seek help from someone else who is (or claims to be) an expert. Providing this education also allows you to appear credible, knowledgeable, and helpful without tackling more than you should in problem solving.

You may find that some of the procedures you have recommended in the past are included in the sections on myths and procedures to avoid. If so, that's a sign that you need to become more familiar with advancements in the field of applied animal behavior, or behavioral medicine, before continuing in or delving deeper into a problem-solving role.

4. Identify the Behavioral Cause of the Problem (Arrive at a Behavioral Diagnosis)

Before attempting to offer management recommendations or devise a treatment plan, you must determine the cause of the problem (arrive at a behavioral diagnosis). Without this step, recommendations would relate only to the symptom, not the cause, and they might be irrelevant or inappropriate for the problem. Using an antibark collar, for example, is a symptomatic treatment, and it might be very inappropriate if the dog's barking is due to fear; confining a cat who is house-soiling does nothing to address the reason for the problem. Behavioral causes of problems are determined by interviewing the owner, making general observations of the animal as well as the problem behavior, and viewing the animal's normal environment. Some of these sources of information may not be available, depending on the type of problem and where behavioral interviews are conducted (in the home, in the office, or through a telephone call). However, the more sources of information available to aid in diagnosis the better.

In this step of the protocol, I have provided a list of common causes for the specific problem being discussed and a lengthy, but not necessarily complete, list of questions to ask owners to help you elicit the information you will need to arrive at a behavioral diagnosis. The answers to these questions will be different based on the cause of the problem. A description of the results to be expected from this questioning is provided for each potential cause listed.

What you are able to accomplish in this step in the protocol will determine what you do next. If you can arrive at a behavioral diagnosis, you can then choose to do any or all of the following: (1) offer specific management suggestions, (2) inform owners of the goals of treatment, (3) devise a treatment plan yourself, or (4) refer the case. If you are *not* able to diagnosis the problem, your options are more limited: (1) offer only general management suggestions that are not based on a behavioral diagnosis, (2) inform owners of the goals of treatment, if this can be done in a general way that is not dependent on a diagnosis, or (3) refer the case or seek assistance in diagnosis from a behavior specialist before proceeding.

5. Discuss Ways to Manage or Control the Behavior over the Short or Long Term

If you don't feel comfortable in problem solving or if you find that the owners are unable or unwilling to implement the procedures necessary to resolve a problem, you can help your clients identify ways in which to manage the problem. However, you need to be absolutely certain that the owners understand that managing a problem is not the same as resolving it or actually changing the animal's behavior. For example, it *may* be possible to manage an aggression problem by muzzling or confining the dog under certain circumstances. The problem may be controlled using these procedures, but the dog's behavior hasn't been changed. Muzzling a dog is managing the behavior; changing his response from aggressive to neutral or friendly is resolving the problem. It's inappropriate to let clients believe that problem management is problem resolution. Some clients may choose management procedures over resolution procedures, which is fine as long as they are aware of the difference. If you choose to limit your recommendations to management procedures, make sure that you give the client the option of being referred to a behavior specialist who can help with problem resolution or actual behavior changes.

6. Explain the Goals of an Appropriate Behavior Modification Plan

In explaining the goals of a modification plan, you may or may not include the actual treatment procedures. Let's say that you have determined a cat is urinating outside the litterbox because of a surface or location preference problem. You can explain to the owner that, in such cases, the goals are to change the litterbox characteristics so that they suit the cat's preferences, to make the soiled areas less attractive, and perhaps to try to change the cat's preferences. Whether or not you have the expertise to help clients achieve these goals, by explaining them you give the owners a perspective on what needs to be done (in addition to what not to do). This not only helps them avoid inappropriate procedures but also provides them with additional information by which to evaluate recommendations that come from other resources they may contact. When you've identified the specific treatment goals, you can ask yourself if you know how to reach them. This will help you determine whether you have the expertise to function as a problem solver in the case.

HOW TO USE THE PROTOCOL

Depending on your goals in a specific case, you can use the response protocol in a very general way, without knowing the cause of a behavioral symptom, or in a very specific way, based on a behavioral diagnosis.

If you don't have the time, interest, or expertise to thoroughly question the owners, the protocols can still be helpful to you. You can either end your involvement at the education step and refer the case or you can talk to the owners in general terms about management procedures and treatment goals. For example, one general *management procedure* in dog aggression cases is to eliminate any opportunity for the dog to bite someone by muzzling him or keeping him away from people when he might be inclined to bite. If two cats are fighting, a general *management procedure* would be to keep the cats separated at all times or when they are likely to fight. You don't need to know what type of aggression the dog or cat is showing to make such recommendations, but you will be better able to predict when the aggression might occur if you know what type of aggression is involved.

A general *treatment goal* in aggression cases is to use techniques that will condition the dog or cat to behave nonaggressively in the situations that are currently a problem. You can explain that general treatment goal and avoid more specific ones without knowing the type of aggression involved.

However, sometimes you will need to have more specific information about a problem before you can make recommendations about management procedures or treatment goals. For example, you don't want to recommend a crate as a management procedure for destructive behavior if separation anxiety is involved. Similarly, you don't want to recommend various changes to a litterbox until you know why the cat isn't using it because you could be suggesting some change that would actually exacerbate the problem. More specific recommendations must be based on the cause of the problem, which you will not know unless you spend time gathering information from the owner.

This is the value of this unique protocol: It allows you to assess your position at each step, so you can make appropriate choices about how you should proceed and what role you should play. The most important choice is whether you should delve into actual problem solving. If you choose not to, the protocol lets you identify all the other roles you can play and the important things you can do to be helpful to both owner and animal.

REFERENCES

1. Askew, H.R. 1996. *Treatment of behavior problems in dogs and cats*. Cambridge, Mass.: Blackwell Science.

2. Hunthausen, W.L., and G.M. Landsberg. 1995. *A practitioner's guide to pet behavior problems: Supplemental information*. Lakewood, Colo.: American Animal Hospital Association.

3. Overall, K. 1997. *Clinical behavioral medicine for small animals*. St. Louis: Mosby.

4. Voith, V.L., and P.L. Borchelt. 1996. History taking and interviewing. In *Readings in companion animal behavior*, ed. V.L. Voith and P.L. Borchelt, 42–7. Trenton, N.J.: Veterinary Learning Systems.

5. Hart, B.L. 1991. The behavior of sick animals. *Vet. Clinics of North Amer. [Small Anim. Pract.]* 21 (2):225–38.

6. Reisner, I. 1991. The pathophysiologic basis of behavior problems. *Vet. Clinics of North Amer. [Small Anim. Pract.]* 21 (2):207–24.

CHAPTER 7

Elimination and Urine-Marking
Problems in Dogs

A simpler title for this chapter might have been "Housesoiling Problems," but the term *housesoiling* describes the outcome or consequence of a behavior, not the behavior itself. I've tried to avoid this kind of description of behavior problems when possible (although I found it to be unavoidable when discussing destructive behaviors—see chapters 8 and 14). The important points are that dogs may urinate or defecate in undesired locations for reasons other than a need to empty the bladder or bowels and that urine has a communicative value that has nothing to do with the need to eliminate.

PROTOCOL

Elimination and urine-marking problems are two of the most common problems you'll encounter. Start working through the protocol by finding out what the dog is actually doing.

1. Obtain a Description of the Problem Behavior

First, you must obtain a description of the behavior from the client that will allow you to determine if the problem involves urinating, defecating, or both. Common euphemistic expressions that owners use may not be helpful in this regard: "He's going on the bed," "He's making a mess in the house," "He's marking all over." This suggests another important discrimination you'll need to make—that is, whether the urination is due to urine marking. If the client says the dog is marking, *do not assume* that this is, indeed, the case. Many owners refer to any urination in the house as marking. You will probably not be able to determine if urine marking is involved without asking the owner the questions detailed in step 4 of the protocol. At this point, you will only be able to determine if the problem pertains to urination, defecation, or both.

2. Evaluate Potential Medical Causes for the Problem Behavior

Any number of medical conditions can cause inappropriate elimination[1]. These include urinary tract infections, internal parasites, diabetes, endocrine disorders, foreign bodies, anal sac problems, neurological conditions, food allergies, any condition that produces physical pain or discomfort and makes the dog reluctant to go outside, a change in diet, inappropriate supplements to a regular diet (e.g., table scraps or too many treats), and many others. If you are a non-veterinarian talking to the owners of a housesoiling dog, be adamant about having them contact the veterinarian first: Without question, that should be the initial step taken. If the owners respond, "But he doesn't act sick," be armed with several effective responses. Point out, for example, that:

- Animals sometimes are good at hiding signs of illness.
- You do not want to waste their time and money with a behavior consultation when a medical problem could be involved.
- If your own dog were housesoiling, you would call your veterinarian first.
- It's the best thing for the dog—suggest the owners would not want to leave an illness untreated.

If all else fails, simply refuse to schedule a behavior consultation until the veterinarian has been contacted.

If you are a veterinarian, make sure that you don't let the client talk you out of any workup you feel is necessary because she is so convinced that her pet has a behavior problem.

3. Educate Owners About the Problem Behavior

Educate the owners about anthropomorphic and other misinterpretations. Housesoiling does not occur because the dog is mad, "acting out," or being spiteful or revengeful; he isn't signaling his dislike of someone in the household or a visitor to the home; and he is not housesoiling for any of the other anthropomorphic explanations for the behavior that pet owners commonly give. Getting owners to view the problem from a behavioral perspective rather than an anthropomorphic one can sometimes be a hard task. Elimination on the bed, on items of clothing, or when the dog is not taken on an outing is most often misinterpreted as an act of spite. However, such behaviors are usually motivated either by urine marking or by separation anxiety. Owners sometimes report that their dog goes off by himself and eliminates after being punished, which could simply be an anxiety behavior, similar to what happens in a veterinary clinic.

It may be helpful to explain that if the elimination was a spiteful act, the dog would need to view urine and feces as distasteful in the same way that people do, which clearly is not the case. Dogs are known to eat feces, and we know that dogs use urine to communicate with each other, two acts that aren't in the repertoire of human behavior. By pointing this out, you are encouraging owners to understand that animals don't perceive the acts of urination or defecation as degrading. Most owners are aware of only two reasons for housesoiling—marking and incomplete housetraining. As you'll see in a later section, these are only two of many possible reasons.

Although scent marking in other species may allow animals to assess each other's dominant status, whether this is true in dogs has never been determined[2]. There is no evidence that there is a relationship between urine marking and dominance status. In other words, it cannot be said that dogs who are more socially dominant are more likely to urine mark. Elimination problems not involving marking certainly have nothing to do with a lack of owner dominance over the dog or a lack of obedience.

Educate the owners about myths regarding problem solving and techniques to avoid. Attempts to punish the dog after the fact, such as showing him what he's done or rubbing his nose in the mess, are not helpful or effective. In fact, these and other types of noncontingent punishment can exacerbate the problem, and depending on its severity, the punishment will at best be unfair and at worst be abusive. Refer to chapter 3 for a discussion of punishment and ways to explain inappropriate punishment to owners. It may be helpful to point out that because it is only possible to punish *behavior*, not the animal, punishment is useless unless owners see the animal perform the behavior.

It is *not* appropriate to recommend a crate until you are certain that the problem is not based on fear or anxiety. Crating a dog who is housesoiling when alone due to separation anxiety has a high probability of increasing his anxiety; it may even result in injury to the dog if he tries to escape from the crate. If the owner is already using a crate and the dog is making extreme attempts to escape, making the crate escape-proof is not the answer. If the dog is clearly anxious and frightened while crated, then this procedure should be abandoned until the problem can be evaluated.

In regard to urine marking, there are many myths about the behavioral effects of neutering, a topic you may need to discuss with your clients. See the section in chapter 9 for more information on this issue.

Educate the owners about realistic expectations. It always amazes me how many calls I get from owners of 4-, 5-, or 6-month-old puppies who are complaining because their puppies aren't yet housetrained! I don't expect a young dog to be completely housetrained until 8, 9, or even 12 months of age. Similarly, adult dogs that are new to the household, as mentioned in chapter 4, should not be expected to be housetrained even if they were well trained in a previous home.

4. Identify the Behavioral Cause of the Problem

Before developing management procedures or treatment goals, you must understand the cause for the housesoiling. If you are going to proceed further in the case, your next job is to ask owners specific questions designed to help you determine the cause of the problem. This is a decision point for you: If you do not have time to ask enough questions to diagnose the problem or at least determine if fear or anxiety is likely involved, you should refer the case to someone who can do so. You may or may not choose to talk to owners in *general* terms about management procedures and treatment goals (refer to the later section on this topic).

After medical conditions have been ruled out, common behavioral causes of inappropriate elimination or housesoiling are:

- Incomplete housetraining
- Separation anxiety
- Fears or phobias
- Urine marking (not an elimination problem)
- Submissive or excitement urination
- Development of undesirable surface or location preferences
- Olfactory cues

Components of a behavioral history. The answers to the following questions will help you distinguish among these causes. For easier organization, they are divided into several categories:

Description of the dog, description of the behavior.
- How old is the dog?
- What breed is the dog?
- Is she spayed/he neutered?
- Does the problem involve urinating, defecating, or both?
- Was the dog found as a stray or obtained from a humane society or shelter?

Specific details of housetraining procedures.
- During housetraining:
    - Did the owner consistently confine or supervise the dog any time he could not be watched?
    - Did "accidents" happen frequently?
    - Did the owner go outside with the dog and *immediately* reinforce elimination behavior?
    - Did the owner keep the dog on a consistent daily feeding schedule?
    - Did the owner provide consistent and frequent opportunities for the dog to eliminate outside?
    - Did the owner punish the dog if he or she caught him soiling? If so, how?
    - Did the owner punish the dog if he or she didn't catch him soiling? If so, how?
    - Would the owner describe the dog as difficult to housetrain?

Description of the dog's daily routine, environment, and behavior patterns.
- Does the dog consistently follow the owner from room to room (is he a "shadow" dog)?
- Does the dog greet the owner frantically when he or she returns home?
- Does the dog display a visible change in behavior as the owner prepares to leave the house without him—e.g., become agitated, restless, nervous, anxious, depressed, or fearful?
- Does the dog frequently and persistently solicit the owner's attention or become anxious or pestering if he is ignored?
- Is the dog known to be afraid of any noises (such as thunder, firecrackers, or hot-air balloons) or of people such as neighbors, mail carriers, or schoolchildren?
- Is the dog reluctant to go outside or stay outside even for short periods by himself?
- Are there frequent conflicts or tension between family dogs?
- What is the owner's schedule for providing opportunities for the dog to eliminate outside? (That is, when and how often does the owner walk him, put him outside in the yard, etc.?)
- Does the dog "ask" to go outside when he needs to eliminate? If yes, how?
- Does the dog have a dog door?
- Does the dog have easy access to the yard or another area where she should be eliminating?
- Does the dog show any reluctance to use this access path?
- Does the dog have a sheltered, grassy area for elimination, one that is near the house and easy to get to?
- What is the dog's feeding schedule?

Specifics about the occurrence of the problem behavior.
- Has the housesoiling been a problem, with varying frequency, for virtually all of the dog's life?
- Has there been a significant period of time (months) when the dog has not housesoiled? If so, when did that occur and how long did it last?
- If the dog has a history of being reliably housetrained, when did the current housesoiling first start?

- Does the housesoiling occur only in the owner's absence? If yes:
  — Does it occur every time the dog is alone or with a consistent pattern of absences, such as only in the evening?
  — Does it occur within the first 30 minutes of the owner's departure? (If this is unknown, the owner can find out by videotaping or returning unexpectedly after a brief absence.)
- Does the housesoiling occur both when the owner is home and when he or she is away?
- Does it occur overnight?
- If the dog is being crated, is he soiling his crate? If so, how frequently?
- Does it occur when the owner is home but not watching the dog?
- Did the beginning of the housesoiling problem correlate with any changes in the family's routine or composition—e.g., a change in work hours, the death of another pet, or a child going away to college?
- If the housesoiling is intermittent, could it be correlated to the occurrence of anything the dog is afraid of (thunder, construction noises, etc.)? If the owner doesn't know this, suggest video- or audiotaping.
- Is the dog urinating relatively small amounts ("sprinkles") or more of a puddle?
- Is the urination occurring on objects new to the home or on the belongings of a visiting friend or new family member? (Examples include baby's toys, suitcases, new clothes, and the like.)
- Is the urination occurring in conjunction with the presence of unfamiliar people or animals, either in the home or passing by outside?
- Is the urination occurring shortly after the dog returns from a walk?
- Is the elimination frequently occurring after the dog has been put outside to eliminate and then comes back inside?
- Does the urination occur only when the dog is being greeted, played with, petted, or disciplined? If yes, does the dog roll over, crouch down, pull her ears back, tuck her tail, "grin," or show any other submissive or fearful postures?
- Are the soiled areas in out-of-the-way locations in the house?
- Have other pets soiled the same area?
- Do the soiled areas have a common type of texture, such as soft surfaces (carpet, bed, clothes, etc.)?
- Do the locations of the soiled areas seem to be more consistent (e.g., in out-of-the-way places, on new items, etc.) than the type of surface on which the elimination occurs?
- Have the owner provide a detailed list of the soiled locations.
- If the family has more than one dog, how has the owner determined which dog is housesoiling? (This is a very important question. It is not sufficient for owners to say that "we just know it's him" or that "the other dog would never do this." Instead, they should be encouraged to provide some concrete justifications—for instance, one dog was confined or out of the house, and it still happened; one dog was observed soiling; there is a significant difference in the sizes of stools produced by the household pets; or the location of the urine corresponds to the leg lifting of a male or the squatting of a female. If owners cannot provide substantiating evidence, you may need to investigate further before determining which dog has the problem.)

Owners' attempts at problem resolution and the dog's response.
- Has the dog been punished, either if caught in the act or not?
- Has the dog been hit or verbally scolded?
- Has the dog been put outside in an angry way?
- Has the behavior improved, gotten worse, or stayed the same since the problem began?
- What products have been used for cleaning the soiled areas?
- What other things have been done to try to resolve the problem? What results have been observed?

Differential results of the behavioral history. Answers to the preceding questions will help you identify the cause of the problem.

Incomplete housetraining. Because the dog has never been entirely housetrained, the history will reveal that housesoiling has been a problem, possibly at varying frequencies, for most, if not all, of the dog's life. Questioning usually reveals that inadequate or inappropriate housetraining procedures were used (see chapter 4), resulting in the dog often having unlimited access to the house without ever being fully trained. Often, but not always, both urination and defecation are involved. Due to an inappropriate use of punishment, the dog may be eliminating where he can't get "caught" (out of the owner's presence) or soiling in infrequently used areas of the house, out of the owner's sight, overnight, or only in the owner's absence (this behavior must be carefully distinguished from separation anxiety problems). Inconsistent daily routines and inadequate opportunities for appropriate elimination may also be noted. Where the elimination occurs can be highly variable, ranging from a few places used repeatedly to virtually anywhere in the house. Owners may have used ineffective deodorizing products (ammonia-based liquids, vinegar, regular carpet cleaners, anything that is not enzymatic) so that the lingering odor continues to attract the dog to the soiled areas.

Separation anxiety. The pattern of occurrence of the housesoiling will be congruent with any problem behavior associated with separation anxiety. The housesoiling will occur within the first 30 minutes or so after the owner's departure, it will occur *only* and *consistently* (i.e., every time, not unpredictably) in the owner's absence (or a particular pattern of absences, such as every time the owner leaves for the evening after a workday absence), and it will *not* occur when the owner is home[3, 4]. Either urination, defecation, or both may be involved. If elimination occurs both in and out of the owner's presence, it is not likely related to separation, although it could be a compound problem involving separation anxiety as well as another motivation.

Confining or restricting a dog with separation anxiety usually exacerbates the problem. If the owner has crated the dog or confined it to a small area of the house and if the dog has injured itself attempting to escape or has soiled the crate, separation anxiety may be the underlying problem.

The dog will also demonstrate some or all of the other signs correlated with separation anxiety, such as following the owner around the house, frantic greeting behavior, and agitation if the owner is briefly out of sight[3, 4]. Because the owner's preparations to leave predict to the dog that he is about to be left alone, there will usually be obvious responses to these departures cues (increased anxiety, agitation, depression). A strong attachment to the owner seems to be characteristic of dogs with separation anxiety, and many of them display a pattern of frequently soliciting social interaction (human attention) and receiving it on demand. This may be part of the explanation for the problem behavior: Such dogs become anxious or frustrated when they cannot immediately interact with their owners.

Dogs with separation anxiety are statistically more likely to be purebreds obtained from a humane society[4]. They are also more likely to have a history of constant companionship and rarely being left alone prior to the onset of the problem behavior.

Triggers for the onset of a separation anxiety problem include a change in the family's schedule, a change in the family composition (including the death of another pet), a move to a new environment, or being boarded, hospitalized, or away from the owner for some other reason. It is important to note that not all housesoiling that occurs in the owner's absence can be attributed to separation anxiety.

Fears or phobias. Dogs will eliminate when they are frightened. The most common stimuli causing fear-related housesoiling seem to be loud noises, such as thunder, firecrackers, car backfires, trash trucks, or the sounds of construction or heavy equipment. Fear of certain people could trigger the problem, as well, although I have not encountered this response very frequently. Some detective work on the owner's part may be necessary to establish the correlation between the occurrence of these noises (or other events) and the housesoiling. Videotaping may be necessary, and it should not only reveal the correlation but also fear-related body postures. The dog may not eliminate in the owner's presence in reaction to the same stimulus because the animal may not be as afraid when the owner is present.

Rather than the feared stimulus actually triggering elimination, the dog could begin eliminating in the house because she is afraid to go outside due to a noise phobia or other fear-related problem. A reluctance to go outside or to stay outside by herself for any length of time will be seen.

In cases of fear- or phobia-related elimination problems, the history should not reveal any difficulties with housetraining procedures and the soiling should occur only in conjunction with the fear-producing stimulus. In some cases, however, the fear may have generalized to a particular location, so that the soiling occurs there even in the absence of the initiating stimulus. Either urination, defecation, or both could be involved.

Urine marking. Urine marking is seen more frequently in males than females and most often in intact males. Urination posture is not diagnostic, for males will lift their legs when marking as well as when eliminating. Dogs typically will not urine mark before puberty, so it would be unusual (although not impossible) to see the problem in a dog younger than 6 months or a year. Most often, urine marking involves relatively small quantities of urine, less than a bladder's worth.

The context in which the behavior occurs is important in diagnosing urine marking. It should be related to some event that the dog perceives as a threat to the integrity of his territory. Examples include other dogs or people passing by; the presence of unfamiliar people or animals in the home; the addition of anything new to the home, including pets, furniture, or people (babies, spouses, roommates); and the odors of other animals on the owner's shoes or clothing. Urine marking can happen shortly after the dog returns from a walk, and it may be more likely in dogs who urine mark frequently on walks. It can also occur if there are conflicts or tensions among family dogs.

Some dogs will repeatedly urine mark a few locations; others will mark widely. Dogs may mark objects new to the home, such as baby's toys, suitcases, new furniture, grocery bags, etc. Marking may also occur near doors and windows. The marking may be occurring at times or in locations where the dog has learned he won't be punished (out of the owner's immediate sight), or the owner may be able to observe the behavior at least occasionally. It's been my experience that the owner may catch the dog early in the course of the problem, but due to interactive punishment, the dog quickly learns to mark only out of the owner's presence.

Submissive or excitement urination. This is usually extremely easy to diagnosis. It most often occurs in young dogs (less than 1 year of age) and in contexts in which the dog is either very excited or is feeling threatened. Examples include greetings, both from family members and visitors, especially if someone reaches to pet the dog (this is particularly true with shy or timid dogs) or if the dog is being punished verbally or physically (appropriately or not). Submissive urination is usually accompanied by other submissive postures, such as rolling over, pulling the ears back, crouching, tucking the tail, or submissively grinning. If the urination is due to excitement, the dog's demeanor should be exuberant, boisterous, and friendly.

Development of undesirable surface or location preferences. This is often, but not always, a corollary of inappropriate housetraining procedures. Most animals develop preferences for where and on what they eliminate (see chapter 4). If the dog has frequent opportunities to housesoil because of inadequate supervision during housetraining, she may come to prefer using these inappropriate areas over eliminating outside.

A lack of appealing surfaces or areas outside can also cause problems. The behavioral history may reveal that it is difficult for the dog to get outside due to environmental factors (I once worked with a dog who was required to walk along a narrow board slanted at a steep angle to reach the backyard, as if he were walking the plank) or health factors (the dog is aging or has difficulty moving around). In addition, the area provided for elimination outside may not be acceptable to the dog because of adverse weather conditions (usually cold and wet weather, but extreme heat and humidity can also be involved); landscaping that only gives the dog access to surfaces such as gravel, cement, bark, prickly weeds, or other rough textures; or a lack of access to established preferred substrates. An example of the latter case would be a dog who has been accustomed to eliminating on grass but who now has access only to cement on his leash walks. The physical characteristics of the dog may influence his willingness to eliminate outdoors in adverse weather conditions: Small, short-coated dogs don't like the snow, and heavy-coated dogs may be reluctant to leave an air-conditioned house in hot, humid weather. In these cases, it is certainly preferable from the dog's point of view to go into a convenient room in a nice warm (or cool) house with soft carpeting rather than braving the unpleasant world outdoors. The dog may display a pattern of being reluctant to go outside, not wanting to stay out for long, and eliminating soon after coming in because he then has access to his preferred location or substrate (this behavior needs to be carefully distinguished from behavior stemming from fear-related problems).

Surface and location preferences for elimination are strongly influenced by early experience. The puppies I observed for my doctoral dissertation were raised on a cement floor until they were 16 weeks of age. When first exposed to grass, they would not eliminate on it but chose concrete sidewalks instead. Finding out what the dog's early experiences were may also be helpful in diagnosing this problem.

Olfactory cues. Many owners view these cues as a very common cause of an elimination problem when, in reality, they are usually at best a contributing factor or one that helps maintain a problem once it begins. Dogs are typically drawn to specific areas for housesoiling for the other reasons already discussed. No odors are present to attract them to the area until they begin to soil there because of some other motivation. It is possible that odors from other pets who have previously eliminated in an area may contribute to the housesoiling problem at hand. However, I think these odor cues are more likely to trigger a urine-marking problem than an elimination problem.

5. Discuss Ways to Manage or Control the Behavior over the Short or Long Term

As mentioned in chapter 6, management procedures can be discussed in a very general way if you have not been able to arrive at a behavioral diagnosis for the problem, or they can be specific to the underlying cause. Remember as well that managing the problem is not necessarily the same thing as resolving it.

General management procedures—no behavioral diagnosis. About the only thing that can be said about management procedures when no behavioral diagnosis has been reached is that the dog should not be given the opportunity to housesoil. (This does not mean recommending a crate unless you know the problem is *not* due to fear or anxiety). Of course, effective odor-neutralizing products can be recommended (see product appendix): For the owner, reducing the odor is usually an important part of management.

Management procedures based on a diagnosis.

Incomplete housetraining. To simply manage the problem of housesoiling caused by incomplete housetraining, recommend increased supervision. For such a straightforward problem, there should be no reason not to explain the relevant treatment, which consists of basic housetraining procedures of which supervision is a part (see chapter 4).

Separation anxiety. In this type of case, the elimination is motivated by anxiety, so management requires keeping the dog from becoming anxious; this, in turn, requires that the owner not leave him alone long enough to trigger the anxiety. Options include:
- Using a doggie day care service, boarding him in the daytime at a kennel or veterinary clinic, letting him stay with friends or family who are home all day, or letting him accompany the owner
- Leaving the dog outside during the day. Usually, however, this backfires because most dogs are more or at least equally anxious outside and other problems often result, such as destructive behavior, escaping, or barking.
- Working with the veterinarian to provide medication on a short-term basis to decrease the dog's anxiety. However, make sure the owner understands that medication alone is not a long-term solution to separation anxiety problems (see chapter 18 for more information about medication).

Fears or phobias. Inappropriate elimination caused by fears or phobias can be managed by changing the dog's daily routine so that she is not exposed to the fear-producing stimulus or by working with the veterinarian to provide medication that will decrease the dog's anxious response on a short-term basis.

Urine marking. An elimination problem stemming from urine marking can be managed by:
- Not allowing the dog to be exposed to the stimuli that trigger the marking
- Supervising or appropriately confining the dog so he does not have the opportunity to urine mark

Drug therapy is not widely used for urine marking in dogs (see chapter 18). Neutering should be the first recommendation for either management or treatment.

Submissive or excitement urination. Manage the problem of submissive or excitement urination by preventing the interactions that trigger the behavior. If such interactions cannot be prevented, try having them occur outside only so that if urination does occur, it will not happen in the house. Owners should be reminded that many of these problems resolve themselves as the dog matures, as long as they are not dealt with inappropriately in the meantime with some sort of aversive approach.

Development of undesirable surface or location preferences. Elimination problems resulting from the development of undesirable surface or location preferences can be managed by not allowing the dog access to his preferred locations or surfaces. This usually means increased supervision, appropriate confinement, or the use of barriers, such as baby gates.

Olfactory cues. Managing this type of problem could initially entail not allowing the dog access to the soiled areas. The best approach is to reduce the odor through the use of enzymatic cleaning products (see product appendix) and take a problem-resolution approach.

6. Explain the Goals of an Appropriate Behavior Modification Plan

As you read through these various treatments, it should be apparent that some are very complex and others are easy and straightforward. Recognizing this should help you decide if you truly want to be the problem solver in the case or if you would rather refer it to someone else. If you don't have a diagnosis or haven't determined the cause of the problem, don't attempt to choose a treatment plan from the recommendations that follow. Instead, either obtain more information from the client to allow you to diagnose the cause or refer the case.

Incomplete housetraining. The dog must be reliably housetrained. Owners should be encouraged to treat the dog as though he were an untrained puppy, regardless of his age. Refer to chapter 4 for a housetraining protocol. Keep in mind that confinement (i.e., crating) is only one option in addressing the issues of supervision and therefore is only a small part of a complete housetraining plan.

Separation anxiety. The dog's anxiety in response to being left alone must be decreased. Counterconditioning and desensitization procedures (see chapter 3) are necessary, since the problem is essentially based in fear. Techniques to make the dog less demanding of attention from the owner may also be helpful. Treatment has nothing to do with dominance issues, giving the dog more exercise, confinement, restricting access to food or water, or making sure the dog eliminates immediately before the owner leaves (although this is always a good idea, it does nothing to decrease the dog's anxiety). Sample steps in a treatment program will be described. *Please note that these procedures do not represent a complete treatment plan, as there are always nuances and differences in each case that will require additional steps or modifications of generally recommended procedures. Failure to implement a complete plan correctly will result in ineffective treatment or even an exacerbation of the problem. The behavior modification procedures for separation anxiety problems are tedious, so these cases require significant client follow-up. Consider these factors as you decide whether to make treatment recommendations yourself or refer the case.*

- The owner can make the departure cues less predictive for the dog and therefore less likely to elicit anxiety by repeating discrete behaviors (picking up keys, approaching the door, putting on shoes, etc.) without leaving. Many repetitions may be necessary (up to 10 or more per day over a period of weeks or months) to counteract the existing predictive value of these cues. Behaviorists vary as to whether the dog should be ignored (habituation), given a treat at the onset of the departure cue (counterconditioning), or required to lie down quietly (countercommanding).
- In the meantime, the owner should vary the sequence of her actual departure routine (e.g., rather than getting dressed and eating breakfast, eat first and then dress) and do as much preparation as possible the night before or well in advance of a departure. She should not pay a lot of attention to the dog during her normal departure routine, as this only serves to focus the dog on her and make her absence more distressing.
- The owner should begin to accustom the dog to being left alone for brief periods so that a nonanxious response can be elicited. Some behaviorists recommend pairing these brief absences with a pleasant stimulus (food, a toy, etc.); others do not.

The pleasant stimulus becomes the cue that the absence will be brief, and it should *not* be used for longer absences. If the owner is already in the habit of giving the dog a treat when she leaves for a prolonged absence, this and similar treats should be avoided during these practice sessions. Other behaviorists use a counter-commanding procedure and have the dog lie down quietly as the owner leaves briefly. The length of the absence is completely dependent on the dog's response— the owner must return before the dog becomes anxious. In some cases, this means returning within seconds; in others, it can mean returning in several minutes. Giving departure cues prior to these absences should be avoided. The length of the absences should then be gradually increased, on an unpredictable schedule.

- As the dog's reaction to the departure cues improves and he can tolerate absences of 20 minutes or so, a departure cue can be combined with a briefer (say, a 10-minute) absence. Longer absences should then be gradually preceded by more cues until this practice procedure is similar to the owner's normal routine.
- The owner should work on out-of-sight stays to prevent the dog from following her around the house and encourage him to be more relaxed out of her presence. The dog can be taught to lie down and stay in return for a tidbit (which should be given as the owner walks away from the dog, not on returning), with the duration of the stay and the time out of sight being very brief at first and increased incrementally. During training, the owner should be in sight/out of sight repeatedly. Initially, the out-of-sight time should be extremely brief. The dog should be calm enough to eat the tidbit; if he is not, the owner should stay in close proximity until he is able to do so.
- Arrivals and departures should be quiet and calm events, with no long speeches made to the dog on leaving and no excited greetings on returning. (I'm always surprised at how much owners complain about not being able to greet the dog in an enthusiastic manner. It would be interesting to know if owners of dogs without separation anxiety have the same attitude.)
- The owner should not pet or interact with the dog when he demands it but instead require the dog to wait, obey a command, or become calm and relaxed before receiving attention. This can be accomplished by ignoring the dog until he lies down and stops pestering. (Popular literature has misinterpreted this approach, with some sources recommending that owners completely ignore their dogs for months at a time. The humaneness of that recommendation should be questioned.)
- The dog's anxiety response *must* be prevented during treatment, using one or more of the management procedures previously discussed.

Fears or phobias. To handle problems stemming from fears or phobias, you must first identify the specific stimulus that is causing the fear and then implement a desensitization and counter-conditioning plan to decrease it (see chapters 3 and 11 for details). Management procedures (described previously) should be implemented in the meantime, as ongoing fear responses will significantly interfere with treatment. If you do not feel confident devising a step-by-step counterconditioning and desensitization plan, refer the case to someone else. If you cannot identify the fear-eliciting stimulus, either the problem has been misdiagnosed, the owner needs to do some detective work, or you should refer the case.

Urine marking. The dog's reaction to the initiating stimulus needs to be changed, usually through counterconditioning. For example, if paper grocery bags on the floor trigger urine marking, the owner should countercondition by hiding food treats under and around the bags, thereby making the bags a source of goodies rather than a trigger for marking. Countercommanding can also be used. For example, after another dog passes by outside the home, the pet could be taught to go to the owner for a tidbit rather than urine marking (but, logistically, this may be difficult to implement). As discussed in chapter 3, the motivation to perform the alternative behavior must be stronger than the motivation to urine mark. Both of these approaches require consistency.

If conflicts between dogs in the family are the cause of the problem, they need to be addressed (see chapter 12). Surfaces where the dog must stand to urine mark can be made unpleasant with double-sided sticky tape, vinyl carpet runners with the pointed side facing upwards, or other environmental booby traps mentioned in the product appendix. This approach is limited in that the dog may simply choose another location for his urine marking unless his motivation for marking is addressed.

Management approaches often need to be a part of the treatment plan. These might include limiting the dog's access to the areas he is marking or not exposing him to the triggers for the behavior. Neutering is a virtual necessity in order to successfully change urine-marking behavior. One study found that neutering eliminated or greatly reduced urine marking in about 50 percent of the cases[5].

Submissive or excitement urination. In such cases, the dog's reaction to the interactions triggering the urination need to be changed. If the behavior is submissive, owners should avoid using postures or gestures that dogs typically view as threatening. These include:

- Direct eye contact
- Bending over the dog
- Reaching toward the dog, especially over the head
- Hugging the dog
- Approaching the dog directly, head on (front to front)

Instead, people should look off to the side when approaching the dog, bend at the knees or sit on the floor, make no arm or hand movements toward the dog, and if the dog approaches to sniff a hand held loosely next to the person's body, pet the dog under the chin, not over the head. These procedures are less important with excitement urination, but keeping the dog calm should be the goal.

Alternatively, the dog can be encouraged to engage in different greeting behaviors, such as playing with a toy or taking a tidbit. Letting the dog take the treat from a standing position is usually better in these cases, as sitting and lying down are comparatively more submissive postures and attempts to encourage the dog to assume them may trigger the urination. In some cases, it may be better just to toss tidbits on the floor for the dog. Owners and visitors can also keep greetings low-key and ignore the dog during arrivals until he is calm.

Punishment or any kind of aversive technique will only exacerbate the problem. Owners should be warned even about subtle changes in facial expressions (scowling or frowning if these have previously preceded punishment) or frustrated comments ("Oh Ashley, you did it again!"), which can trigger the behavior.

Development of undesirable surface or location preferences. The goal of treatment in such a case is to identify the dog's preferences, provide appropriate surfaces and locations for elimination that suit those preferences, and either prevent access to the undesired areas or make them less attractive. Elimination in appropriate areas needs to be elicited and reinforced by using basic housetraining procedures.

Make sure that the dog has an acceptable area (from his point of view) where he can eliminate outside. Most, but not all, dogs seem to like a soft surface such as grass; they also seem to choose an area of the yard that is separate from the areas they use to rest and play. Many don't like inclement weather (perhaps that's a personal, biased observation as I have always had short-coated dogs in a snowy climate). I have recommended that owners plant a small patch of grass somewhere on their property if there isn't any at present. One owner who lived in a high-rise condominium came up with a creative solution: She obtained several litterboxes and used them as planters for sod, which she placed on her balcony for her dog.

The dog's preferred but unacceptable areas for elimination need to be made either inaccessible or unappealing. The former can be accomplished by supervision or using barriers, the latter by changing textures or booby-trapping the area as described in the earlier section on urine marking and in chapter 4.

Olfactory cues. If olfactory cues from the dog's own soiling have become a contributing factor to a housesoiling problem motivated by other reasons, the underlying cause must still be addressed. It is likely that secondary surface and location preferences have developed. Because the odors from other animals are more likely to trigger a urine-marking problem, refer to the section on urine marking. The odors should be neutralized with an enzymatic cleanser (see product appendix).

SUMMARY

This chapter has illustrated the wide range of causes for inappropriate elimination, including urine marking. Elimination problems can sometimes be very difficult to diagnose, and others have multiple causes. Because their persistence puts animals at risk of surrender to a shelter[6], accurate diagnosis and effective treatment are crucial. Given that the causes are so varied, it is imperative to know why a problem is occurring before attempting to resolve it.

REFERENCES

1. Reisner, I. 1991. The pathophysiologic basis of behavior problems. *Vet. Clinics of North Amer. [Small Anim. Pract.]* 21 (2):207–24.

2. Voith, V.L., and P.L. Borchelt. 1996. Elimination and related problems in dogs. In *Readings in companion animal behavior*, ed. V.L. Voith and P.L. Borchelt, 168–78. Trenton, N.J.: Veterinary Learning Systems.

3. McCrave, E.A. 1991. Diagnostic criteria for separation anxiety in the dog. *Vet. Clinics of North Amer. [Small Anim. Pract.]* 21 (2):247–56.

4. Voith, V.L., and P.L. Borchelt. 1996. Separation anxiety in dogs. In *Readings in companion animal behavior*, ed. V.L. Voith and P.L. Borchelt, 127–39. Trenton, N.J.: Veterinary Learning Systems.

5. Hopkins, S.G., T.A. Schubert, and B.L. Hart. 1976. Castration of adult male dogs: Effects on roaming, aggression, urine marking, and mounting. *JAVMA* 168:1108–10.

6. Patronek, G.J., L.T. Glickman, A.M. Beck, G.P. McCabe, and C. Ecker. 1996. Risk factors for relinquishment of dogs to an animal shelter. *JAVMA* 209:572–81.

CHAPTER 8

Destructive Behavior in Dogs

Labeling a behavior as "destructive" actually refers to the *result* of that behavior, not the behavior itself. The same is true of "escape" behaviors, which are discussed in the next chapter. Thus, the terms *destructive* and *escape* are not strictly comparable to *fear, elimination*, and other words used to categorize problems that refer more to the actual behavior. However, because pet owners most often use these terms, I chose to employ these designations here for ease in accessing information on these topics. This chapter refers to behaviors dogs direct toward the environment; it does *not* refer to self-destructive behavior.

Destructive behavior and inappropriate elimination are two of the most common problems seen by anybody in the field—behavior specialists, trainers, veterinarians, or animal shelter personnel. To put it simply, dog owners don't like their pets damaging their stuff. In fact, destructive behavior and housesoiling put dogs at greater risk of surrender to shelters[1]. Owners may more readily tolerate behaviors that are actually much more serious, such as growling or snapping, than those that damage their possessions. Destructive behavior can be very straightforward (such as the playful or investigative behavior typical of young dogs) or much more complex (such as the behavior arising from separation anxiety). It's crucial that you determine what motivation you're dealing with before making any recommendations. Also refer back to chapter 4 on problem prevention for additional information about destructive behavior.

PROTOCOL

As you work through the protocol, determining exactly what the dog is doing and when he's doing it (as well as when he isn't) is crucial to arriving at a behavioral diagnosis for the destructive behavior.

1. Obtain a Description of the Problem Behavior

A client usually begins a conversation about destructive behavior with a comment such as, "He's destroying my house," "He's chewing everything in sight," or "He's done hundreds of dollars of damage to my home." Clearly, these are not behavioral descriptions but rather expressions of frustration. To obtain a behavioral description, you will have to ask the owner exactly what the dog is damaging, as well as how and when he is doing so. Be prepared for replies such as, "Everything!" (more frustration), "Whenever my back is turned," or "When nobody's around to catch him." If you respond with the question "Can you give me some examples?" you'll usually begin to obtain the information you need.

Destruction indoors. What the dog is damaging can provide a clue to the motivation for the behavior. Often, the items the dog is damaging indoors fall into one of two types: things that the dog has found are fun to tear up or get into and things that involve more severe structural damage to the house and its contents. When dogs are just having fun ("dogs just wanna have fu-un!"), they might get into the trash; pull things off the counters; tear up pillows; chew on furniture legs; tear up books, newspapers, magazines, or computer disks; unravel the fringe on a throw rug (or an expensive Persian carpet); or chew up the children's toys.

When dogs are fearful or anxious, the destruction often takes on a different intensity, marked by such behaviors as chewing or clawing through doors or drywall, removing the molding around doors or windows, chewing through furniture, pulling down drapes, tearing up blinds, pulling up carpet or linoleum, and overturning bookcases or storage shelves.

Although these distinctions can be *helpful* in diagnosis, they are not reliable in distinguishing between motivations. I recently saw a Yorkshire terrier who went down to the basement and tore into the Christmas paper and decorations as she was trying to find a hiding place during a thunderstorm. That was not the severe damage usually seen with thunderphobic dogs. Destruction involving items of clothing and other objects with a strong scent of the owner (such as eyeglasses, the TV remote control, or couch cushions) could be caused by either anxiety or fun. Another point of confusion arises when owners say that the dog is only chewing on wood objects, which may mean only door molding or other wooden objects as well, such as furniture. Have owners list as many things as they can think of that the dog has destroyed, as it will be helpful later in diagnosis. Be sure to include any destructive behavior resulting from a dog attempting to escape from a crate because this is often a sign of separation anxiety.

Destruction outdoors. When dogs are being destructive outdoors, similar categorizing may be helpful. Chewing on or digging up plants, chewing on the garden hose, digging holes in the yard, or chewing on the patio furniture may have a different motivation than tearing up the siding on the house, clawing at doors or windows, or digging under or chewing through the fence (see chapter 9 on escape behavior). The former are more likely the result of playful or "boredom" behavior; the latter may be caused by separation anxiety or some other fear-related problem. You'll need more information about when the behaviors are occurring, as well as information about the dog's behavior patterns, to make such distinctions.

2. Evaluate Potential Medical Causes for the Problem Behavior

Destructive chewing in puppies is often the result of normal teething. The degree of medical workup necessary for destructive behavior problems may vary with the age of the dog, with more extensive testing being recommended for older dogs[2]. If the behavior leads to the ingestion of potentially harmful materials, an appropriate evaluation should be done to protect the dog's health. For specific recommendations, refer to E. Lindell's work[2].

In my experience, cases involving destructive behavior are much less likely to have a medical component than problems such as aggression and inappropriate elimination or even fear-related problems. However, in older dogs or if pica (ingesting of nonfood items) is involved, veterinarians should carefully consider whether some workup is advisable prior to referring the case or treating it as a behavior problem.

3. Educate Owners About the Problem Behavior

Destructive behavior problems often require an enormous amount of owner education. Owners are often angry and frustrated; they may have erroneous beliefs or unrealistic expectations about even normal puppy chewing behavior; they may be convinced that the dog "knows" he shouldn't be doing this and believe they are completely justified in punishing him after the fact. The sad truth is that dogs suffer a lot of unfair and sometimes downright abusive treatment as a result of their owners' misconceptions about destructive behavior. Even without getting into problem solving, you can make a major difference in a dog's life by getting his owners to stop engaging in inappropriate punishment procedures and inappropriate confinement.

Educate the owners about anthropomorphic and other misinterpretations. With the possible exception of elimination, there is no single problem about which owners consistently anthropomorphize more than destructive behavior. When I'm talking to owners, before I start talking about why the dog *may* be being destructive, I talk about why he *isn't*. Owners must understand that destructive dogs are not being spiteful, are not mad at them, and are not acting out or being rebellious. When a dog chooses to chew on the possessions of one person in the family, such as gloves, hats, or a briefcase, this especially elicits the conclusion that the dog bears some grudge against that person. In fact, the opposite may well be true: As you'll see later, this is often a sign of attachment to that person.

Owners must come to understand that destructive behavior is not malicious if they are to stop unfairly treating the dog with punishment after the fact or holding a grudge against him. Only at that point can they become willing participants in efforts to work on the problem. If they aren't attributing it to spite, owners often attribute destructive behavior to "boredom." This anthropomorphic term is not even included under the list of common causes discussed in a later section because it isn't really a motivation for destructiveness. Dogs may chew because they have nothing else to do in a relatively impoverished environment (a more objective description of "boredom"), or they may be playing or investigating their environment, even though they have numerous toys of their own.

Dogs are not destructive because their owners are not dominant over them. Destructive behavior and dominance are not related to one another. There is also no evidence that dogs who are more obedient to commands are less destructive.

Most often, dogs are destructive because they are either anxious or fearful or because they are doing what dogs do—exploring the world with their mouths or paws and finding something to do to amuse themselves. They may choose objects other than their own toys simply because something unusual that's been left lying around or something they've never played with before is more interesting than the same old toys they play with day after day. There is no malice in their intent or in their behavior.

Educate the owners about myths regarding problem solving and techniques to avoid. As with elimination problems, it is neither helpful nor fair to the dog to show him his "mess" while asking him, "Did you do this?"; nor is it helpful to hit, scruff shake, verbally scold, or employ any other type of punishment after the fact. Owners are more likely to think that punishment after the fact is appropriate if some evidence of the dog's misbehavior is left in its wake. For example, most owners wouldn't think about coming home and punishing a dog for barking all day—for which there is no telltale evidence—but many have no problem doing so in response to destructive and elimination problems. Some of the old-style dog training methods recommend blatantly cruel procedures, such as filling a hole the dog has dug in the yard with water and holding his head under water or using duct tape to tape the dog's mouth shut as he holds the item he chewed[3]. Dogs have died from these procedures. Refer to chapter 3 for a discussion of appropriate punishment and how to explain it to owners.

Recommending a crate is not appropriate until you know the problem is not based in fear or anxiety. If the owner is already using a crate and the dog is making extreme attempts to escape, trying to make the crate escape-proof is not the answer. If the dog is clearly anxious and frightened while crated, this procedure should be abandoned until the problem can be evaluated.

Educate the owners about realistic expectations. I tell new pet owners that they should expect to lose something of value as a result of owning a pet. This could be something expensive, such as a piece of furniture or an item of clothing, or something of sentimental value. When my Dalmatian Mocha was about 8 months old, he reached through his crate to a nearby bookshelf and tore up the last picture that was taken of my grandparents prior to my grandmother's death. I was devastated and found myself going through all those judgmental reactions that I hear from pet owners—"Mocha, how could you! Why did you have to pick that picture? Didn't you know how much it meant to me?" Of course, Mocha's only responses would have been, "Because it was there" and "No, Mom, I had no idea."

When talking to pet owners about destructive behavior, sometimes a sense of humor and a sense of perspective can be invaluable. You might ask them about how much their kids have cost them—such as a teenager who wrecked the car. You can also share your own war stories; just be sure it doesn't turn into a "my dog is worse than your dog contest" but rather serves the purpose of letting owners know that you understand how they feel and that you and your dog have survived similar problems.

Before proceeding to management procedures or treatment goals, you must understand the cause for the destructive behavior. Consequently, your next job is to ask owners questions in order to determine the cause of the problem. This becomes a decision point for you. If you do not have time to ask enough questions to diagnose the problem or at least determine if fear or anxiety are likely involved, you should refer the case. You may or may not choose to talk to owners in *general* terms about management procedures or treatment goals (refer to later section).

4. Identify the Behavioral Cause of the Problem

Common behavioral causes for destructiveness are:

- Separation anxiety
- Playful, investigative, or teething behavior
- Social isolation/barren environment
- Fears or phobias
- Attention-getting behavior
- Territorial behavior
- Comfort-seeking behavior
- Hyperkinesis

Components of a behavioral history. The answers to the following questions will help you distinguish among these causes. For easier organization, they are divided into several categories.

Description of the dog, description of the behavior.
- How old is the dog?
- Is the dog young enough to still be teething?
- What breed is the dog?
- Is she spayed/he neutered? (This is always good to know, but it may not be very helpful in diagnosing reasons for destructive behavior.)
- What specifically is the dog destroying?

    — Is the dog damaging random objects in the household or outside that he could be perceiving as toys or things that are fun to tear up?

    — If the behavior occurs indoors, is the damage focused on doors, windows, carpet in front of the door, drapes, or blinds? If outdoors, is it focused on the house, doors, windows, the fence, or gate?

    — Ask the owner to list as many examples as possible, in chronological order (to determine if the type of items that the dog is destroying has changed over time)

- Was the dog found as a stray or obtained from a humane society or shelter? How many owners/homes has the dog had?

Description of the dog's daily routine, environment, and behavior patterns.

- Does the dog consistently follow the owner from room to room (is he a "shadow" dog)?
- Does the dog greet the owner frantically (acting more than excited, almost panicky) when he or she returns home?
- Does the dog display a visible change in behavior as the owner prepares to leave the house without him—e.g., become agitated, restless, nervous, anxious, depressed, or fearful?
- Does the dog frequently and persistently solicit the owner's attention or become anxious or pestering if he is ignored?
- Is the dog known to be afraid of any noises (such as thunder, firecrackers, or hot-air balloons) or of people such as neighbors, mail carriers, or schoolchildren?
- What kinds of toys and chewies does the dog have? How often does the dog receive new toys and chewies?
- What opportunities does the dog have for physical exercise, such as walks and runs?
- How often and for how long does the owner play actively with the dog (e.g., play fetch, tug-of-war, wrestle, etc.)?
- Is the dog a high-energy, active individual or content to be a couch potato?
- Is the dog very reactive to passersby, the mail carrier, or other delivery people? What about other dogs?
- Does the dog threaten visitors to the home, or is he friendly and accepting?
- Has either urine marking or excessive barking in reaction to the presence of visitors or strangers been a problem?
- Is the dog primarily an outdoor dog?
- Is the dog often restless, inattentive to the owner, difficult to train (especially in learning sit, down, and stay commands)?
- Has the owner observed the dog digging or pawing at things prior to lying down, as though he is building a nest or bed?
- Does the dog have a soft, comfortable bed indoors and a doghouse outside that is protected from the weather and that provides a soft surface to lie on? Does the dog use the bed and house?
- Does the dog have a dog door?
- Has the dog been obedience trained to the level of performing a stay with the owner out of sight?

Specifics about the occurrence of the problem behavior.

- Does the destructive behavior occur only in the owner's absence? If yes,
    — Does it occur every time the dog is alone or with a consistent pattern of absences, such as only in the evening?

— Does it occur within the first 30 minutes of the owner's departure? (If this is unknown, the owner can find out by videotaping or returning unexpectedly after a brief absence.)

- Does the destructive behavior occur both when the owner is home and when he or she is away?
- Does it occur when the owner is home but not watching the dog?
- Did the beginning of the destructiveness correlate with any changes in the family's routine or composition—e.g., a change in work hours, the death of another pet, or a child going away to college?
- If the destruction is intermittent, could it be correlated to the occurrence of anything the dog is afraid of (such as thunder, construction noises, etc.)? If the owner doesn't know this, suggest video- or audiotaping.
- If the destruction is intermittent, is it correlated with times when the dog has less opportunity for play and physical exercise? If the owner doesn't know, suggest that he or she keep a behavioral log or diary for a few weeks.
- Does the behavior occur only in the owner's presence? Does the dog turn the situation into a game?
- Does the behavior seem to occur completely at random or unpredictably?
- How often, on average, is the behavior occurring (e.g., everyday, once a week, once a month)?
- If crated when alone, is the dog being destructive in an attempt to escape from the crate? Is the dog harming himself in the process?
- Is the dog reluctant to enter the crate when the owner prepares to leave?
- Does the dog voluntarily enter the crate when the owner is home?
- Has the dog's behavior when home alone ever been audio- or videotaped?

Owners' attempts at problem resolution and the dog's response.
- Has the use of a crate or confinement in a small area such as a mudroom made the problem worse?
- Has the dog been punished, either if caught in the act or not?
- Has the dog been hit or verbally scolded?
- Has the dog been played with and/or exercised more?
- Has the dog been seen by a veterinarian for this problem?
- Has the behavior improved, gotten worse, or stayed the same since the problem began?
- What other things have been done to try to resolve the problem? What results have been observed?

Differential results of the behavioral history. Answers to the preceding questions will help you identify the cause of the problem:

Separation anxiety. The pattern of occurrence of the destructive behavior will be congruent with any problem behavior associated with separation anxiety. The destructive behavior, whether indoors or out, will occur within the first 30 minutes or so after the owner's departure, it will occur *only* and *consistently* (i.e., every time, not unpredictably) in the owner's absence (or a particular pattern of absences, such as every time the owner leaves for the evening after a work-day absence), and it will *not* occur when the owner is home. If destructive behavior occurs both in and out of the owner's presence, it is not likely related to separation, although it could be a compound problem involving separation anxiety as well as another motivation.

As discussed under obtaining a behavioral description of the problem, consider what is being destroyed. With a classic pattern of destructive behavior caused by separation anxiety, the dog is often damaging doors and windows or tearing up the carpet in front of these structures, pulling down drapes or blinds, chewing the siding off the house, damaging the fence in escape attempts (see chapter 9), or destroying items that have a strong scent of the owner (such as bedclothes or couch cushions). The destructive behavior may involve other items and still be related to separation anxiety, so this will need to be considered in light of the rest of the behavioral history.

Confining or restricting a dog with separation anxiety usually exacerbates the problem. If the owner has crated the dog or confined her to a small area of the house and if the dog has injured herself attempting to escape or has displayed even more profound destructiveness, separation anxiety may be the underlying problem.

The dog will also demonstrate some or all of the other signs correlated with separation anxiety, such as following the owner around the house, frantic greeting behavior, and agitation if the owner is briefly out of sight. Because the owner's preparations to leave predict to the dog that he is about to be left alone, there will usually be obvious responses to these departures cues (increased anxiety, agitation, depression). A strong attachment to the owner seems to be characteristic of dogs with separation anxiety, and many of them display a pattern of frequently soliciting social interaction (human attention) and receiving it on demand. This may be part of the explanation for the problem behavior: Such dogs become anxious or frustrated when they cannot immediately interact with their owners.

Dogs with separation anxiety are statistically more likely to be purebreds obtained from a humane society[4]. They are also more likely to have a history of constant companionship and rarely being left alone prior to the onset of the problem behavior.

Triggers for the onset of a separation anxiety problem include a change in the family's schedule, a change in the family composition (including the death of another pet), a move to a new environment, or being boarded, hospitalized, or away from the owner for some other reason. It is important to note that not all destructiveness that occurs in the owner's absence can be attributed to separation anxiety.

Playful, investigative, or teething behavior. Dogs play and explore their world with their mouths and paws. Items that can be treated as prey and shaken, carried around, and torn up are attractive to most dogs. Examples include pillows, children's stuffed toys, throw rugs, tissues from the trash, and other soft items. However, on any given day, any dog can turn anything into a toy.

Dogs also simply like to chew. They may have preferences for what they like to chew. If hard items such as wood are preferred, furniture legs, banisters, and cabinets are likely targets. Other dogs will focus on plastic or soft items. Sometimes, a dog may choose anything that is convenient. I once caught Ashley chewing a hole in the drywall in a hallway simply because as she was lying on her side, her chewbone slipped out of her mouth and the next surface her mouth contacted was the drywall—an instant chewing surface. Outside, dogs may dig holes, chew up plants and shrubs, tear up the garden hose, or shred the lawn furniture. (Ashley took a liking to the corners of the redwood deck.) All of these behaviors can satisfy a dog's need to chew and play. Again, on any given day, any dog can turn anything into a chewie. Young dogs who are teething are even more prone to this behavior, as are active dogs who do not have sufficient outlets for play and physical exercise.

Dogs may also learn that trash containers, kitchen counters, or the dining room table can be a source of food, so if foraging there is productive, they'll continue to get up or into these areas and make a mess.

In my experience, young dogs are much more likely to engage in this type of exploratory, playful behavior. Yet some high-energy dogs may be prone to this type of problem throughout life. For these dogs, the destructiveness may be occurring relatively consistently when they are alone but not in the owner's presence because they have been punished when caught. This type of problem can usually be differentiated from a separation anxiety problem by (1) looking for other signs correlated with separation anxiety (see the preceding discussion), (2) determining if the destructiveness is consistently occurring within that first critical 30 minutes after the owner's departure (usually this is not a consistent pattern except with separation anxiety problems), (3) determining if the behavior also occurs at other times, as it usually does if it is prompted by play and related motivations, and (4) considering what is being destroyed, as described earlier.

Destructiveness tied to play and related motivations may also come and go for no apparent reason—the "on any given day" phenomenon. A dog may have bouts of it for several days or weeks and then have no problems for indefinite periods. Sometimes, but not always, these bouts can be correlated with the dog receiving less exercise or being alone more.

A dog may choose to destroy household items even if she has a number of toys of her own. This can happen simply because the other items are more appealing or because the dog has so many toys that to her, anything in the house can be considered a toy. I'm convinced that Ashley thinks wastebaskets are containers that we put little pieces of paper into so she can reach them more easily. Most dogs seem to mature out of normal, young-dog destructive behavior somewhere between 2 to 3 years of age. I'm *hoping* Ashley makes this change by the time she's 3!

Social isolation/barren environment. Destructive behavior stemming from social isolation or a barren environment can usually be diagnosed by obtaining a description of the dog's physical and social environment and of a typical day in his life. What often emerges is a picture of a "back-yard dog"—which raises the question of why the owner obtained the dog at all since no one in the family seems to pay any attention to him. This dog is outdoors for the majority of his life; perhaps he comes into the garage, mudroom, or a similar area at night or if the weather is bad. He gets no exercise, has very little or no social time with the family, and is probably chewing up everything in the backyard (including trees, plants, the fence, and the house itself) and digging holes. The pattern of the behavior may not be too different from that of the playful, investigative category, except that it may be occurring more often and the standard of care given the dog may be very different.

Fears or phobias. Dogs can be destructive when they are frightened. Some common stimuli causing fear-related destruction seem to be noises such as thunder, firecrackers, car backfires, hot-air balloons, trash trucks, the sounds of construction or heavy equipment, or any other loud, startling sound. I've had cases of very destructive dogs who live near airports and firing ranges; another lives in the mountains and was afraid of the explosions used to set off avalanches. Some detective work on the owner's part may be necessary to establish the correlation between the occurrence of these noises or other events and the destructive behavior. Videotaping may be necessary, and it should not only reveal the correlation but also fear-related body postures as well. If the fear has generalized to a particular location, the destructive behavior may now occur there even in the absence of the original triggering stimulus.

Dogs may destroy things by attempting to find a "safe" place. Furniture, carpet, and a variety of other items may be damaged if the dog is trying to burrowing behind or underneath something because he's afraid. If he's in the yard and trying to get into the house, windows, doors, and siding on the house may be torn up as a result. Digging and damage to the fence is also common. In the owner's presence, the dog may not be as afraid of the same stimuli and may only pant, whine, or be restless instead.

Attention-getting behavior. The desire for attention is not a common cause of destructive behavior, but when it occurs, it is usually easy to diagnosis. Because the dog engages in the destructive behavior in order to get the owner's attention, the behavior naturally occurs only in the owner's presence, and it does, indeed, produce the desired result. This attention can be the owner's attempts to punish the dog, which are usually relatively mild and which, to the dog, actually serve as positive reinforcement in the form of social interaction (refer back to chapter 3 on learning). Questioning of the client may reveal that either the dog is rarely given much attention except when he is misbehaving or that, at the other extreme, he is often the center of attention and tends to get into things when he is not.

A classic example of attention-getting behavior is the dog who takes socks from the drawer or tissues from the trash, begins to tear them up in a location where he is sure to be seen by the owner (e.g., he goes to the room where the owner is), then runs when the owner approaches him, which results in a game of chase around the house—a fun doggie game! For some dogs, this can result in defensive aggression at the end of the game if the owner begins to hit or threaten the dog in order to take the item away (see chapters 3 and 12).

Territorial behavior. When territorialism is at the root of destructive behavior, the destructiveness is secondary to another problem. If the dog is very territorial and reacts strongly to someone passing by the house or yard, he may lunge and paw at windows, doors, or the fence in an attempt to get to the passerby. Some dogs react in this manner only to the mail carrier or other delivery people. Letters or packages, if they come through a door slot, may be torn up as the dog redirects his aggression.

To diagnose territorial behavior as the cause of the destructiveness, the behavior must be linked with the presence of passersby or other dogs. Videotaping may be necessary if it is happening in the owner's absence. The owner may also report that the dog shows similar behavior when he or she is at home but to a lesser degree, probably because the animal has been punished for the destructive behavior. Other territorial behaviors may be observed, as well, such as barking or urine marking.

Comfort-seeking behavior. Dogs may damage items when they are trying to find a comfortable place to lie down or rest. They may dig holes, scratch at the carpet, or damage a couch cushion by pawing at it. I frequently find lines through the pile of the carpet when I return home, which I assume are the result of Mocha pawing at the carpet prior to lying down. He's never damaged anything with this behavior, although I recently spoke with a client whose dog had damaged the couch cushion by scratching at it prior to lying down.

Hyperkinesis. Physiological hyperkinesis is rare in dogs. Many owners describe their dogs as "hyper" when they really mean they are unruly, poorly trained, or high-energy animals. Physiologic hyperkinesis involves a dysfunction of the dopaminergic system, although other neurotransmitters can also be involved[5]. Behavioral symptoms vary and may include destructiveness, being difficult to train, being easily distracted and excitable, and having a short attention span. Diagnosis is based not just on the behavioral history but also on the dog's response to a test dose (recommended dosage varies depending on source) of d-amphetamine, including measurement of changes in respiration, pulse, salivation, muscle tone, and general activity[3, 7]. Thus, veterinary involvement in the diagnosis is required. For information on treating this disorder with medication, see chapter 18.

5. Discuss Ways to Manage or Control the Behavior over the Short or Long Term

As mentioned in chapter 6, management procedures can be discussed in a very general way if you have not been able to arrive at a behavioral diagnosis, or they can be specific to the underlying cause. Remember as well that managing the problem is not necessarily the same thing as resolving it.

General management procedures—no behavioral diagnosis. Very few recommendations can be made without a behavioral diagnosis. One such recommendation would be to keep the dog away from situations in which he has the opportunity to be destructive, either through increased supervision or confinement. Confinement in a crate or other area should be recommended *only* if you know the problem is unrelated to fear or anxiety. Alternatively, you can suggest that the owner provide the dog with additional toys or give him more exercise or social playtime. Owners should, however, be cautioned that additional play and exercise, though certainly not harmful, may ultimately be ineffective because they may not be relevant to the cause of the problem.

Management procedures based on a diagnosis.

Separation anxiety. In this type of case, destructiveness is motivated by anxiety, so management requires keeping the dog from becoming anxious; this, in turn, requires that the owner not leave him alone long enough to trigger the anxiety. Options include:

- Using a doggie day care service, boarding him in the daytime at a kennel or veterinary clinic, letting him stay with friends or family who are home all day, or having him accompany the owner.
- Leaving the dog outside during the day if he has been destructive inside. Usually, however, this backfires because most dogs are more or at least equally anxious outside and either the destructiveness continues or other problems result, such as escaping or barking. Sometimes, dogs will be less anxious inside if they have been destructive outside, but there is no guarantee of this. If you suggest this approach to an owner, tell him or her to try it for very short periods initially to see how the dog responds. You must caution the owner about the potential for destructiveness inside.
- Working with a veterinarian to provide medication on a short-term basis to decrease the dog's anxiety. However, make sure the owner understands that medication alone is not a long-term solution to separation anxiety problems (see chapter 18 for more information about medication).

Playful, investigative, or teething behavior. Managing the problem of destructiveness stemming from playful, investigative, or teething behavior means not giving the dog the opportunity to destroy things by either watching him more closely or confining him in a crate or other small area. Confinement by itself should always be viewed as a short-term management tool, not a long-term solution. Excessive confinement, without concurrent attempts to resolve the problem, is not appropriate, as it may significantly decrease the dog's quality of life. Crating or confinement is acceptable for short periods only, as long as the dog's social and exercise needs are being met. However, problem-resolution techniques should also be used (see subsequent section).

Social isolation/barren environment. One approach to the management of destructiveness resulting from social isolation or a barren environment might be to deny the dog an opportunity to be destructive. However, further restriction or isolation of a dog who is already in a substandard environment is not appropriate. Management could also mean finding the dog a new home if it is not possible for the family to meet his needs. Problem resolution through environmental enrichment (discussed in a later section) is in the best interest of the dog.

Fears or phobias. Destructiveness caused by fears or phobias can be managed by changing the dog's daily routine so that she is not exposed to the fear-producing stimulus or by working with the veterinarian to provide medication that will decrease the dog's anxious response on a short-term basis (see chapter 18).

Attention-getting behavior. Managing the destructiveness that results from attention-getting behavior might entail avoiding those situations in which the dog has the opportunity to set up the "behavioral trap" of forcing the owner to pay attention to him to prevent the destructive behavior. This may mean modifying the dog's environment—for example, not allowing him access to the sock drawer (see previous example) by using a baby gate, closing the door to the room, or keeping him tethered to the owner with leash and collar as necessary.

Territorial behavior. Managing territorial behavior that results in destructiveness means keeping the dog from those stimuli that trigger the territorial reaction. This might require preventing the dog from seeing out the window, keeping him inside if the behavior is triggered when he is in the yard, or perhaps building him a dog run instead of allowing him to charge the fence.

Comfort-seeking behavior. As with destructiveness caused by social isolation, attempting to manage comfort-seeking destructiveness by prohibiting the dog from trying to create a comfortable place to lie down may compromise his welfare. This depends on the circumstances. Not allowing the dog on the couch and requiring that he sleep on his own doggie bed is not the same thing as forcing a dog to lie on rocks so that he can't dig in the dirt. Managing the behavior in other ways is probably not that much different from resolving the problem, which would inherently be easier and better for the dog (see later section).

Hyperkinesis. Again, management of destructiveness caused by hyperkinesis means not allowing the dog the opportunity to be destructive, which, with a hyperkinetic dog, may be very difficult to accomplish. Confinement of hyperkinetic dogs usually worsens their symptoms, so increased supervision is the other management alternative. Problem resolution through medication makes more sense.

6. Explain the Goals of an Appropriate Behavior Modification Plan

The causes of destructive behavior are varied, so the treatment or behavior modification plans are diverse as well. That is why you must arrive at a behavioral diagnosis before proceeding. Without an accurate diagnosis, it is all too likely that you will make irrelevant or ineffective recommendations. Consequently, if you don't have a diagnosis or haven't determined the cause of the problem, don't attempt to choose a treatment plan from the recommendations that follow. Instead, either obtain more information from the client to allow you to diagnose the cause or refer the case.

Separation anxiety. The dog's anxiety in response to being left alone must be decreased. If the dog is being destructive due to separation anxiety when left alone outside, it is possible he may not be anxious if left inside. However, if the problem persists inside, the following type of treatment will be necessary. Counterconditioning and desensitization procedures (see chapter 3) are necessary, since the problem is essentially based in fear. Techniques to make the dog less demanding of attention from the owner may also be helpful. Treatment has nothing to do with dominance issues, giving the dog more exercise, confinement, booby-trapping items the dog has damaged, or providing more toys. Sample steps in a treatment program will be described. *Please note that these procedures do not represent a complete treatment plan, as there are always nuances and differences in each case that will require additional steps or modifications of generally recommended procedures. Failure to implement a complete plan correctly will result in ineffective treatment or even an exacerbation of the problem. The behavior modification procedures for separation anxiety problems are tedious, so these cases require significant client follow-up. Consider these factors as you decide whether to make treatment recommendations yourself or refer the case.*

- The owner can make the departure cues less predictive for the dog and therefore less likely to elicit anxiety by repeating discrete behaviors (picking up keys, approaching the door, putting on shoes, etc.) without leaving. Many repetitions may be necessary (up to 10 or more per day over a period of weeks or months) to counteract the existing predictive value of these cues. Behaviorists vary as to whether the dog should be ignored (habituation), given a treat at the onset of the departure cue (counterconditioning), or required to lie down quietly (countercommanding).
- In the meantime, the owner should vary the sequence of her actual departure routine (e.g., rather than getting dressed and eating breakfast, eat first and then dress) and do as much preparation as possible the night before or well in advance of a departure. She should not pay a lot of attention to the dog during her normal departure routine, as this only serves to focus the dog on her and make her absence more distressing.
- The owner should begin to accustom the dog to being left alone for brief periods so that a nonanxious response can be elicited. Some behaviorists recommend pairing these brief absences with a pleasant stimulus (food, a toy, etc.); others do not. The pleasant stimulus becomes the cue that the absence will be brief, and it should *not* be used for longer absences. If the owner is already in the habit of giving the dog a treat when she leaves for a prolonged absence, this and similar treats should be avoided during these practice sessions. Other behaviorists use a countercommanding procedure and have the dog lie down quietly as the owner leaves briefly. The length of the absence is completely dependent on the dog's response—the owner must return before the dog becomes anxious. In some cases, this means returning within seconds; in others, it can mean returning in several minutes. Giving departure cues prior to these absences should be avoided. The length of these absences should then be gradually increased, on an unpredictable schedule.
- As the dog's reaction to the departure cues improves and he can tolerate absences of 20 minutes or so, a departure cue can be combined with a briefer (say, a 10-minute) absence. Longer absences should then be gradually preceded by more cues until this practice procedure is similar to the owner's normal routine.
- The owner should work on out-of-sight stays to prevent the dog from following her around the house and encourage him to be more relaxed out of her presence. The dog can be taught to lie down and stay in return for a tidbit (which should be given as the owner walks away from the dog, not on returning), with the duration of the stay and the time out of sight being very brief at first and increased incrementally. During training, the owner should be in sight/out of sight repeatedly. Initially, the out-of-sight time should be extremely brief. The dog should be calm enough to eat the tidbit; if he is not, the owner should stay in close proximity until he is able to do so.
- Arrivals and departures should be quiet and calm events, with no long speeches on leaving and no excited greetings on returning.
- The owner should not pet or interact with the dog when he demands it but instead require the dog to wait, obey a command, or become calm and relaxed before being given attention. This can be accomplished by ignoring the dog until he lies down and stops pestering. This does not, of course, mean that the owner should completely ignore the dog for months at a time.

- The dog's anxiety response *must* be prevented during treatment using one or more of the management procedures previously discussed.

Playful, investigative, or teething behavior. The goal with this type of problem is *not* to stop the dog from playing, exploring, or teething but to (1) find acceptable outlets for these behaviors (yes, I know teething isn't a behavior, but the chewing that results from it is!) and (2) prevent the behaviors from being expressed in ways that are problems for the owner.

Find acceptable outlets for these behaviors. Most toys that owners leave with their dogs during the day are boring (or quickly become so). A tennis ball, for example, is only fun if the owner throws it. Many of the new, commercially available toys that require the dog to manipulate them to release a food treat do provide acceptable outlets for playful destructiveness. Examples are included in the product appendix. Other toys that provide opportunities for long-duration chewing without gastrointestinal upset can also be considered, such as Booda Velvets (made of pressed cornstarch), Beefy Bones, Combones (a marrow cavity of sterilized beef bones filled with beef-, cheese-, or liver-flavored rawhide pieces), Smoked/Plain Sterilized Bones (see product appendix), or rawhides (although some people caution against leaving a dog home alone with these because of a concern about choking). Veterinarians have varied opinions as to acceptable products for dogs to chew, and dogs differ in their tolerance of these items as well.

Of course, playing interactively with the dog not only more often but also more consistently is always a good thing to do. However, if the destructive behavior is occurring when the owner is gone and the dog is looking for ways to occupy his time, how much playtime he has had when the owner is home may not make much difference. With young, active dogs who are prone to these problems, it's hard to tire them out so much that they aren't interested in looking for something to do when they are alone.

Prevent these behaviors from being expressed in problematic ways. This means either confining or supervising the dog or, alternatively, booby-trapping off-limit items. Examples of booby traps are included in the product appendix. Refer to chapter 3 for the criteria for appropriate punishment using such remote devices.

If the behavior is intermittent, without pattern, or of the on-any-given-day sort, it may be very difficult to entirely resolve, as it is hard to predict what the dog will get into next. For example, I have several coffee-table books that have been in the same place for the 2 years we've had Ashley. One Sunday morning, for no apparent reason, she decided to chew one of them up when she was by herself in the living room. I still have no idea what attracted her to it.

Social isolation/barren environment. The treatment goal for cases stemming from social isolation or a barren environment is to enrich the dog's environment so that he has acceptable outlets for play and social interaction. This may include allowing him inside more often, as well as requiring the owners to interact with him more. If other problem behaviors prevent this, they, too, must be addressed. If the dog is chained or tied up, the reason why he is must be addressed so that such restraints are no longer necessary. Suggested toys for environmental enrichment can be found in the section on play, investigative, or teething behavior and in the product appendix. Giving the dog more control over his environment by installing a dog door that allows him access to the garage or some part of the house may also be helpful.

Fears or phobias. To handle problems stemming from fears or phobias, you must first identify the specific stimulus that is causing the fear and then implement a desensitization and counter-conditioning plan to decrease it (see chapters 3 and 11 for details). Management procedures (described previously) should be implemented in the meantime, as ongoing fear responses will significantly interfere with treatment. If you do not feel confident devising a step-by-step counterconditioning and desensitization plan, refer the case to someone else. If you cannot iden-tify the fear-eliciting stimulus, then the problem has been misdiagnosed, the owner needs to do some detective work, or you should refer the case.

Attention-getting behavior. The goal in treating attention-getting destructiveness is to change the nature of the interactions between dog and owner so that the dog can receive atten-tion when she is behaving appropriately and so that inappropriate behavior does not result in reinforcing social interactions. This can be accomplished in a number of ways, depending on the details of each interaction.

The dog can be kept away from off-limit items through the use of booby traps, as mentioned earlier. A Snappy Trainer could be placed in the sock drawer or the trash, for example. If the dog already has the item, she can be encouraged to engage in another behavior—the owner can call her into the kitchen, have her sit, lay down, or perform any basic command in return for a tidbit, and then remove the "stolen" item (see chapter 3 for an explanation as to why this is not rein-forcing inappropriate behavior). If the item can be sacrificed and if the dog will not harmed by chewing on it, the chewing behavior can be ignored, and in fact the owner can go into another room and shut the door. This technique is extinction (removing the reinforcement), and it should be effective unless there is still sufficient internal reinforcement value for the dog in chewing the item.

The dog can also be started on a "nothing in life is free" program, meaning she must obey a command before receiving anything she wants (being let outside or up on furniture, fed, given a treat, and *especially* petted or played with). The value of this approach is that the dog cannot demand things from the owner on her own terms, and, in addition, she learns appropriate behaviors that will result in attention. Dogs who display attention-getting destructive behavior often have a history of demanding attention from the owner and have a wide repertoire of annoying behaviors they display if their demands aren't met.

Territorial behavior. The goal of treatment in territorial destructiveness is to change the dog's territorial reaction to passersby. The dog should eventually react to people in at least a neutral way and ideally in a positive, welcoming manner. In other words, the dog should no longer view people as territorial intruders but rather as folks he'd like to have drop by because they cause good things to happen for him. This requires a counterconditioning and desensitization program, and it may require the judicious use of punishment, usually remote. For more information on ter-ritorial behavior, see chapter 12 on aggressive behavior in dogs. If you don't feel comfortable devising a plan using these techniques, then refer the case.

Comfort-seeking behavior. Several approaches exist for destructive problems caused by com-fort-seeking behaviors. One would be to provide the dog with a comfortable resting place, such as a doggie bed or a pile of soft blankets. Another would be to make the area he is scratching or digging less appealing, using some of the booby traps previously mentioned or by limiting his access to the area. A third approach would be to provide him an acceptable outlet for digging or pawing prior to lying down. Make him a digging pit in the yard, filled with loose soil or sand. Put it in the shade so it will be even more attractive. If the behavior is occurring inside, give him a nest of old throw rugs or blankets that he can bunch up and turn into a bed.

Hyperkinesis. The treatment for destructiveness caused by physiological hyperkinesis includes medication prescribed by a veterinarian as well as behavior modification specific to the problem behavior being displayed. Hyperkinesis has been successfully treated using methylphenidate HCl (Ritalin), dextro-amphetamine sulfate (Dexadrine), and even clomipramine or buspirone[5]. For more information, see chapter 18.

SUMMARY

Destructive behavior presents a significant threat to the human-animal bond and can result in mistreatment of the dog, relinquishment of the dog, or both. Prevention, as discussed in chapter 4, is the best alternative whenever possible. Proper diagnosis combined with early *and appropriate* intervention can improve the welfare of many companion dogs and result in happier owners, as well.

REFERENCES

1. Patronek, G.J., L.T. Glickman, A.M. Beck, G.P. McCabe, and C. Ecker. 1996. Risk factors for relinquishment of dogs to an animal shelter. *JAVMA* 209:572–81.

2. Lindell, E. 1997. Diagnosis and treatment of destructive behavior in dogs. *Vet. Clinics of North Amer. [Small Anim. Pract.]* 27 (3):533–48.

3. Koehler, W. 1967. *The Koehler method of guard dog training.* New York: Howell Book House.

4. Voith, V.L., and P.L. Borchelt. 1996. Seperation anxiety in dogs. In *Readings in companion animal behavior*, ed. V.L. Voith and P.L. Borchelt, 127–39. Trenton, N.J.: Veterinary Learning Systems.

5. Luescher, U.A. 1993. Hyperkinesis in dogs: Six case reports. *Can. Vet. J.* 34:3368–70.

6. Campbell, W.E. 1975. *Behavior problems in dogs.* Santa Barbara, Calif.: American Veterinary Publications.

7. Voith, V.L. 1980. Hyperactivity and hyperkinesis. *Mod. Vet. Pract.* 61:787–9.

CHAPTER 9

Canine Escape Problems

Because of the unfortunate consequences that can occur when a dog runs loose, behaviors that result in the dog escaping from the house or yard are decidedly not trivial. Dogs at large can be hit by cars, shot at, or purposely hurt or abused in other ways. In addition, they endanger themselves by getting into trash and other refuse or chasing wildlife. Intact dogs may mate during their forays away from home, resulting in puppies that contribute to the already acute overpopulation problem. Loose dogs can present a danger to the community by biting people, chasing or threatening them, chasing and injuring cats, getting into fights with other dogs, and leaving their waste in public places. Moreover, people walking their own dogs on leash do not appreciate being approached by a loose dog. Thus, for the owner's, the dog's, and the community's sake, escape problems must be taken seriously. It is not acceptable to minimize these problems or suggest the owner tie or chain the dog as a permanent means of dealing with the behavior, as will be discussed.

Dogs will occasionally have an indoor escape problem, involving either door dashing or breaking out of windows. This chapter will not cover the former, as door dashing is more of an obedience issue. The latter is almost always due to separation anxiety, thunderphobia, or some other fear-related problem. Separation anxiety is discussed later in this chapter; fear-related problems are covered in more detail in chapter 11.

PROTOCOL

To resolve escape problems, you must first determine why and how the dog is escaping.

1. Obtain a Description of the Problem Behavior

When a dog is escaping over the fence, owners almost always say their pet is jumping the fence. Rarely, however, is this the case. More often than not, the dog is climbing the fence by hooking his front paws over the top or pushing off with his back feet from somewhere on the fence. (Occasionally, a large dog will be able to clear a 4-foot or shorter chain-link fence, in which case he could accurately be described as jumping the fence.) The distinction between jumping and climbing is important if either the management or treatment options include making it more difficult or unpleasant for the dog to get out. Other means of escape include digging under the fence, chewing through the fence, opening the gate (yes, dogs do learn to do this!), or a combination of methods. Thus, describing the problem means first determining how the dog is getting out and then discovering what he does once he's escaped. Find out if he stays close to home, sits on the front porch, goes to the neighbor's house or yard, races away and roams far and wide, goes to the school bus stop, visits all the dogs in the neighborhood, etc. You also need to know the pattern of escaping—when the behavior does and does not occur—as well as the dog's body postures immediately prior to and during the escape (see step 4).

2. Evaluate Potential Medical Causes for the Problem Behavior

I can't think of any case I've had in which a medical condition was the cause of an escape problem. If anything, the reverse seems to be true: Dogs get injured attempting to escape or when they are roaming outside of the yard. Thus, I always encourage owners to call their veterinarians if the dog has come home limping or injured in any way or if he soon thereafter develops diarrhea or refuses to eat.

3. Educate Owners About the Problem Behavior

Educate the owners about anthropomorphic and other misinterpretations. Owners often don't understand why their dog is escaping ("I don't know why he wants to get out—he's got plenty of toys in the backyard"), but they do seem less inclined to anthropomorphize escape behaviors as compared to destructiveness or housesoiling. When they do anthropomorphize, the common interpretations are that the dog was mad about being left behind, was not getting enough attention, or was trying to follow them. There may be a grain of truth to the last two interpretations (see the section on causes of escape problems), so your role is to assess the situation and reinterpret it from a behavioral viewpoint. Owners may also believe or have been told that their dog is escaping in order to defy their authority or because he isn't obedient. In fact, escaping problems are unrelated to dominance or obedience issues.

Educate the owners about myths regarding problem solving and techniques to avoid. By the time owners call for behavioral help, they often say they have "tried everything" to keep the dog in the yard. What they likely mean is that they have tried everything to make it harder for the dog to get out of the yard or deny him the chance to try. As an educator, your job is to change the owners' focus from escape-proofing their yard to discovering what is motivating the escape behavior. When fear or anxiety is the motivation, it can be virtually impossible to keep a dog in the yard just by building barricades without addressing the cause of the problem. In fact, fearful dogs often hurt themselves in escape attempts. Furthermore, if owners successfully prevent the escape, the fear will be expressed in some other way, such as howling or destructive behavior.

When the problem involves an intact male dog who just likes to roam, myths about neutering may need to be addressed. There is no need to tell an audience of veterinarians, shelter personnel, and dog trainers that there are no behavioral disadvantages to neutering. However, one myth that seems to be widespread among nonveterinary dog professionals is that once a dog is neutered, weeks or months are required for testosterone to be cleared from the body. In fact, testosterone is metabolized rapidly, and blood concentrations are reduced to essentially zero within hours of castration[1]. Behavioral changes may be more gradual, sometimes taking several months.

A second myth is that past a certain age, neutering won't change behavior. This doesn't seem to be the case. One study found that age at neutering was not correlated with the degree of behavior change[2].

Tying or chaining a dog is *not* an acceptable long-term option for dealing with an escape problem. Dogs who are tied or chained are more likely to bite than those who are not[3], although it is not known if this is a cause-and-effect relationship or simply because the dog has more opportunity to bite. No objective studies of this have been done, but many people in the field, including myself, believe that consistently tying a dog is not good husbandry and actually decreases the quality of the dog's life. Dogs can become tangled in their ropes or chains, resulting in injury or in being deprived of access to food, water, or shelter; they can hang themselves; and they may be prone to frustration-related problems such as destructiveness, aggression, or excessive barking. In fact, tying or chaining is no longer approved by the Animal Welfare Act as a method of confinement for dogs maintained for research purposes. Do companion dogs deserve less?

Another technique to avoid is punishing the dog when he comes home or when he is caught outside the yard. This technique does not address the escape behavior. Moreover, all it does is to create a secondary problem by making the dog more difficult to catch. It does nothing to deter the escaping (see chapter 3 on learning). Any other kind of punishment after the fact, such as dragging the dog back to the fence, crating him, confining him, or ignoring him, is ineffective and inappropriate.

I no longer suggest using antijump harnesses because one client's dog broke her leg attempting to jump while wearing a harness.

Educate the owners about realistic expectations. Expecting a 3-foot fence to contain a Siberian husky or other large dog is not realistic. I recently talked with an owner of a golden retriever who was jumping (truly jumping) a 3-foot split-rail fence to visit with other dogs who were passing by. From the dog's point of view, this was reasonable behavior: He could clear the fence without difficulty, nothing bad happened to him on a consistent basis when he did it, and it was, of course, great fun to play with a visiting dog. It is surprising what flimsy structures owners think can be used to contain a dog. If a lack of secure fencing is contributing to the problem, owners should be instructed about the structural changes they need to make.

4. Identify the Behavioral Cause of the Problem

Before developing management procedures or treatment goals, you must understand the cause for the escape behavior. As mentioned, finding ways to turn an owner's yard into an obstacle course may be a waste of time and energy. If you are going to proceed further in the case, your next job is to ask the owner specific questions to determine the cause of the problem. This becomes a decision point for you. If you do not have time to ask enough questions to diagnose the problem or at least determine if fear or anxiety is likely involved, you should refer the case. You may or may not choose to talk to the owner in *general* terms about management options (refer to later section).

Common behavioral causes for escaping are:

- Separation anxiety
- Fears or phobias
- Sexually motivated roaming
- Territorial behavior
- Play, investigative, or social behavior
- Predatory behavior

Components of a behavioral history. The answers to the following questions will help you distinguish among these causes. For easier organization, they are divided into several categories.

Description of the dog, description of the behavior.
- How old is the dog?
- What breed is the dog? (Some breeds have a reputation as "roamers," which may or may not be accurate.)
- Is she spayed/he neutered?
- Specifically how is the dog getting out? Is he:
    — Jumping the fence by clearing it without touching it?
    — Climbing the fence by using the fence to pull himself over or push off from?
    — Chewing through the fence?
    — Digging under the fence?
    — Opening the gate?
    — Breaking through windows or screens to get out of the house?
    — Crossing through an electronic boundary system?
- What does the dog do or where does he go after he gets out of the yard? Does he:
    — Stay around the house or sit on the front porch?
    — Visit the neighbors or other dogs nearby?
    — Roam a considerable distance from home?
    — Chase people?
    — Chase or kill animals such as cats?
- Where was the dog obtained?
- How long has the dog lived with the family?

Description of the dog's daily routine, environment, and behavior patterns.
- Does the dog consistently follow the owner from room to room (i.e., is he a "shadow" dog)?
- Does the dog greet the owner frantically when he or she returns home?
- Does the dog display a visible change in behavior as the owner is preparing to leave the house without him, e.g., become agitated, restless, nervous, anxious, depressed, fearful?
- Does the dog frequently and persistently solicit the owner's attention or become anxious or pestering if he is ignored?
- Does the owner know if the dog is afraid of any noises (such as thunder, firecrackers, or hot-air balloons) or any people (such as neighbors, mail carriers, or schoolchildren)?
- Does the dog seem reluctant or afraid to go in the backyard either by himself, with the owner, or both?
- What kinds of opportunities does the dog have for physical exercise, such as walks and runs?
- How often and for how long does the owner play actively with the dog (e.g., play fetch or tug-of-war, wrestle, chase, etc.)?
- Is the dog a high-energy, active individual or content to be a couch potato?
- Is the dog very reactive to passersby or the mail carrier and other delivery people? What about other dogs?
- Does the dog threaten visitors to the home, or is he friendly and accepting?
- Have either urine marking or excessive barking in reaction to the presence of visitors or strangers been a problem?
- Is the dog primarily an outdoor dog? How much time does he spend outside each day on average?

- Where does the dog sleep at night?
- What specific type of fence or other containment system is being used?
    — Does the fence seem adequate and well constructed?
    — Is the fence too short, or does it have gaps or areas the dog can easily push through?
    — Are there structures or debris close to the fence that provide a launching pad for the dog?
    — Does the dog have a dog door?

Specifics about the occurrence of the problem behavior.
- Does the dog escape occur only in the owner's absence? If yes,
    — Does escape occur every time the dog is alone or with a consistent pattern of absences, such as only in the evening?
    — Does it occur within the first 30 minutes of the owner's departure? (If the owner doesn't know this, suggest he or she find out by videotaping or returning unexpectedly after a brief absence.)
- Does the dog escape from the yard both when the owner is home and when he or she is away?
- Does the escape occur when the owner is home but not watching the dog or if the animal has been outside for a considerable length of time?
- Did the beginning of the escape problem correlate with any changes in the family's routine or composition (e.g., different work hours, the death of another pet, or a child going away to college, etc.)?
- If the escaping is intermittent, could it be correlated to the occurrence of anything the dog is afraid of, such as thunder, construction noises, etc.? If the owner doesn't know, suggest video- or audiotaping.
- If the escaping is intermittent, is it correlated with times when the dog has less opportunity for play and physical exercise? If this is unknown, suggest that the owner keep a behavioral log or diary for a few weeks.
- Does the behavior seem to occur completely at random or unpredictably?
- How often, on average, is the behavior occurring? (e.g., every day, once a week, once a month)?

Owners' attempts at problem resolution and the dog's response.
- Has the dog been confined in a crate, garage, or a small area such as a mudroom instead of being left in the yard? If so, how has he behaved?
- Has the dog been punished either if caught in the act of escaping or later?
- How has the dog been punished? Has he been hit or verbally scolded? Have other techniques been used?
- Has the dog been played with and exercised more often?
- Has the behavior improved, gotten worse, or stayed the same since the problem began?
- What modifications have been made to the fence or yard (or windows in the house) to thwart the dog's escape attempts?
- Has an electronic containment system been installed or the use of an existing one discontinued?
- Has the dog been spayed or neutered in an attempt to stop the escape behavior? Did this result in any change in the behavior?
- What other things have been tried to resolve the problem? What results have been observed?

Differential results of the behavioral history. Answers to the preceding questions will help you identify the cause of the problem.

Separation anxiety. The pattern of occurrence of the escaping will be congruent with any problem behavior associated with separation anxiety. The dog will escape, or attempt to escape, within the first 30 minutes or so after the owner's departure, he will do so *only* and *consistently* (i.e., every time, not unpredictably) in the owner's absence (or a particular pattern of absences, such as every time the owner leaves for the evening after a workday absence), and he will *never* try to leave the house or yard when the owner is home. The only exception to this rule is if the owner is outside gardening, getting the mail, etc., in which case the dog may attempt to escape in order to reach the owner. If the dog escapes both in and out of the owner's presence, it is not likely related to separation, although it could be a compound problem involving separation anxiety as well as another motivation.

A classic behavioral pattern observed in a dog with separation anxiety is that once out of the yard, she will sit on the front porch waiting for the owner to return. There is one caveat here: The owner may be fooled by a dog who runs around the neighborhood for most of the day and then, exhausted, rests on the front porch until someone gets home. Usually, these different patterns can be discerned by talking to the neighbors or with animal control personnel if they have been involved. In addition, a dog who has been roaming around all day may be dirty, her coat may be matted, her paws may be blistered or bleeding, or she may be panting if she has recently returned (but since anxious or overheated dogs pant, too, don't rely too heavily on this observation). Instead of going to the front porch, the dog with separation anxiety may go to a house nearby (or even at a distance) where there is someone at home with whom she can spend the day.

If a yard has been made escape-proof, the separation anxiety will manifest itself in tandem with another symptom, such as destructiveness or barking or howling most of the day. However, dogs with separation anxiety can find ways through barriers that would contain a less motivated dog.

The dog will also demonstrate some or all of the other signs correlated with separation anxiety, such as following the owner around the house, frantic greeting behavior, and agitation if the owner is briefly out of sight[4, 6]. Because the owner's preparations to leave predict to the dog that he is about to be left alone, there will usually be obvious responses to these departures cues (increased anxiety, agitation, depression). A strong attachment to the owner seems to be characteristic of dogs with separation anxiety, and many of them display a pattern of frequently soliciting social interaction (human attention) and receiving it on demand[6]. This may be part of the explanation for the problem behavior: Such dogs become anxious or frustrated when they cannot immediately interact with their owners.

Dogs with separation anxiety are statistically more likely to be purebreds obtained from a humane society[6]. They are also more likely to have a history of constant companionship and rarely being left alone prior to the onset of the problem behavior.

Triggers for the onset of a separation anxiety problem include a change in the family's schedule, a change in the family composition (including the death of another pet), a move to a new environment, or being boarded, hospitalized, or away from the owner for some other reason. It is important to note that not all escapes that occur in the owner's absence can be attributed to separation anxiety.

Fears or phobias. Dogs sometimes escape because they are frightened. Some common stimuli causing fear-motivated escape attempts seem to be noises such as thunder, firecrackers, car backfires, hot-air balloons, airplanes, gunshots, trash trucks, sounds of construction or heavy equipment, or any other loud, startling noise. Dogs are probably attempting to get away from the noise by going anywhere other than where they are or trying to find a "safe" place. In the initial stages of a fear-related escaping problem, the behavior is correlated with the occurrence of the noise. Owners may need to observe the dog or even video- or audiotape him to establish this connection. However, if the dog is frightened in the yard repeatedly or consistently, he may exhibit a generalized reaction, as if thinking, "The yard is a bad place to be," even when the initial triggering stimulus is absent. With some dogs, that generalization can occur after one or only a few experiences. Owners should also look for any traumatic experiences the dog has had in the yard. Some electronic devices such as antibark collars or electronic fences can cause fear-related problems that motivate escape behavior.

The dog may also show a reluctance to go outside, even when the owner is home, or he may want to go back inside immediately. This pattern may also be seen with separation anxiety. With some fear-motivated escaping problems, the dog will escape from the yard even if the owner is home, particularly if he is not let inside when the fear reaction begins. A fear-motivated dog can successfully escape through barriers that would normally contain a calm dog.

Sexually motivated roaming. Sexually motivated roaming is a problem primarily with intact male dogs, who have a tendency to want to roam particularly if there is a female in season nearby. If a male dog has a history of roaming and is subsequently neutered, this may not decrease the behavior because it has already become more of a learned pattern. However, in one study, roaming was decreased after neutering in about 90 percent of the cases[2], and the beneficial effect was seen regardless of the age at the time of neutering.

In the behavioral history, the pattern of escaping may be extremely varied. Roaming may occur daily for a time if the dog's sense of smell tells him that there are females in season nearby (something that would be very hard to find independent evidence for unless you went door to door and asked!), or roaming may occur randomly. The behavior may occur both in the owner's presence and absence. However, if the dog has been caught and punished when the owner is home, the behavior may be restricted only to times when the owner is gone. This should not be misdiagnosed as separation anxiety. Typically, dogs escaping for these reasons are not front-porch sitters but may be found several blocks or even much farther from home. The dog may have found an easy way out through some weakness in the fence, or he may have worked hard to find a way through a well-constructed barrier.

Territorial behavior. Dogs can be motivated to get out of the yard to chase or threaten people or other dogs passing by whom they perceive as intruding on their territory. These dogs will usually have a pattern of "on-patrol" behavior, reacting to people and dogs passing by with barking, lunging, and even growling. These dogs may not be well socialized. Sometimes, owners view such behavior as the dog's job and not only don't *discourage* these alerting or threatening behaviors but actually *encourage* or reinforce them. The dog's reactions can escalate to the point of escaping and chasing.

Territorial escaping will correlate with the presence of people or other dogs passing the house or yard. Mail carriers and other delivery people are commonly triggers for the behavior. The behavior may not occur when the owner is home, as most owners have done something to prevent the behavior from escalating to that intensity in their presence. It may occur more often when owners are gone and cannot exert their inhibitory influence. Other territorial behaviors may be observed, such as barking or urine marking.

Play, investigative, and social behavior. Escape problems can occur just because the dog finds it is more fun to be out of the yard and roaming, sniffing, playing with people or other dogs, digging in the park, and so on. This behavior is more likely to develop in dogs whose home or yard environment provides little opportunity for social interaction, play, and exercise. A dog who escapes for these reasons may be primarily an outdoor dog whose owner ignores him much of the time; for him, the world beyond his yard is a more rewarding environment. Unfortunately, if such a dog is not well socialized, he can threaten or bite people who attempt to approach him.

However, some well cared for dogs also escape for these reasons. I once saw a golden retriever who became so excited when another dog walked by that he would climb a 6-foot fence to say hello. There was nothing territorial or aggressive in his behavior—he just couldn't resist making a new friend.

In the behavioral history, look for what the dog is doing once he gets out, as well as what his home environment is like. The pattern of occurrence of the behavior may also be extremely varied, or it may be correlated with the presence of people or other dogs—not because they represent territorial intruders but because they provide opportunities for social interaction and play. This is an important distinction when it comes to formulating a treatment plan.

Predatory behavior. Some dogs are motivated to get out of the yard to chase and hunt cats, birds, squirrels, or other animals, such as deer. Owners will usually be aware of these tendencies in their dogs, and the escaping will occur in response to these stimuli.

5. Discuss Ways to Manage or Control the Behavior over the Short or Long Term

With escaping problems, management usually means finding a way to prevent the dog from getting out of the yard or house, at least in the short term. Remember that managing the problem is usually not the same thing as resolving it.

General management procedures—no behavioral diagnosis. If you are not armed with a behavioral diagnosis, making suggestions about how to manage the problem is a somewhat risky proposition. For example, if you recommend leaving the dog inside, the owner may come home to a destroyed house if the escaping is caused by a separation anxiety problem, if it is the result of playful or investigative behavior, or if the dog is just not accustomed to being left indoors. Leaving the dog in the garage on a short-term basis is another possibility—if temperatures are not too extreme and if all chemicals (especially antifreeze) and tools the dog could be injured by are removed—but the possibility for the dog being destructive or barking still exists.

Similarly, installing a dog door that would allow the pet access to the garage or house does not avert the risk of destructive behavior, and there is, of course, no guarantee the dog will choose to go inside the house or garage rather than escaping from the yard.

It would be inappropriate to suggest medication without first knowing whether fear or anxiety is involved. One safe recommendation might be for the owner to either take the pet to doggie day care, leave him with a friend who will be home to supervise him, or take him to work (although few people have that luxury).

Tying the dog in the yard should be done only as a last resort and only for a day or two, as this is a potentially dangerous way to manage the problem. One owner who resorted to this method came home to find her dog's leg caught in the chain, which resulted in swelling and tissue damage, and there are cases in which dogs have hung themselves by attempting to get over the fence while tied up. If tying the dog is a short-term necessity, most animal control agencies can provide recommendations on how to do it safely. If your facility can board the dog during the day for a brief time until the owner can find another solution, I would recommend that approach, rather than risking the dog being injured or killed from being chained up. Also refer to the later section discussing possible modifications to the fence.

Management procedures based on a diagnosis.

Separation anxiety. With escaping motivated by anxiety, management requires preventing the dog from becoming anxious, which requires not leaving him alone for long enough periods to trigger the anxiety. Options include:

- Using a doggie day care service, boarding the dog during the day at a kennel or veterinary clinic, letting him stay with friends or family who are home all day, or allowing him to accompany the owner throughout the day.
- Leaving the dog inside during the day if he escapes when outside. Many dogs are less anxious inside, but some are not, and if a dog is still anxious indoors, she may be destructive, bark, or housesoil. If you suggest owners try this approach, tell them to do so for very short periods initially to see how the dog responds.
- Working with a veterinarian who can prescribe medication on a short-term basis to decrease the dog's anxiety. Medication alone should not be viewed as a long-term solution to separation anxiety problems (see chapter 18).

Fears or phobias. Manage the problem by changing the dog's daily routine so that she is not exposed to the fear-producing stimulus. If triggering noises (gunshots, airplanes, hot-air balloons, etc.) are more intense outside than inside, the dog may be fine if left indoors. Another alternative is for a veterinarian to prescribe antianxiety medication, which will decrease the dog's anxious response on a short-term basis (see chapter 18).

Sexually motivated roaming. The problem of sexually motivated roaming can be managed by leaving the dog inside or building a secure dog run. The possibility for destructive behavior or other problems exist if the dog is not used to being left inside. Any weaknesses in the fence can be repaired, or additional obstacles can be added (see the following section). Neutering the dog is probably a better solution for all concerned and less time-consuming for the owner.

Territorial behavior. Managing an escape problem due to territorial behavior involves either preventing the dog from being exposed to the people or animals triggering the behavior or denying her the opportunity to escape. In both cases, this could mean changing her environment, perhaps by leaving her inside or in a specific part of the house where she can't see passing people or animals, or by building her a run in the yard, which accomplishes the same thing. The fence could be changed to make it more difficult for the dog to escape (see the following section). If the escaping is triggered when the dog *sees* the individual, a privacy fence or some other visual barrier could be installed.

Play, investigative, or social behavior. Escape caused by play, investigative, or social motivations can be managed by denying the dog the opportunity to escape by using the methods mentioned earlier—building a dog run, leaving the dog inside (although the risk of destructive behavior exists), or making changes to the fence so that escaping is more difficult or impossible (more on this in the following section). However, putting more restrictions on the dog (in a run, in the garage, inside) without meeting his play and social needs may result in other behavioral manifestations, such as destructiveness or barking. A problem-resolution approach that enriches the animal's environment and provides appropriate outlets for these behaviors is preferable (see subsequent section).

Predatory behavior. Management options for escaping caused by predatory behavior are similar to those for other causes—that is, making it more difficult for the dog to escape (see the discussion that follows) or managing his environment so the dog doesn't encounter the triggers for the predatory behavior. Instead of changing the dog's environment, this could mean discouraging cats, birds, squirrels, and other dogs from entering his territory. Use of a motion detector (see the product appendix) is a possibility. However, most motion detectors have a limited range, which may not be sufficient for the large area of many backyards. For example, even if a squirrel avoids the area in which it would trigger the detector, it could still run across the rest of the fence and stimulate the dog's predatory instincts and subsequent escaping behavior. Another option would be to install a privacy fence if that would prevent the dog from seeing the species of animal triggering his predatory behavior.

Modifying the fence. When making it more difficult for the dog to escape is an appropriate management or treatment approach, the ideas discussed in this section may be helpful. However, always remember that unless the motivation for the behavior is addressed, the dog will often keep trying to escape or display other problem behaviors.

If the dog is digging out under the fence.
- Partially bury large rocks (one client used bowling balls) along the entire fence line. Keep in mind, however, that if this is done only in the place where the dog is escaping, he will most likely move to another location, especially if only management options are being applied.
- Place lengths of chain-link fencing on the ground and extend them a foot or so up the side of the fence (the chain link will bend as it moves from the ground to the fence). Dogs cannot dig under the chain link.
- Install an electric wire (a "hot wire") along the bottom of the fence (the wire will short out if it touches the fence or ground). This option is *not* appropriate for fear- or anxiety-based problems, as punishing a fearful dog is unacceptable.

If the dog is climbing the fence.
- Attach a border of inward-facing heavy wire that meets the top of the fence at a 90° angle (this may require attaching some supports as well) to prevent the dog from gaining a foothold at the top of the fence.
- Install an electric wire along the top of the fence or any horizontal support bar that the dog may be using to push off from. Other booby traps are feasible, such as placing vinyl carpet runners with the pointy side up (mentioned in other chapters) or hanging tin cans or Snappy Trainers (see product appendix) that may startle the dog. These methods are not appropriate for fear- or anxiety-based problems.
- Make sure to remove any objects near the fence that the dog may be using as climbing aids.

If the dog is chewing through the fence.
- Apply a foul-tasting substance (see product appendix) to the fence in a thick layer. Of course, this may be impractical if a large area of fence must be treated.
- Cover a picket fence with pieces of vinyl carpet runner with the pointy side out; again, this method may be impractical if a large area must be covered.
- Hang Snappy Trainers or balloons that the dog will pop in an attempt to escape.

If the dog is jumping the fence (clearing it).
- Make the fence taller.
- Add a second, inner fence, trench, or hedge to interrupt the dog's running approach or prevent him from having access to his required take-off point (if he has to stand too close to the fence or too far away, he can't make the leap to clear the fence).

- Add a visual barrier that prevents the dog from seeing where he is going to land—some dogs won't jump if they can't see the landing zone.
- Remove any objects near the fence that the dog may be using as a launching pad.

If the dog is crossing through an electronic boundary system. An electronic boundary system consists of a buried wire and a receiver attached to the dog's collar. When she approaches within a set distance of the wire, she receives a shock through the collar. It is possible to adjust the intensity of the shock on most (but not all) models. A relatively new type of boundary system delivers a spray of citronella under the dog's chin rather than a shock (see product appendix).

There are disadvantages to this method. First, if the dog's motivation to leave the yard exceeds the aversiveness of either the shock or the citronella, she will tolerate the punishment in order to cross the boundary (although the vast majority of dogs will not recross the boundary to get back into the yard). Second, these systems cannot keep people or animals out of the yard. This may be a minor or a very serious disadvantage, depending on the environment.

If the dog is breaking through the boundary, retraining may be necessary. This usually entails reinstalling the boundary flags, allowing the dog to experience the shock if she comes too close to the flags, and then encouraging and reinforcing her for moving away from the boundary. The intensity of the shock may need to be increased. If the system is used inappropriately, the dog may learn to tolerate gradually increasing intensities of shock and its effectiveness may be diminished. In some cases, owners may need to use a physical fence instead.

Some dogs reportedly display what is assumed to be redirected aggression toward people who are standing nearby when the animals receives a shock at the boundary of a yard[5]. The boundary systems based on the citronella spray are a more humane alternative to shock, in my opinion.

6. Explain the Goals of an Appropriate Behavior Modification Plan

For escaping problems, the appropriate treatment often combines addressing the cause of the problem and using management options and modifications to the fence if necessary. If a dog has been successful at escaping, even on an intermittent basis, this will encourage him to continue his attempts. Consequently, the behavior needs to be prevented and the motivation for it must be addressed. Fear and anxiety motivations for escaping are treated very differently than other causes, so you must arrive at a behavioral diagnosis before proceeding. If you don't have a diagnosis or haven't determined the cause of the problem, don't attempt to choose a treatment plan from the recommendations that follow. Instead, either go back and obtain more information to allow you to diagnosis the cause or refer the case.

Separation anxiety. When separation anxiety causes the problem, the dog's anxiety in response to being left alone must be decreased. Some dogs with separation anxiety may not be anxious if left inside, and if so, this can be a sufficient treatment procedure (see management section). If not, counterconditioning and desensitization procedures are necessary because the problem is essentially based in fear. Techniques to make the dog less demanding of attention from the owner may also be helpful. Remember that treatment has nothing to do with dominance issues, giving the dog more exercise, making it more difficult for the dog to get out (assuming the fence is in good repair and of appropriate height), or providing more toys. Sample steps in a treatment program will be described. *Please note that these procedures do not represent a complete treatment plan, as there are always nuances and differences in each case that will require additional steps or modifications of generally recommended procedures. Failure to implement a complete plan correctly will result in ineffective treatment or even an exacerbation of the problem. The behavior modification procedures for separation anxiety problems are tedious, so these cases require significant client follow-up. Consider these factors as you decide whether to make treatment recommendations yourself or refer the case.*

- The owner can make the departure cues less predictive for the dog and therefore less likely to elicit anxiety by repeating discrete behaviors (putting the dog outside, backing the car out of the garage, etc.) without leaving. Many repetitions may be necessary (up to 10 or more per day over a period of weeks or months) to counteract the existing predictive value of these cues. Behaviorists vary as to whether the dog should be ignored (habituation), given a treat at the onset of the departure cue (counterconditioning), or required to lie down quietly (countercommanding).

- In the meantime, the owner should vary the sequence of her actual departure routine (e.g., back the car out of the garage first thing) and do as much preparation as possible the night before or well in advance of a departure. She should not pay a lot of attention to the dog during her normal departure routine, as this only serves to focus the dog on her and make her absence more distressing.

- The owner should accustom the dog to being left alone for brief periods so that a nonanxious response can be elicited. Some behaviorists recommend pairing these brief absences with a pleasant stimulus (food, a toy, etc.); others do not. The pleasant stimulus becomes the cue that the absence will be brief, and it should *not* be used for longer absences[6]. If the owner is already in the habit of giving the dog a treat when she leaves for a prolonged absence, this and similar treats should be avoided during these practice sessions. Other behaviorists use a countercommanding procedure and have the dog lie down quietly as the owner leaves briefly. The length of the absence is completely dependent on the dog's response—the owner must return before the dog becomes anxious. In some cases, this means returning within seconds; in others, it can mean returning in several minutes. Giving departure cues prior to these absences should be avoided. The length of the absences should be gradually increased, on an unpredictable schedule.

- As the dog's reaction to the departure cues improves and he can tolerate absences of 20 minutes or so, a departure cue can be combined with a briefer (say, a 10-minute) absence. Longer absences should then be gradually preceded by more cues until this practice procedure is similar to the owner's normal routine.

- The owner should work on out-of-sight stays to prevent the dog from following her around the house and encourage him to be more relaxed out of her presence. The dog can be taught to lie down and stay in return for a tidbit (which should be given as the owner walks away from the dog, not on returning), with the duration of the stay and the time out of sight being very brief at first and increased incrementally. During training, the owner should be in sight/out of sight repeatedly. Initially, the out-of-sight time should be extremely brief. The dog should be calm enough to eat the tidbit; if he is not, the owner should stay in close proximity until he is able to do so.

- Arrivals and departures should be quiet and calm events, with no long speeches made to the dog on leaving and no excited greetings on returning.

- The owner should not pet or interact with the dog when he demands it but instead require the dog to wait, obey a command, or become calm and relaxed before receiving attention. This can be accomplished by ignoring the dog until he lies down and stops pestering. This does not, of course, mean that the owner should completely ignore the dog for months at a time.

- The dog's anxiety response *must* be prevented during treatment using one or more of the management procedures previously discussed.

Fears or phobias. To handle problems stemming from fears or phobias, you must first identify the specific stimulus that is causing the fear and then implement a desensitization and counterconditioning plan to decrease it (see chapters 3 and 11 for details). Management procedures (described previously) should be implemented in the meantime, as ongoing fear responses will significantly interfere with treatment. If you do not feel confident in devising a step-by-step counterconditioning and desensitization plan, refer the case. If you cannot identify the fear-eliciting stimulus, either the problem has been misdiagnosed, the owner needs to do some detective work, or you should refer the case.

Sexually motivated roaming. The goal in treating sexually motivated roaming is to decrease the dog's desire to roam. First, the animal should be neutered. Second, steps can be taken to make it more difficult for the dog to escape, using any appropriate procedures described previously in the section on modifying the fence. Third, if the dog is caught in the act of escaping, the behavior can be punished by throwing water at the dog or turning the hose on him as he comes over the fence or by using a startling noise (blowing an air horn, banging pots and pans, etc.). Because punishment must be immediate and consistent to be effective (see chapter 3), it may have limited value, as those criteria are difficult to meet. If punishment is used, the dog must literally be caught in the act of getting out: Catching him running around several seconds later is not good enough. It is difficult to set up remote punishers that are automatically triggered, so the punishment may need to be administered by the owner as in the prior examples. If the dog can predict that the owner is lying in wait for him, he will discriminate when he can chance an escape and when he can't.

Territorial behavior. The goal in treating territorially motivated escaping is to change the dog's territorial behavior to either tolerant, relaxed behavior or friendly expectation, both of which should decrease the dog's desire to escape. This will probably require a counterconditioning and desensitization approach. If the dog is motivated enough to escape the yard to pursue territorial intruders, it is highly likely that aggressive behavior will be part of the problem as well (see chapter 12). If "on-patrol" behaviors (barking, charging windows and gates, etc.) are part of the problem, counterconditioning, which can be combined with countercommanding, can be used. The careful use of remote punishment may be helpful, but this cannot be the only constituent of or even the focus of the behavior modification plan. If you don't feel comfortable devising a plan using these techniques, refer the case. Making it more difficult for the dog to escape is also a reasonable part of the treatment plan, as is the management option of changing the dog's environment so he isn't exposed to the stimuli that trigger the territorial behavior.

Play, investigative, or social behavior. As with destructive behavior motivated by play, investigative, or social behaviors, the goal in resolving this type of escaping problem is to meet the dog's needs for play, investigation, and social interactions through other means that keep him in the yard. The dog's environment in the yard should be enriched, providing him with activities to occupy his time and give him a reason to stay in the yard. Use some of the toys described in chapter 8 and in the product appendix. Sometimes, installing a dog door, which gives the animal another choice as to where he spends his time during the day, could be part of an environmental enrichment program. The dog can also be taken for walks and supervised runs to meet his need to explore areas outside of his yard. Consistent, immediate, remote punishment for the behavior as described in the section on roaming behavior, as well as changes to the fence, also may need to be incorporated into the treatment plan.

Predatory behavior. One goal of treatment for escape caused by predatory behavior would be to change the dog's predatory response to another, incompatible behavior. For example, he could be trained to tolerate the presence of the "prey" by sitting and watching it rather than trying to chase and catch it (which is resulting in the escaping behavior). However, predatory behavior is very difficult to countercondition or countercommand because it is generally highly motivated. Providing acceptable outlets for predatory behavior is also difficult, unless the behavior can be redirected onto toys: A fake rabbit skin or stuffed toy in the shape of a prey animal, such as a squirrel, may be an option. In addition, appropriate punishment may be needed. If barking is part of the escaping sequence, the owner could try using a citronella antibark collar (see chapter 10), which may have a general calming or inhibitory effect and prevent the escape attempt. If the dog can consistently be caught trying to escape, other types of punishment can be used, as described earlier in the roaming section. However, consistency is usually a problem here, as it is not practical for an owner to be home every time a squirrel or cat makes an appearance.

Giving the dog something else to do, as described previously, may be somewhat helpful. Management options such as leaving the dog inside, building a run, discouraging the presence of the prey, and making modifications to the fence may all need to be part of the plan.

SUMMARY

The treatment of escaping problems often requires not only changing the dog's behavior but also using management approaches. Environmental management, including modifying the fence and changing where the dog is housed, as well as environmental enrichment may be required.

REFERENCES

1. Hart, B.L. 1985. *The behavior of domestic animals.* New York: W.H. Freeman and Company.

2. Hopkins, S.G., T.A. Schubert, and B.L. Hart. 1976. Castration of adult male dogs: Effects on roaming, aggression, urine marking, and mounting. JAVMA 168:1108–10.

3. Gershman, K.A., J.J. Sacks, and J.C. Wright. 1994. Which dogs bite? A case-control study of risk factors. *Pediatrics* 93 (6):913–7.

4. McCrave, E.A. 1991. Diagnostic criteria for separation anxiety in the dog. *Vet. Clinics of North Amer. [Small Anim. Pract.]* 21 (2):247–56.

5. Polsky, R.H. 1998. Shock collars and aggression in dogs. *Animal Behavior Consultant Newsletter* 15 (2):1–2.

6. Voith, V.L., and P.L. Borchelt. 1996. Separation anxiety in dogs. In *Readings in companion animal behavior,* ed. V.L. Voith and P.L. Borchelt, 127–39. Trenton, N.J.: Veterinary Learning Systems.

CHAPTER 10

Barking Problems in Dogs

Excessive barking is one of the more common behavior problems seen by animal behaviorists[1]. Interestingly, whether a dog's barking is a problem is often determined by the community. A dog kept inside who barks all day due to a separation anxiety problem may not be viewed as a problem if the barking is not disturbing the neighbors. However, a dog in the backyard who barks in response to things she sees or hears may actually bark less than the dog with separation anxiety but be labeled as a problem because of complaints from neighbors.

A dog who barks or vocalizes excessively can create a variety of negative consequences for the community, her owner, and herself. For the community, dealing with complaints about barking dogs often involves a significant investment of money, time, and other resources by animal control and other law enforcement agencies. For the owner, a noisy dog can result in sleepless nights, disruptions in activities, general aggravation, angry neighbors, legal actions, and even the loss of the dog. For the dog, a barking problem can result in restricted activity, ill treatment or abuse by owners or neighbors, surgical debarking, or even death. Furthermore, dogs who bark excessively are probably stressed, and their welfare is likely to be negatively affected.

Barking seems to be such a simple, basic, and uncomplicated behavior. Either because they think it is a simple problem or because they are under pressure from animal control personnel or their neighbors, owners expect and sometimes demand quick solutions for the problem. In most cases, there aren't any. The availability of antibark collars suggests that quick solutions do indeed exist, and use of an antibark collar, when appropriate, may result in a quick solution. However, before recommending a collar, you must first reach a behavioral diagnosis.

PROTOCOL

There are many possible reasons for excessive barking, and you will need to work through the protocol to decide how a particular problem should be handled.

1. Obtain a Description of the Problem Behavior

Usually, describing this behavior is a pretty straightforward task—the dog is barking. However, to develop a meaningful diagnosis, it is important to know whether other types of vocalizations are involved as well and to determine exactly when and for how long the dog is vocalizing. Rather than relying on the secondhand reports of neighbors or animal control personnel, it may be wise to audio- or videotape the dog to accurately describe the behavior.

The problem description should also note what the dog looks like when he's barking, as a good description of body postures can be helpful in diagnosis. This is another justification for videotaping the dog if the behavior is occurring in the owner's absence.

2. Evaluate Potential Medical Causes for the Problem Behavior

Dogs can vocalize when they are in pain, physically uncomfortable, thirsty, hungry, or ill. Older dogs who don't hear or see well or who are experiencing "senility" changes may also become more vocal. Vocalizations may involve not only barking but whining, yelping, whimpering, or even howling. At a minimum, dogs with barking problems should be given a thorough physical examination to be sure they are not ill and that no source of discomfort, such as an ear infection or an abscessed tooth, exists. In addition to the physical exam, blood work and a urinalysis may be warranted in case any antianxiety medications are later indicated, based on the behavioral diagnosis[2].

3. Educate Owners About the Problem Behavior

Educate the owners about anthropomorphic and other misinterpretations. Owners generally don't anthropomorphize barking behavior too much, apart from sometimes believing that the dog barks because he is mad at them. Perhaps this is because barking is such a "doggie" behavior that it is less amenable to anthropomorphism. Or perhaps it is because, unlike destructive and elimination behaviors, barking doesn't produce any physical evidence that can be used to show the dog he has "done wrong." When owners receive citations about excessive barking from animal control, they may be told their dog needs more training. However, obedience training has nothing to do with how much a dog barks or doesn't bark. It also is unrelated to the owners' "lack of dominance" over the dog. Most barking problems occur in the owners' absence, so logically, the owners' relationship with the dog could have no influence over his behavior. Barking and dominance are not related to one another.

Educate the owners about myths regarding problem solving and techniques to avoid. As mentioned at the outset, many owners want quick solutions for barking problems. This is especially true if they've received complaints from animal control officers. When I get a call about a barking problem, more often than not the owner asks about using a bark collar. However, I rarely if ever recommend a bark collar of any kind as a first or only approach. Above all, I do not feel comfortable suggesting these devices until I know the motivation for the barking, because punishment devices like these are usually not appropriate for a barking problem caused by fear or anxiety. These products will be discussed more in the section on treatment goals.

Another common question from owners involves the debarking procedure. Whether debarking is humane or ethical is a matter of personal opinion. Veterinarians make individual choices about performing the procedure: Some will only do so in certain cases, others will do the procedure simply if the owner requests it, and still others refuse to perform it at all. Unfortunately, debarking surgery is often less expensive than a behavior consultation appointment or a good-quality antibark collar.

No studies have investigated the behavioral effects of debarking. Certainly, though, many dogs who are debarked continue to vocalize at the same frequency. The sound they make is usually sufficiently attenuated to placate neighbors, although this is not always the case. If I'm asked about the procedure, I always suggest the owner contact her veterinarian to discuss what the surgery involves. Although I must admit I don't like the idea of debarking, I can't in good faith tell an owner that the procedure has a detrimental effect on the dog's behavioral well-being because there are no data to support that statement.

As mentioned earlier, antibark devices are generally not appropriate for barking problems motivated by fear or anxiety. Muzzles cannot be considered for long-term management either, as it is not safe to leave a muzzled dog alone for the day.

When I was working at an animal shelter, I was shocked at the number of complaints the cruelty department received about owners who had left their dogs outside and alone all day with rubber bands around their muzzles or with their muzzles tied shut with cords in order to stop them from barking. Obviously, such techniques are inhumane and completely unacceptable.

Educate the owners about realistic expectations. Owners need to have realistic expectations about when barking is acceptable and when it isn't. They should also recognize that they themselves may have played a role in creating the barking problem. Most people want and encourage their dogs to alert them to sounds such as people passing by the house. Too often, though, dog owners fail to discourage or set limits on this kind of barking for fear that the dog won't alert them to *any* sound of impending danger. Owners will sometimes even turn a dog's barking into a game: Inciting a dog to "get the cat" or teasing him with "Where's that squirrel?" or "Who's there?" can certainly contribute to a barking problem. The dog then becomes constantly on patrol—barking at every noise and difficult to quiet down once he's alerted. I believe this pattern may predispose dogs to develop territorial aggression problems as well (see chapter 12), and certainly it is a contributing factor to some stimulus- or territorially motivated barking problems. Ultimately, it is necessary to set limits on a dog's natural tendency for alarm barking so that he does not develop an excessive barking problem.

Because most owners seek professional help for a barking problem only when they are panicked by complaints from neighbors or a visit from animal control, they are often desperate for quick solutions. Consequently, it sometimes takes real salesmanship to convince owners to invest the time needed to determine the motivation for the barking, choose the best treatment approach for the problem, and implement a behavior modification plan. Most would rather just put a bark collar around the dog's neck and be done with it. This approach, however, can backfire: Some dogs bark in spite of the punishment delivered by the collar, and other behavior problems may erupt, as well. In my consulting practice, I will not rent or sell a bark collar to an owner without at least a brief (20-minute) consult. My preference is to work with collars only within the context of a complete behavioral consultation so that I can determine the appropriateness of this technique for the particular problem.

If you work at an animal shelter or animal control agency and it is your job to deal with barking complaints, you, too, must have realistic expectations. As you will see in the pages ahead, few barking problems can be resolved overnight: Just leaving the dog inside is often not feasible, for reasons that will be discussed. You can, however, be helpful in a number of ways. You can assist dog owners who in good faith are attempting to resolve the problem by working with a trainer, veterinarian, or behavior specialist and by not citing them during the treatment process. You can reassure angry neighbors that something is being done, while cautioning that an immediate cessation to the barking may not be possible. If the barking complaints are tied to other neighbor-to-neighbor conflicts, you might even refer the case to mediation. In such situations, the duration and frequency of barking may, in fact, be only moderate, but the dog's behavior has become a flash point for extraneous reasons. Addressing the other personal conflicts involved may be more practical or even necessary, rather than attempting to create a silent dog.

4. Identify the Behavioral Cause of the Problem

Before proceeding to management procedures or treatment goals, you must understand the cause of the barking behavior. Thus, if you are going to be further involved in the case, your next job is to ask owners questions in order to determine the cause of the problem. This is a decision point for you. If you do not have time to ask enough questions to diagnose the problem or at least to determine if fear or anxiety are likely involved, you should refer the case and not attempt to make recommendations in the absence of a behavioral diagnosis. In the interim, you may or may not choose to talk to owners in *general* terms about management options (refer to later section).

You'll notice that "boredom barking," which is commonly referred to in the popular literature, has not been mentioned in the preceding passages. This is because boredom (whatever that means from the animal's perspective) is not in and of itself a motivation for barking. Dogs who live in impoverished environments with little stimulation (which is a more concrete description of what may lead to boredom) may have lowered thresholds for barking, but the actual reason for the barking is usually subsumed under one of the following categories:

- Separation anxiety
- Territorial or protective
- Excitement or greeting
- Play
- Attention getting or care seeking
- Fear, distress, or anxiety
- Pain
- Defensive
- Frustration
- Group-motivated
- Stereotypic behavior

Components of a behavioral history. The answers to the following questions will help you distinguish among these causes. For easier organization, they are divided into several categories.

Description of the dog, description of the behavior.
- What breed is the dog?
- How old is the dog?
- Is she spayed/he neutered?
- What kind of vocalizations is the dog making?
- What does the dog look like when barking? Describe his body postures? (Dogs may have mixed motivations and display body postures that are congruent with more than one emotional state.)
    — Ears back, tail down, crouching, hiding (all indicative of fearfulness)
    — Ears back, tail down, growling or barking, tense body, showing teeth, possibly piloerection (all indicative of defensiveness)
    — Ears forward, tail up, stiff-legged, upright, staring, tense body, growling or barking, charging target, possibly piloerection (all indicative of offensively threatening behavior)
    — Crouching, play bow, tail wagging, body relaxed (all indicative of friendliness or playfulness)
- Does the dog show other repetitive behaviors, such as circling, spinning, or jumping, while barking?
- Does the dog have any chronic illnesses or conditions that cause physical discomfort or pain?

Description of the dog's daily routine, environment, and behavior patterns.
- Does the dog consistently follow the owner from room to room when he or she is home (is he a "shadow" dog)?
- Does the dog greet the owner frantically when he or she returns home?
- Does the dog display a visible change in behavior when the owner is preparing to leave the house without him—e.g., does he become agitated, restless, nervous, anxious, depressed, or fearful?
- Does the dog frequently and persistently solicit the owner's attention or become anxious or pestering if he is ignored?
- Does the owner know if the dog is afraid of any noises (such as thunder, fire-crackers, or hot-air balloons) or any people such as neighbors, mail carriers, or schoolchildren?
- What toys and chewies are available to the dog to occupy his time when left alone? How often does the dog receive new toys and chewies?
- Does the dog have a dog door so he can enter the garage or house for part of day?
- What opportunities does the dog have for physical exercise, such as walks and runs?
- How often and for how long does the owner play actively with the dog (play fetch or tug-of-war, wrestle, chase, etc.)?
- Is the dog a high-energy, active individual or content to be a couch potato?
- Is the dog very reactive to passersby, the mail carrier, and other delivery people? What about other dogs and other animals?
- Does the dog threaten visitors to the home, or is he friendly and accepting?
- Has urine marking in reaction to the presence of visitors or strangers been a problem?
- Is the dog primarily an outdoor dog? How much time does the dog spend outside?
- How would the owner describe the indoor or outdoor environment in which the dog spends most of his time? Is it complex, with opportunities for play and social interaction? Or is it barren and impoverished, without much stimulation?
- Is the area surrounding the dog's home or yard a high-traffic area—i.e., with people, delivery trucks, and so forth frequently passing by?
- Are there other dogs in the neighborhood who often bark, howl, or vocalize in other ways?
- Does the dog's normal play pattern involve a lot of vocalizing?
- Are multiple dogs left alone together during the day? If so, how has it been determined which one is barking excessively?
- Has the dog been encouraged to be alert to noises? Has he been "teased" with "Go get the squirrel" kinds of games?
- What kind of fence does the dog have? Does the fence allow the dog to see through to the other side? Is an electronic fence being used?
- Does the dog run along the fence with dogs in the next yard and bark?

Specifics about the occurrence of the problem behavior.
- Does the barking occur only in the owner's absence? If yes:
  — Does it occur every time the dog is alone or with a consistent pattern of absences, such as only in the evening?
  — Does it occur within the first 30 minutes of the owner's departure? (If the owner doesn't know, suggest finding out by videotaping or audiotaping.)

- Does excessive barking occur both when the owner is home and away?
- Does it occur when the owner is home but not supervising the dog?
- Did the beginning of the barking problem correlate with any changes in the family's routine or composition—different work hours, death of a pet, a child going away to college, a move to a new environment, etc.?
- If the barking is intermittent, could it be correlated to the occurrence of anything the dog is afraid of (such as thunder or construction noises) or with other stimuli (such as people walking by or other dogs, squirrels, cats)? If the owner doesn't know, suggest video- or audiotaping.
- If the barking is intermittent, is it correlated with times when the dog has less opportunity for play and physical exercise? If the owner doesn't know, he or she should keep a behavioral log or diary for a few weeks.
- Does the behavior occur only in the owner's presence?
- Does the dog bark at the owner to get her to do things for him or when he is being ignored?
- Does the behavior seem to occur completely at random or unpredictably?
- How often, on average, is the behavior occurring (every day, once a week, once a month)?
- What is the temporal pattern of the barking (e.g., a few barks, quiet, a few barks [constantly repeated]; frantic yapping for several minutes, then a long period of quiet, etc.)?
- Is the dog known to react to squirrels, birds, and other small animals by barking? Is the dog frequently exposed to these stimuli—that is, does he have frequent opportunities to bark at them without interruption?
- In general, does the dog have a fairly low threshold for barking at anything? In other words, is his attitude, "If you don't know what else to do, bark at it"?
- Is the excessive barking triggered by other dogs barking?
- Is the barking occurring shortly before the time the owner generally arrives home?
- Is the barking triggered by the sight of the neighbors or their pets in the adjacent yard? Is the barking dependent on what the neighbors or the animals are doing?
- If outdoors, is the dog barking at the fence, gate, or back of the house?
- Does the dog appear to be barking at nothing?
- Does the barking appear to be somewhat ritualistic (stereotyped) or accompanied by ritualized behaviors such as spinning or whirling?
- Does the dog react to stimuli that typically don't trigger barking, such as pictures on the wall, opening doors, etc.? Does this type of barking continue for long periods? Is it difficult to interrupt?
- Can the owner provide a list of everything that triggers the problem barking, including discrete stimuli, as well as the contexts in which the barking occurs?

Owners' attempts at problem resolution and the dog's response.
- If the barking has been a problem when the dog is left outside alone, has he been left inside instead? If so, has the barking decreased, stayed the same, or worsened? Have other behavior problems occurred when the dog is inside?
- Has the dog been punished for barking?
- Has the dog been hit or verbally scolded?
- Has the dog been given more exercise and playtime?
- Has the dog been seen by a veterinarian since the excessive vocalizing began?

- Has the behavior improved, gotten worse, or stayed the same since the problem began?
- Has any antibark collar or other device been used? If so, what was the result?
- What other things have been done to try to resolve the problem? What were the results?

Differential results of the behavioral history. Answers to the preceding questions will help you identify the cause of the problem.

Separation anxiety. As social animals, dogs will sometimes become anxious or distressed when separated from their owners or other people or animals to whom they are attached. Barking, whining, whimpering, or yelping are possible symptoms of separation anxiety. Destructiveness, attempts to escape, or housesoiling can also occur in response to separation anxiety. If separation anxiety is the cause, the vocalization will occur within the first 30 minutes or so after the owner's departure, it will occur *only* and *consistently* (i.e., every time, not unpredictably) in the owner's absence (or a particular pattern of absences, such as every time the owner leaves for the evening after a workday absence), and it will *not* occur when the owner is home. The dog may appear to be barking at the gate or door through which the owners departed, at the window from where the owners could be seen leaving, or just vocalizing without any apparent stimulus or target.

Dogs with separation anxiety are statistically more likely to be purebreds obtained from humane societies[3]. They are strongly attached to their owners or other family animals, they tend to follow these individuals around when with them, and they may often solicit or "pester" their owners for attention. Frantic greeting behavior, agitation if their owners are out of sight even briefly, and reactions (anxiety, agitation, depression) to their owners' preparations to leave the home are other characteristics of dogs with separation anxiety. A recent change in the dog's ownership, a change in family work schedules, a move to a new home, or the death of another pet or person can all trigger separation anxiety problems. Dogs with separation anxiety may not have been accustomed to being left alone prior to the onset of the problem. This is one of the most common causes of problem vocalizations that occur *only* when dogs are left alone. In summary, excessive vocalization due to separation anxiety:

- Occurs *only* when the dog is separated from the owners or others to whom he is attached
- Can occur inside, outside, or in a vehicle
- Occurs consistently when the owners are gone (or with a specific pattern of absences)
- Begins within the first 30 minutes after departure
- May be accompanied by destructiveness, escape attempts, or elimination
- May be associated with fearful body postures
- May not appear to be directed *at* anything or may be directed toward doors, windows, or gates
- Is associated with other characteristics of separation anxiety

Territorial or protective vocalizations. Dogs may bark, growl, or vocalize in other ways to warn or drive away people or animals whom they view as intruders on their territories. Dog territories can be small (the area around their beds, for example) or large (the entire block) and have nothing to do with the owners' property boundaries. Many dogs consider the car to represent their territory, and they bark and threaten when people approach the vehicle. Children walking to school, delivery people, loose dogs and cats, and even neighbors or dogs in their own yards can all be perceived as territorial intruders and trigger territorial barking. The doorbell or a knock at the door (or even these sounds coming from the TV) or the sound of a car or the sight of its headlights can all be powerful triggers for territorial barking because they so perfectly predict the arrival of an intruder. Dogs may display offensive or defensive threat behavior while engaged in this kind of barking. The barking usually ceases when the stimulus ends or the intruder is "driven off." Owners may contribute to the problem by encouraging the dog to bark or growl at unfamiliar people, animals, or noises. The behavior is also reinforced if the dog believes that it drives away the intruders—as if thinking, "I bark, and the mail carrier leaves!"

These same vocalizations and behaviors can be displayed off the dog's territory if he is being protective of people or other animals to whom he is attached. It must be determined if the dog is trying to protect himself (defensive behavior) or a member of his social group (protective behavior). More often, it is the former, not the latter. I tell owners that it's usually not about *them*, it's about how the dog feels about someone approaching *him*. If a dog is protecting someone, he will put himself between this individual and the one approaching them. Furthermore, the dog will not show protective barking if he is by himself or with an unfamiliar person when someone approaches.

In summary, the following points can be made about territorial or protective barking:

- It usually occurs on or near what the dog perceives to be his property (territorial barking) or in the presence of his social group (protective barking), in the face of a *perceived* threat.
- Territorial barking may occur when the owners are home or away, although it may be less frequent in the owners' presence if they have corrected the dog for the behavior.
- Vocalizations are directed *at* people or other animals.
- The behavior lasts only as long as the eliciting stimulus is present.
- The dog usually displays offensive threats while barking, but he may also be ambivalent or even defensive.

Excitement or greeting vocalizations. Barking, howling, whining, whimpering, yelping, and growling can all occur in the context of greeting people or other dogs or in exciting situations. These vocalizations are frequently shown when owners return home from work or when the dog sees or hears someone she knows. The dog usually appears friendly, playful, or submissive during this kind of barking. The behavior can be exacerbated if the owners or other people encourage this kind of greeting or if the behavior results in pleasant social interaction. Barking for these reasons:

- Is elicited by the approach of a person or another dog
- Is generally accompanied by friendly body postures
- Sometimes may involve other vocalizations and sound as though the dog is in pain (e.g., high-pitched yelps)

Playful vocalizations. During play, dogs emit a variety of vocalizations, such as barking, yelping, whining, whimpering, growling, panting, and tooth snapping. The sounds are either intended to elicit play behavior from a person or other animal or are an integral part of the play sequence itself. For example, a dog may bark or whine to entice a person to play with her, or as two dogs are playing, they may bark, growl, or otherwise vocalize at each other. Friendly and playful postures such as the play bow are often seen during play barking. This kind of barking often happens when dogs are together in a backyard or if they see one another through adjacent fences.

Playful vocalizations:

- Are directed toward people, other animals, or an object such as a ball
- Can occur anytime and anywhere
- Are accompanied by playful body postures

Attention-getting or care-seeking vocalizations. Barking, whining, or whimpering may occur to solicit attention from people or other animals. A dog put outside may whine or bark at the back door because doing so usually results in being let inside. Even negative attention, such as being yelled at, may be perceived by the dog as reinforcing, causing the behavior to continue. Dogs may bark at their owners to get what they want or when they are being ignored. Interestingly, owners often report their dogs begin to bark when they talk on the telephone. Body postures may vary. These kinds of vocalizations are:

- Directed at people or animals or the places where these individuals are (e.g., at the house if the dog is in the yard)
- Heard when the dog is by himself in a particular location but when people or animals are in close proximity (usually not when owners are gone from the home; although dogs can bark to be let inside even when no one is home—my neighbor's dog is a prime example! This type of barking may be related to barking caused by separation anxiety.)
- Accompanied by friendly, submissive, or playful body postures
- Is sometimes associated with other behaviors—jumping up, scratching, digging, pawing, etc.

Fear, distress, or anxiety vocalizations. Dogs who are afraid of specific stimuli (such as thunderstorms, fireworks, or people) may bark, whine, whimper, yelp, scream, pant, or growl in the presence of these stimuli. It is not uncommon, for instance, for dogs to bark or yelp if left out during high winds or thunderstorms or exposed to other stimuli that commonly elicit fearful behavior, such as hot-air balloons, construction equipment, backfiring cars, gunshots, and airplanes. Dogs barking for these reasons will display fearful body postures while doing so or may attempt to leave the area to get away from the feared stimulus. If a dog has several frightening experiences in the same location, such as the backyard, the fear may be generalized and the dog may bark in the yard even when the original fear-eliciting stimulus isn't present. Fear-related vocalizations:

- Are associated (at least initially) with the presence of a fear-producing stimulus
- Are accompanied by other fearful behaviors, such as hiding, avoidance, escape attempts, and fearful body postures
- Can continue for long periods, especially if the behavior has been generalized to the location, in the absence of the stimulus itself

Painful vocalizations. Dogs in pain may whine, whimper, yelp, pant, or scream, depending somewhat on the severity of the discomfort, although dogs in chronic or severe pain may not vocalize at all. Dogs in pain also display characteristic body postures, varying from fearful postures or hiding to attempts to protect the painful area by curling up, not moving, limping, etc. Painful vocalizations can also be elicited by punishment. Painful vocalizations:

- Can occur when the dog is injured or ill
- Can occur in response to some antibark collars, such as the shock collar
- Can occur in response to owner-delivered punishment, such as hitting and kicking
- Are accompanied by fearful or painful body postures

- May be associated with pacing, circling, lethargy, or other behavioral or physical signs of injury or illness

Defensive vocalizations. When dogs are threatened by other dogs or people and attempt to protect themselves, they may bark, whine, whimper, yelp, or growl. In such situations, dogs frequently show defensive body postures: Their ears may be back, their tails may be down, they may exhibit piloerection (have their hackles up), their eyes may be dilated, they may crouch or lean away from the stimulus, and they may show their teeth by horizontal retraction of the lips (see chapter 12). Defensive reactions are a type of agonistic behavior, which will be discussed in chapter 12. Defensive vocalizations:

- Are directed at specific people or animals
- Can be accompanied by defensive threats or aggression
- Are heard only as long as the threatening stimulus is present

Frustration vocalizations. The barks, yelps, whines, or howls of frustration vocalization can occur when the dog is prevented from engaging in a particular behavior or doing what he wants to do. For example, a dog may bark at a squirrel on top of the fence that she cannot reach or at children playing across the street whom she is prevented from joining. Alert body postures are usually seen, and the vocalizations may be accompanied by attempts to engage in the thwarted behavior, such as jumping up, pawing or digging at restraining objects, pacing, or circling. Frustration vocalizations are characterized by:

- Attempts to engage in another behavior or accomplish a certain goal—e.g., digging under the fence to play with another dog or jumping up to catch a squirrel or cat on top of the fence
- Prolonged barking if the dog continues to be thwarted
- A lack of fearful behavior but may be accompanied by a variety of other body postures ranging from threatening to playful

Group-motivated vocalizations. Dogs may bark, howl, whine, whimper, or growl simply because other dogs are doing so. An individual dog may begin barking for any reason, and other dogs nearby may join in. This is the common "neighborhood barkfest" that often is heard in response to sirens or other noises. Although it is not clear why dogs bark at sirens, train whistles, and other high-pitched sounds, many behaviorists believe that these sounds are similar to the long-distance vocalizations that trigger group howling in wolves.

In summary, group vocalizations:

- Occur only in response to vocalizations from other dogs
- May be directed at other animals if they are visible
- May be accompanied by a variety of body postures

Stereotypic behavior. I dislike vague descriptions, but stereotypic barking is genuinely hard to describe. Nonetheless, you know it when you hear it and see the accompanying behaviors. Stereotypic behavior is defined as a repetitive behavior that has a rigidly fixed form, has no apparent purpose, and is not normal behavior for the species as a whole[4]. The dog who is barking stereotypically may appear to be barking at nothing or at a stimulus that normally doesn't trigger barking[2]. Some owners report that these dogs don't seem to be aware of their surroundings. I once saw a sheltie who barked at a picture on the wall (the sheltie is the only breed in which I have seen this type of barking, although I'm sure other behaviorists have encountered it in other breeds, as well). He would jump up and spin as he was doing so, and it was very difficult to interrupt this behavior. The dog would be more likely to do this when he was agitated or excited—when he came back from a walk, after the doorbell rang, etc.

5. Discuss Ways to Manage or Control the Behavior over the Short or Long Term

Management of excessive vocalization problems means finding a way to prevent the barking from occurring or at least preventing it from being a problem for the neighbors. It does not necessarily mean changing the dog's reaction to the stimuli or situations that are triggering the barking; that is more of a problem-resolution approach.

General management procedures—no behavioral diagnosis. As you can see from the previous section, there are many reasons why dogs bark excessively. Without knowing why the dog is barking, it is difficult to make any general statements about management. Note that bark collars should *not* be considered a general management procedure: They should be used only after a behavioral diagnosis has been made. In the absence of a diagnosis, one management option is to house the dog in a different way so that the barking is not a problem. Perhaps the dog could be left inside if the barking occurs outside. If, however, the barking is a problem when the dog is inside, as it might be in an apartment or condominium, management becomes more difficult. In that situation, owners might leave the dog with someone else while they are away from home or use a doggie day care service until the problem can be diagnosed and treated.

Another management principle is to prevent the dog from experiencing the stimuli that trigger the barking. A behavioral diagnosis may be necessary to do so. Practically, this may result in housing changes similar to those already mentioned.

Management procedures based on a diagnosis.

Separation anxiety. This type of barking is motivated by anxiety, so management requires keeping the dog from becoming anxious. Specifically, this means not leaving him alone long enough to trigger the anxiety. Options include:

- Using a doggie day care service, day boarding at a kennel or veterinary clinic, letting him stay with friends or family who are home all day, or allowing him to accompany the owner
- Leaving the dog inside during the day if he has been barking outside, but this may backfire. Some dogs remain anxious even if left inside, and if that is the case, they may continue barking, be destructive, or housesoil. If you suggest an owner try this approach, caution him or her to do so for very short periods initially to see how the dog responds.
- Working with a veterinarian to provide medication on a short-term basis to decrease the dog's anxiety. Medication alone should not be viewed as a long-term solution for separation anxiety problems (see chapter 18).

Territorial or protective. Managing territorial behavior means preventing the dog from being exposed to those stimuli that trigger the territorial reaction. This might require not allowing the dog to see out the window, keeping the dog inside if the behavior is triggered when he is in the yard, or building him a run or putting up a visual barrier of some sort so that he can't see people passing by, instead of allowing him access to the fence. If the behavior happens at the door, the dog can be confined in another room before the owner answers the doorbell or before the doorbell rings if visitors are expected.

Managing a protectively or territorially barking dog in the car may be accomplished by crating him so he can't see outside. Managing the behavior on walks may be more difficult and may require walking the dog in an isolated location, changing direction when approached by another person, or even muzzling the dog. A head collar may also be a good management, as well as treatment, tool.

Excitement or greeting. Managing this type of barking depends on what stimuli are actually triggering the problem. If greeting is the primary trigger, arrivals can be kept very low-key to prevent the dog from becoming excited. Perhaps the dog can be taken to a different location immediately on the owner's arrival (e.g., inside) so any barking that does occur will not disturb the neighbors. The dog could also be housed in a quieter environment, away from whatever triggers the excited barking.

Play. If the barking is occurring when two dogs are playing together, they could temporarily be housed separately when the owner is away. If the dogs are barking over toys or bones, the owner could either remove these items when the barking can't be controlled or provide so many (e.g., a dozen balls) that possession of one becomes unimportant.

Attention getting or care seeking. In the short term, management of this type of barking would involve avoiding situations in which the dog has the opportunity to set up the behavioral trap of forcing the owner to pay attention to him to quiet the barking. For example, if the dog barks to be let inside, the owner should let him in *before* he starts barking. If the dog barks while the owner is on the phone, he can be given something to chew prior to the phone call or he could be confined away from the owner.

Fear, distress, or anxiety. As with all fear-related problems, management of this type of barking means either not putting the dog in the situation that triggers the fear or decreasing his fearful behavior with short-term medication prescribed by a veterinarian.

Pain. In virtually all cases of barking caused by pain, there should be no difference between treatment and management: The source of the pain must be eliminated. If the pain is a result of punishment, this should be stopped, and other ways to deal with the misbehavior should be identified. The owner should have the dog checked by a veterinarian if the source of pain cannot be identified. If the source can't be eliminated because of a chronic or terminal condition, then the owner should work with a veterinarian to provide an analgesic or other appropriate medication.

Defensive. Management options for defensive barking are similar to those for territorial or protective barking. Once the stimuli that trigger the defensive reaction have been identified, the dog's environment could be changed to isolate him from such situations.

Frustration. Management approaches for frustration barking focus on isolating the dog from the source of frustration or removing the source. Squirrels or cats might be discouraged by the use of motion detectors. One type emits loud noises and has a flashing light; another activates a garden hose when triggered (see product appendix).

Group-motivated. Unless the owner can find a neighborhood without other barking dogs (which, of course, is not very realistic), the dog may need to be left inside or somewhere else where his barking won't be triggered by the barking of other dogs.

Stereotypic behavior. Stereotypic barking can be managed by isolating the dog from the stimuli that trigger the behavior (if they can be identified) or using medication (see chapter 18).

A discussion of antibark collars. In recent years, a number of remote and automatic devices have become available to punish a dog when he barks or vocalizes. Most take the form of a collar with a sensor that responds to the vibration from the dog's vocal chords. Older or less expensive models that use a microphone to pick up the sound of the dog's bark should not be used because they can be activated by other environmental sounds, including the barking of other dogs. When operating and used correctly, antibark collars meet most of the criteria for effective punishment: They deliver immediate, consistent, and remote punishment, and the aversive stimulus occurs only momentarily. Whether the aversive stimulus is of the appropriate intensity (that is, if it stops behavior quickly without provoking fear or aggressive responses) will depend on the stimulus used and the individual dog.

The aversive stimuli the collars produce are either shock (which the collar should be able to deliver at varying intensities), an ultrasonic or audible noise, or a spray of citronella oil that is released under the dog's chin. In my experience:

- Shock collars are almost always aversive enough to stop the behavior, but there are exceptions. Fearful and aggressive reactions are common.
- Ultrasonic or audible-noise collars may be aversive to some dogs but not to others; further, even if these collars are aversive initially, many dogs habituate or adapt to the noise they deliver and resume barking.
- Citronella collars are usually effective; in fact, they are probably as effective as shock collars and are generally more acceptable to owners (and to me!).

One study[5] found that in a sample of nine dogs, the citronella collar was more effective than the TriTronics Bark Diminisher shock collar (see product appendix). Owners in the study also found the citronella collar to be more acceptable and humane than the shock collar. In my experience, shock collars elicit more fearful and aggressive behavior than do the citronella collars. In fact, I have seen dogs become afraid of their own backyards (either in the short or long term) subsequent to use of the shock collar, and I have also seen this type of collar cause dogs to attack other family dogs when the shock was delivered. If shock is to be used, a variable-intensity collar should be selected so that the intensity of the shock can be adjusted according to the dog's reaction.

A unique remote device is the Super Barker Breaker by Amtek (see product appendix). This device contains both a microphone and electronics tuned to the sound of the dog's bark, and it automatically emits a high-pitched sound similar to that of a smoke alarm. Unfortunately, the device sometimes activates in response to other noises, as well. The device will reset and can be triggered repeatedly. It can also be activated manually, via a push button.

Punishment devices should not be used for any vocalization problem motivated by fear or anxiety. Not only would this be cruel, it would also be likely to create additional problems even if the vocalizations are decreased. Any such device should not be the first or only technique used to resolve the barking problem.

Of course, there are exceptions to every rule. I once worked with a cocker spaniel who had a separation anxiety problem manifested by excessive barking. The owner had been crating the dog because of previous elimination problems, as well. A counterconditioning and desensitization program was implemented for the separation anxiety, and medication was administered as a short-term therapy. After the crating was discontinued on my recommendation, housesoiling was not a problem and the dog did improve, but the barking still continued at levels sufficient enough to annoy neighbors in the owner's condominium. Reluctantly, I agreed to try the citronella collar because the owner was either going to move or give up her dog if the problem persisted. I asked the owner to videotape the dog to better monitor his reaction. In previous videotaping sessions, we had discovered that the more the dog barked, the more anxious he became, which only increased the barking. Thus, it seemed the barking itself was not only a symptom of the problem but also a contributing factor. Our second round of videotaping revealed that use of the citronella collar stopped the barking, and the dog became calmer. He was still restless and could be seen pacing from time to time on the tape, but his anxiety declined to a manageable level for both his own and his owner's well-being.

Keep in mind that there was a direct rationale for using the collar in that case and that it was used in conjunction with behavior modification techniques and medication.

6. Explain the Goals of an Appropriate Behavior Modification Plan

Because the causes of barking behavior are so varied, the treatment or behavior modification plans you develop must be based on the behavioral diagnosis. If they are not, you will likely make recommendations that are irrelevant or ineffective or that create other problems. If you don't have a diagnosis or haven't determined the cause of the problem, then either take the time to do so or refer the case. Once again, I would stress that antibark devices should *not* be recommended without a behavioral diagnosis.

Separation anxiety. If excessive barking is caused by separation anxiety, the dog's anxiousness in response to being left alone needs to be decreased. If the dog is barking due to separation anxiety when left alone outside, it is possible he may not be anxious if left inside. However, if the problem persists inside, the following type of treatment will be needed. Counterconditioning and desensitization procedures (see chapter 3) are necessary, since the problem is essentially based in fear. Techniques to make the dog less demanding of attention from the owner may also be helpful. Treatment has nothing to do with dominance issues, giving the dog more exercise, or providing more toys. Sample steps in a treatment program will be described. *Please note that these procedures do not represent a complete treatment plan, as there are always nuances and differences in each case that will require additional steps or modifications of generally recommended procedures. Failure to implement a complete plan correctly will result in ineffective treatment or even an exacerbation of the problem. The behavior modification procedures for separation anxiety problems are tedious, so these cases require significant client follow-up. Consider these factors as you decide whether to make treatment recommendations yourself or refer the case.*

- The owner can make the departure cues less predictive for the dog and therefore less likely to elicit anxiety by repeating discrete behaviors (picking up keys, approaching the door, putting on shoes, etc.) without leaving. Many repetitions may be necessary (up to 10 or more per day over a period of weeks or months) to counteract the existing predictive value of these cues. Behaviorists vary as to whether the dog should be ignored (habituation), given a treat at the onset of the departure cue (counterconditioning), or required to lie down quietly (countercommanding).

- In the meantime, the owner should vary the sequence of her actual departure routine (e.g., rather than getting dressed and eating breakfast, eat first and then dress) and do as much preparation as possible the night before or well in advance of a departure. She should not pay a lot of attention to the dog during her normal departure routine, as this only serves to focus the dog on her and make her absence more distressing.

- The owner should accustom the dog to being left alone for brief periods so that a nonanxious response can be elicited. Some behaviorists recommend pairing these brief absences with a pleasant stimulus (food, a toy, etc.); others do not. The pleasant stimulus becomes the cue that the absence will be brief, and it should *not* be used for longer absences[3]. If the owner is already in the habit of giving the dog a treat when she leaves for a prolonged absence, this and similar treats should be avoided during these practice sessions. Other behaviorists use a counter-commanding procedure and have the dog lie down quietly as the owner leaves briefly. The length of the absence is completely dependent on the dog's response—the owner must return before the dog becomes anxious. In some cases, this means returning in seconds; in others, it can mean returning in several minutes. Giving departure cues prior to these absences should be avoided. The length of the absences should then be gradually increased, on an unpredictable schedule.

- As the dog's reaction to the departure cues improves and he can tolerate absences of 20 minutes or so, a cue can be combined with a briefer (say, a 10-minute) absence. Longer absences should then be gradually preceded by more cues until this practice procedure is similar to the owner's normal routine.
- The owner should work on out-of-sight stays to prevent the dog from following her around the house and encourage him to be more relaxed out of her presence. The dog can be taught to lie down and stay in return for a tidbit (which should be given as the owner walks away from the dog, not on returning), with the duration of the stay and the time out of sight being very brief at first and increased incrementally. During training, the owner should be in sight/out of sight repeatedly. Initially, the out-of-sight time should be extremely brief. The dog should be calm enough to eat the tidbit; if he is not, the owner should stay in close proximity until he is able to do so.
- Arrivals and departures should be quiet and calm affairs, with no long speeches made to the dog on leaving and no excited greetings on returning.
- The owner should not pet or interact with the dog when he demands it but instead require the dog to wait, obey a command, or become calm and relaxed before receiving attention. This can be accomplished by ignoring the dog until he lies down and stops pestering. This does not, however, mean that the owner should completely ignore the dog for months at a time, as some popular litera-ture has suggested.
- The dog's anxiety response *must* be prevented during treatment, using one or more of the management procedures previously discussed.

Territorial or protective. The goal of treatment for territorial or protective barking is to change the dog's territorial reaction to passersby. (Also see chapter 12.) The dog should eventu-ally react to people in at least a neutral way and ideally in a positive, welcoming manner. In other words, if he no longer views people as territorial intruders, he will have no need to bark threat-eningly at them. Instead, he will view passersby as folks he's glad to see because they cause good things to happen for him. Though he may still bark a bit in anticipation, the behavior should be substantially lessened, and he will no longer appear dangerous.

Achieving this requires a counterconditioning and desensitization program (see chapters 3 and 11), and it may require the judicious use of punishment, usually remote, as well as counter-commanding. In some cases, a head halter such as a Gentle Leader can have a calming effect on the dog, and use of such a devise may make counterconditioning easier. An example of a behavioral starting point for such a program, in the backyard, might be to allow the dog to see the "intruder" at a distance, before the barking begins. As soon as the individual comes into view, the dog can be given a tasty treat (the "intruder" predicts the goodie, classical condition-ing). The treatment can gradually progress in incremental steps until the dog is quietly antici-pating a treat from the visitor who is near the fence. This change in response may require many repetitions to be successful. In some cases, the desensitization component (gradual exposure) may not be practical, and counterconditioning alone may be used (the intruder gives the treat regardless of the dog's behavior). This means that the dog will likely, in the initial stages of treatment, receive a treat while he is barking. This should not serve as positive reinforcement for the barking because classical conditioning is occurring—the dog is learning the person will provide him with a treat, which changes the dog's "attitude" from a territorial response to a more tolerant, quiet one (refer to chapters 3, 11, and 12). The success of this type of approach is dependent on making an accurate behavioral diagnosis, having a thorough understanding of the learning principles involved, doing adequate follow-up on the case to ensure correct implementation, and having many different people providing treats so the dog can generalize the response.

If you don't feel comfortable devising a plan using these techniques, you should refer the case. Antibark devices, especially those involving shock, should be used with extreme caution because they can trigger additional aggressive behavior. During treatment, it is beneficial to keep the dog away from situations that trigger the territorial response, as this interferes with the learning of new responses.

If the territorial barking problem occurs as someone comes to the door when the owner is home, the following sequence can be used. Suggest that the owner:

- Allow the dog a small but consistent number of barks (three or four) or a consistent amount of time to bark (a few seconds).
- Immediately give the dog a command, such as "Quiet!" This may need to be a new word if the dog has learned to ignore previous commands.
- Immediately follow this command with a startling noise, such as a blast from an air horn.
- When the dog momentarily stops barking, call him away from the door or even to another room (using a leash if necessary at first), require him to sit, and reinforce him with a special tidbit.
- The dog can then either be required to stay or be released. If he resumes barking, repeat the sequence. Ultimately, the dog should give a few alerting barks, stop barking, and then run to the owner for his reinforcement.

For more information on territorial behavior, see chapter 12 on aggression in dogs. If the barking also involves additional threats and aggression, appropriate precautions discussed in that chapter must be taken.

Excitement or greeting. To solve this type of barking, greeting routines need to be changed in two respects. First, the barking should not be reinforced by giving the dog attention or social interaction while he is barking. Second, quiet behavior needs to be taught through either counterconditioning or countercommanding. If the barking occurs only during greetings at the end of the day when the owner arrives home, requiring the dog to wear an antibark collar throughout the day is excessive. However, if the dog is excited throughout the day, an antibark device may be appropriate. Management procedures can also be used to modify the environment so that the dog doesn't become excessively excited.

Play. To minimize playful barking, the owner should provide or encourage alternative outlets for play that do not trigger barking or other vocalizations. For example, the dogs might be provided with interactive toys (see product appendix), which may decrease the time spent in wrestling with each other that includes barking. Noisy play when the owner is home can be dealt with by ending the opportunity to play, but this approach will not, of course, work when the dogs are home alone, as they will quickly learn that such opportunities will not be taken away when the owner is not present. Ultimately, it may be difficult to change a dog's natural play patterns.

As mentioned in the section on management procedures, the dogs could be kept in separate areas when the owner is gone if barking is a problem. Antibark devices could also be considered, but it is wise to introduce the dogs to them when they are not together, as those that employ shock can trigger aggressive responses and potentially initiate fighting between the dogs. The citronella antibark collar, I believe, is a safer option (see later section for an explanation of the device). My Dalmatian Ashley is very vocal during play, and I have successfully used a citronella collar to stop her barking when she is left alone outside with our other dog, Mocha.

Attention-getting or care-seeking. The goal in treating any attention-getting problem is to identify how the behavior (in this case, the barking) is being reinforced and to modify the interactional pattern so that barking no longer works for the dog. From the dog's point of view, verbal scolding has become a positive reinforcement for the behavior because it involves attention from the owner; it is not perceived as punishment, as the owner intended.

Many dogs will bark when their owners converse with visitors to the home and they are being ignored. With cooperative visitors (or in situations purposely designed as sessions to work on the problem), the dog's barking can be ignored until it stops (extinction). Patience is required (and possibly a set of earplugs!). Expect the dog to engage in other annoying behaviors for a time, which is a result of the extinction process (as explained in chapter 3). Negative punishment in the form of walking away from the dog can also be used. This is negative punishment because it removes something desirable (the opportunity to be with the owner).

Alternatively, the dog can be operantly reinforced to receive the attention he wants only when he is quiet and engaging in other appropriate behavior. Remote positive punishment, such as a loud noise, may be helpful to interrupt the behavior so that countercommanding can proceed. Positive reinforcement can be used by paying attention to the dog any time he is quiet.

Fear, distress, or anxiety. To handle problems stemming from fear, distress, or anxiety, you must first identify the specific stimulus that is causing the dog's fear and then implement a desensitization and counterconditioning plan to decrease it (see chapters 3 and 11 for details). Management procedures (described previously) should be implemented in the meantime, as ongoing fear responses will significantly interfere with treatment. If you do not feel confident devising a step-by-step counterconditioning and desensitization plan, refer the case to someone else. If you cannot identify the fear-eliciting stimulus, either the problem has been misdiagnosed, the owner needs to do some detective work, or you should refer the case. In some cases, psychotropic medication can be helpful as a short-term therapy (see chapter 18).

Pain. The treatment for barking caused by pain is no different from the management of this problem: The source of the pain must be identified and removed. Any punishment techniques that are triggering the vocalizations should be halted. If the dog appears to be in pain for unidentified reasons, he should be taken to a veterinarian for a thorough evaluation and any necessary medication or other treatment.

Defensive. Counterconditioning and desensitization techniques will probably be needed to change the dog's defensive reaction to either a neutral or a friendly one, using procedures similar to those described in the section on territorial barking. If the dog is defensive because of a lack of socialization, socialization experiences should be created (see chapter 4) through which the dog can interact with people positively and without barking. During treatment, the dog's environment should be modified so that the defensive barking is not elicited. Because defensive behavior is usually a combination of fear and threats, punishment or the use of antibark devices is usually not indicated in such cases. The techniques discussed in chapter 12 for dealing with defensive aggression may also be required. In addition, psychotropic medication may be helpful over the short term (see chapter 18).

Frustration. To treat frustration barking, the source of the frustration must first be identified. After that, management options such as changing the dog's environment to prevent the frustration should be implemented. Antibark devices or other remote punishment can also be considered. The dog's environment can be enriched to encourage alternative behaviors. If the behavior is occurring in the owner's presence, the conditioning sequence outlined in the section on territorial barking at the door can be implemented.

Group-motivated. If the barking is occurring in the owner's presence, the conditioning sequence presented in the section on territorial barking at the door can be implemented. Management procedures may also need to be incorporated in the treatment plan; these might include modifying the dog's environment to shield him from hearing other dogs or using an antibark device (perhaps for all the other neighborhood dogs as well!).

Stereotypic behavior. Treating stereotypies can be tricky. They can be a conflict behavior, so the first step is to determine if a conflict exists for the dog in the context in which he barks (see chapter 11). If the behavior is triggered in high-arousal situations, the dog can be taught quiet, calm behavior using a combination of desensitization and countercommanding techniques. This means first teaching a behavior such as a quiet down-stay, using positive reinforcement, when the dog isn't aroused. The same behavior is then encouraged and reinforced in situations that gradually become more like the eliciting contexts. Punishment may not be appropriate, as it can create further conflict or arousal and may actually exacerbate the problem. The treatment of stereotypies often requires medication (see chapter 18).

SUMMARY

Perhaps the biggest challenges in working with a barking problem are, first, diagnosing it because of the many possible causes and, second, convincing an owner to invest the time and effort required to determine the best method of treatment, rather than immediately demanding a quick fix. Although antibark collars, especially the citronella type, are very beneficial when indicated, owners usually need assistance from someone knowledgeable about animal behavior to help them make the best decision about treatment. Because animal control officers so often become involved in barking complaints, they can provide a valuable service by helping owners find this assistance, or they can provide it themselves. Veterinarians, dog trainers, behavior consultants, and other professionals should work with animal control agencies to help owners find appropriate solutions.

REFERENCES

1. Beaver, B.V. 1994. Owner complaints about canine behavior. *JAVMA* 204:1953–5.

2. Juarbe-Diaz, S.V. 1997. Assessment and treatment of excessive barking in the domestic dog. *Vet. Clinics of North Amer. [Small Anim. Pract.]* 27 (3):515–32.

3. Voith, V.L., and P.L. Borchelt. 1996. Separation anxiety in dogs. In *Readings in companion animal behavior*, ed. V.L. Voith and P.L. Borchelt, 127–39. Trenton, N.J.: Veterinary Learning Systems.

4. Immelmann, K., and C. Beer. 1989. *A dictionary of ethology*. Cambridge, Mass.: Harvard University Press.

5. Juarbe-Diaz, S.V., and K.A. Houpt. 1996. Comparison of two antibarking collars for the treatment of nuisance barking. *J. Am. Anim. Hosp. Assoc.* 32:231–5.

CHAPTER 11

Fears and Phobias in Dogs

This chapter is organized somewhat differently than most of the others dedicated to specific problems. With housesoiling, destructiveness, escaping, and so forth, it is important to know the cause or understand why the dog is engaging in these behaviors before implementing a behavior modification plan: Providing the dog with more toys, for example, will not help destructive behavior motivated by separation anxiety. In other words, for these types of problems, the plan must be relevant to the cause of the problem. When it comes to fears and phobias, however, causes are somewhat irrelevant. It doesn't really matter whether the dog is afraid of something because of a genetic predisposition, a traumatic experience, a lack of socialization, or a combination of these factors. The problem will be treated similarly regardless of what caused the dog to become fearful[1].

However, there are two other reasons why identifying the cause of a fear-related problem is important. The first is prognosis. If a dog was inadequately socialized, the resulting behavioral deficits can't be completely overcome, as J.P. Scott and J.L. Fuller demonstrated over 40 years ago[2]. In addition, some animals' genetic tendencies result in inherently fearful personalities or temperaments. It has been shown experimentally that it is possible to selectively breed for fearful temperaments or for a low threshold for fearful behavior[3]. If the fear-related problem is caused by a lack of socialization, genetic tendencies, or both, there is probably a limit as to how much improvement can be made. The second reason why it is important to identify the cause of a fear-related behavior is to become aware of any ongoing traumatic experiences resulting from abuse, mishandling, inappropriate use of punishment, etc., so that steps can be taken to put a stop to these procedures.

To better understand the causes of fear-related problems as well as the basic biology and physiology of fearful behavior, I encourage you to do some additional reading[1,4,5].

It is most important in working with fear-related problems to identify the triggering stimuli, whether they be thunder or other startling noises, men, children, hot-air balloons, or some other common or uncommon source. I've worked with animals who had some odd triggers–dogs who were afraid to go up stairs, dogs who were afraid of the dark, a dog who was afraid of her owner's snoring, a cat who was afraid of a new ceiling fan in the kitchen. These could be called types of fears—fear of men, fear of thunder, fear of children, etc. In reality, there are an infinite number of types of fears, but all are most often treated using counterconditioning and desensitization. Flooding is another technique that is sometimes used to treat fears, but it has some significant disadvantages. These techniques will be explained in the section on behavior modification plans later in the chapter.

Because of the different method of categorizing fear-based behaviors, this chapter's protocol will not include differential management and treatment goals based on the potential cause of the fear (as defined earlier). Instead, it will give examples of treatment procedures for different *types* of fear. The behavioral history questions will focus on identifying the *triggers* for the fear rather than on its cause, as well as the specific behavioral manifestations of fear and related behaviors.

PROTOCOL

The protocol for fear-related problems differs from the protocols for other problems because of the focus on types of fear rather than causes. Fear-related behaviors must also be identified.

1. Obtain a Description of the Problem Behavior

Fear, as defined in Box 11.1, can be manifested through many different behaviors, and it has emotional, physiological, and behavioral components[6]. Generally speaking, the behavioral manifestations of fear are most readily observable and relevant to treating fear-related problems. However, physiological measures such as heart rate can also be valuable in measuring the success of treatment, as well as determining a starting point for a behavior modification program.

> **Box 11.1 Glossary**
>
> **Anxiety:** anticipation of a danger or threat; its source may or may not be identifiable. Anxious behavior may be displayed in the absence of a specific eliciting stimulus.
>
> **Counterconditioning:** teaching (conditioning) the animal to associate a stimulus that previously predicted something "bad" to instead predict something "good"
>
> **Displacement behaviors:** behaviors that occur when an animal is thwarted, in a conflict situation, or anxious. They are irrelevant to the situation or out of context.
>
> **Fear:** a normal, whole-body response to a perceived threatening stimulus that has physiological, emotional, and behavioral components. It is associated with specific triggering stimuli.
>
> **Flooding:** a behavior modification technique requiring prolonged exposure to the feared stimulus until the fearful response terminates
>
> **Phobia:** a fear response that is persistent, maladaptive, and out of proportion to the situation
>
> **Stereotypy:** a ritualized, repetitive behavior that has no apparent goal or function and is not part of the normal behavior pattern of the species
>
> **Systematic desensitization:** exposing the animal to a low-intensity version of a stimulus and gradually increasing the stimulus intensity

Fearful behaviors. When owners describe their dogs as being afraid, it is important to ask exactly what the dog is doing. Common behavioral manifestations of fear are listed in Box 11.2. Some of these behaviors can also be manifestations of submission (body postures) or of pain or

---

Box 11.2 Behavioral manifestations of fear

Body postures
- Ears down or back
- Tail down or tucked
- Head held low
- Body crouched or curled up
- Rolled over on back
- Exposed inguinal area

Vocalizations
- Barking
- Whining
- Whimpering
- Yelping
- Growling

Other manifestations
- Dilated eyes
- Hiding
- Shaking
- Drooling
- Panting
- Avoidance (fleeing, escaping)
- Destructive behavior (which is often manifested as attempts to escape or avoidance)
- Pacing
- Freezing
- Threats or aggression
- Urination or defecation
- Expression of anal sacs
- Footpad sweating
- Shedding hair

---

physical discomfort (drooling, panting, shaking), so additional information regarding the context in which the behavior is occurring should be obtained.

Phobic behavior. As defined in Box 11.1, phobic behavior is fearful behavior that is out of proportion to the situation, occurs persistently, and is maladaptive[1]. Normal fearful behavior can be beneficial because animals can avoid or be cautious about approaching unfamiliar stimuli that may be harmful. Phobic behavior is not helpful because it prevents the animal from functioning normally and can actually result in harm. Based on this definition, separation anxiety might more accurately be termed *separation phobia*. Dogs suffering from thunderphobia (brontophobia) or other noise phobias often hurt themselves as they try to escape the sound or find what they consider to be a safe place. I've seen dogs who have broken their teeth chewing on metal doorknobs, cut themselves jumping through windows and screens, and injured themselves jumping off balconies during thunderstorms or in response to the sound of fireworks. Although I have no statistical evidence of this, it is my opinion that these severe, intense reactions are much more difficult to change than normal fearful reactions. It's surprising to me how often the owner's primary reaction to such a problem is anger if the dog has destroyed something during one of these episodes, rather than sympathy for the dog and what it must be like for him to be in such a panicked state.

Recognizing anxious, stereotypic, and displacement behaviors. Anxiety is difficult to define (see Box 11.1). Anxiety is an anticipatory response to a fear-producing event[6], such as a dog's reaction to the owner's departure cues prior to leaving the house. A thunderphobic dog may become anxious every summer afternoon in anticipation of a storm. Anxiety can be associated with any number of stimuli, such as anticipation of feared noises, chronic conflicts or harassment from other family pets, anticipation of the owner leaving, or contexts in which unpleasant things have occurred previously. Anxious behaviors can be early warning signs of more intense fearful behaviors to come. They are thus important in determining when the problem behavior actually begins and what triggers it.

Anxiety may have some of the same behavioral manifestations as fear, such as pacing, but it may be manifest in other ways as well. Self-injurious behaviors such as hair pulling and excessive licking can be motivated by anxiety, and these can become stereotypic behaviors. Stereotypies, also sometimes referred to as compulsive behavior (the *obsessive* part of the term associated with human disorders—*obsessive-compulsive behavior*—is anthropomorphic when applied to animals because we can't know if the animal is obsessing), are ritualized, repetitive behaviors that have no apparent goal or function and are not part of the normal behavior pattern of the species. Thus, the thunderphobic dog can develop a lick granuloma as the result of stereotypic licking.

Box 11.3 An ethological view of calming signals

"Calming signals," as described by T. Rugaas[8], supposedly calm and reassure other dogs. In reality, these signals are a mixture of many types of behavior, mostly submissive or appeasement behaviors (see chapter 12) and displacement behavior, which was defined in this chapter. Appeasement behaviors in dogs include:

- Avoiding direct eye contact
- Turning the head to the side and away from another individual
- Turning the side of the body to another individual rather than facing him head on
- Grinning by retracting the lips vertically and exposing the front teeth (this is not to be confused with baring the teeth as a threat)
- Rolling over on the back to expose the inguinal area

Appeasement behaviors definitely have a communicative or signaling function. The dog is indicating she is not a challenge or a threat to the other individual and that she is willing to give in or defer to the other dog.

There is no scientific evidence, however, that displacement behaviors in dogs such as yawning, lip licking, and grooming have communicative value. If they did, because they indicate the dog is in conflict or anxious, it would seem this is what would be communicated. In other words, if displacement behaviors do communicate something to other individuals, they would most likely signal anxiousness and therefore make the other dogs anxious as well. Neither this effect nor the supposed "calming" effect of displacement behaviors on other dogs have been scientifically or objectively documented.

Anxiety can also be triggered when a dog is in conflict about how to respond in a given situation. For example, a dog may be unsure of how the owner wants him to behave, and he anticipates being punished for an incorrect response. If he can't decide how to react, he may engage in a displacement behavior such as grooming. Displacement behaviors[7] are those that are irrelevant to a situation and can occur in a variety of contexts, including aggressive encounters, when an animal is thwarted from achieving a goal, or in a training context when he is unsure of whether a particular behavior will be reinforced or punished. A common example is the dog who is told to come and, while on the way to his owner, has to stop and scratch himself. He may be anxious and unsure of what response he'll receive from his owner, and he displays that anxiety through displacement grooming. Other examples of displacement behaviors in dogs are lip licking, yawning, excessive self-grooming, sniffing the ground, and even sleeping[1]. Popular literature has labeled some of these and other behaviors as "calming signals"[8] and has somewhat misinterpreted them (see Box 11.3).

Determining the eliciting stimuli. The concepts discussed in the last section can be very important, first, in identifying a problem as fear-related and, second, in determining the triggering stimuli. For example, if there are conflicts between two dogs in the house, in which one dog is harassing the other, the second dog may begin to lick himself excessively even when the other dog is not bothering him. This licking is an anxious behavior because the dog may be anticipating the next bout of harassment. If you were unaware of the concepts discussed in the previous section, you might not recognize that the licking was related to the harassment. Examples of chronic stressors or fear-eliciting stimuli that can trigger anxiety problems are listed in Box 11.4.

Box 11.4 Examples of common conflict- or anxiety-producing situations

- Excessive confinement (crating, chaining, or tying the dog out)
- Addition or loss of other family pets
- Barren, impoverished, or restricted environments
- Social isolation
- Unpredictable, changeable daily routines (unfamiliar people in and out of the house frequently, owner's changing routines, repeated moves to new environment)
- Noncontingent punishment
- Inconsistent social interactions involving punishment (sitting in the owner's lap is acceptable one time but the next time results in severe punishment)
- Social conflicts or continued harassment between family pets
- Chronic exposure to fear-producing stimuli (e.g., thunderstorms every afternoon, sound of airplanes taking off and landing when dog's house is near the airport)

Other examples of cases in which early signs of fear are manifested include the thunderphobic dog who initially paces restlessly as the clouds move in and ultimately escalates to destructive behavior when he hears the thunder. Similarly, a dog who is fearful of men may yawn (a displacement behavior) as a man approaches and escalate to snapping when the man reaches toward him. It is crucial to identify what triggers the earliest sign of fear or anxiety, as this will help you determine the appropriate starting point for behavior modification procedures.

2. Evaluate Potential Medical Causes for the Problem Behavior

As mentioned, some of the manifestations of fear, both physiological and behavioral, can also be signs of illness or disease. Especially if the fearful behavior is of sudden onset, the dog should be thoroughly evaluated by a veterinarian before assuming the problem is behavioral. A dog can also become fearful when he can't see or hear well, common conditions in geriatric dogs, so sensory function should be evaluated as well. Stereotypies involving excessive auto-grooming should be thoroughly evaluated for medical causes such as allergies, skin infections, or other systemic disorders before presuming them to be caused by fear or anxiety.

3. Educate Owners About the Problem Behavior

Educate the owners about anthropomorphic and other misinterpretations. Owners usually don't have a problem recognizing a fearful dog when they see one (for exceptions to this statement, see later section), but they may have trouble attributing the *results* of behavior to fear. In other words, when people come home to the results of destructive or housesoiling behavior or if they find their dog has left the yard, their first thought is usually *not* "This happened because the dog was afraid or anxious." They may instead explain such behaviors using anthropomorphic interpretations (assuming the dog is mad at them, etc.). Refer to the appropriate chapters for assistance in determining whether these problem behaviors are caused by fear or some other motivation.

There are widespread misconceptions among dog owners, as well as some animal professionals, about how fear and aggression relate to one another. In my experience, many cases of fear-motivated aggression are misdiagnosed as either dominance issues or some other type of aggressive behavior (see chapter 12). Body postures, as well as the context in which the behavior occurs, are important clues in arriving at a diagnosis.

Another widespread belief, which I hear almost every day, is that fearful dogs who have been adopted from previous homes or shelters have been abused. Quite often, when an animal exhibits an unexplained fearful reaction to a harmless stimulus, people jump to the conclusion that the dog was mistreated at an earlier point. Although this may occasionally have happened, I doubt that it is as prevalent as most people believe. In fact, there are several alternative explanations for these fearful reactions. First, the dog may not have been well socialized. Dogs who have not had a variety of pleasant experiences with different places, people, and things during the sensitive period for socialization (see chapter 4) may react with fear to anything out of the ordinary, and it is difficult for poorly socialized dogs to be at ease with unfamiliar things.

Second, some dogs seem to be innately predisposed to be afraid of certain stimuli. These include certain behaviors from *conspecifics* (an ethological term for peers), as well as startling noises, including thunder[1]. Similarly, many dogs seem to be afraid of behaviors exhibited by men (speaking in a deep voice, making abrupt movements) even though they have never had a traumatic experience with a male human.

Third, fears can be classically conditioned (see chapter 3), resulting in fearful responses to what should be neutral stimuli. For example, if a dog was frightened by a clap of thunder at the same time someone rattled a newspaper, the dog may then fear the newspaper rattling even if such a coincidence occurred only once.

Educate the owners about myths regarding problem solving and techniques to avoid. Owners often ask if their dogs will "grow out of" fear-related problems. Although dogs sometimes can *habituate* (stop responding after repeated exposures without any positive or negative consequences) to a fear-producing stimulus, this usually only happens with mild fears. When fearful behaviors do habituate, it has nothing to do with maturation (outgrowing the fear); instead, it is the result of the repeated exposures that have had neutral outcomes.

Another common misconception about the treatment of fears involves a misunderstanding of the concept of socialization. Some believe that forcing the dog to experience what she is afraid of and showing her it won't hurt her will help her overcome her fear. Thus, an owner is often told to take a fearful dog to unfamiliar places and have unfamiliar people pet her, even if she is shaking in fear or trying to avoid them the entire time. There are several ways this approach can go wrong. First, if the dog is taken to public places and walked around while in a fearful state and then taken home while still afraid, nothing good has been accomplished. The dog's fear was not decreased or dissipated, and from the dog's point of view, her fearful behaviors may actually have worked for her—i.e., they kept her safe and resulted in being taken out of the fearful environment. Moreover, nothing pleasant happened to her. This type of procedure is often erroneously referred to as either desensitization or socialization.

True socialization should involve pleasant experiences that don't elicit fear, and desensitization (which will be discussed more fully) should involve a gradual process of exposing the dog to modified or less intense versions of the things she fears in such a way that fear is never elicited. Neither of these requirements is met in the example just mentioned.

Punishing the dog for being afraid, even if his fear is manifested as threatening or aggressive behavior, is not going to be helpful. Punishment will not make the dog less afraid, which is a requirement of successful treatment. In fact, it may have the opposite effect.

Crating or confining a fearful dog to prevent destruction of property, housesoiling, or escaping generally makes the dog more afraid, particularly if he is not accustomed to confinement. This is even more true if he is exposed to the fear-producing stimulus while confined.

There is a widespread belief that "reassuring" a fearful animal will make the problem worse because attention and reassurance will reinforce or reward the fearful behavior. This is a view that, I must admit, I subscribed to as well, until I learned more about it from some colleagues who are very knowledgeable about animal learning theory. Understanding why reassurance may actually have a beneficial effect requires a good grasp of the principles of classical, operant, and counterconditioning (see chapter 3 and later discussion in this chapter). If talking soothingly to the dog as soon as he reacts fearfully serves to quiet and calm him, then counterconditioning (which is based on classical conditioning) may be occurring, rather than operant reinforcement for fearful behavior (for another example, see chapter 10 on the treatment for territorial barking). In other words, if thunder comes to predict soothing words from the owner, then thunder will also be able to elicit calm behavior rather than fear (counterconditioning). If, however, the dog remains too fearful and can't calm down, the reassurance may not have a beneficial effect and could exacerbate the problem.

Consider reading more about these complex topics (see the references in chapter 3 and the additional readings at the end of the book). The take-home message is this: Don't be too quick to discourage the reassurance approach, for if it is used appropriately, it may be beneficial.

Educate the owners about realistic expectations. *If* the stimuli triggering the fear can be identified, *if* the dog can be prevented from getting into a fearful state during treatment, and *if* the stimuli can be presented to the animal in a controlled, gradual fashion, fear-related problems are generally fairly treatable. However, in some cases, these "ifs" are substantial.

For many thunderphobic dogs, some of the fear-eliciting stimuli—barometric pressure changes, the smell of ozone, the darkening of the sky, etc.—cannot be presented in a controlled fashion. Consequently, it is not possible to desensitize the dogs to these stimuli. Many thunderphobic dogs do not react to either audiotapes or CDs of thunder, which suggests that in many cases, the dogs are responding to an entire stimulus complex involving many elements of the storm, not just the thunder. Also, thunder from a stereo speaker probably sounds different from the real thing. For these reasons, counterconditioning and systematic desensitization (CCSD) programs for thunderphobia can be problematic.

With some poorly socialized dogs, it is essentially impossible to prevent exposure to the feared stimuli during treatment because they are afraid of virtually everything. In these types of cases, medication may be helpful (see chapter 18).

4. Causes Versus Types of Fear-Related Problems

As mentioned at the opening of this chapter, determining what causes a fearful problem (whether genetic or innate tendencies, inadequate socialization, or traumatic experiences) is, for the most part, immaterial. What *is* important is identifying the triggering stimuli or the type of fear-related problem (fear of men, children, thunder, other noises, etc.) and the behavioral manifestations. If you do not have the time or experience to ask enough questions to identify at least these basic factors, you should refer the case. Because counterconditioning and desensitization are involved in the treatment of many fear-related problems, you should be able to design such a program, explain it to the owners, and demonstrate the initial stages of the program if the consultation setting allows. If you don't know how to do this, you should refer the case and, if you are interested in treating fear-related problems in the future, learn more about these techniques. You may or may not choose to talk to owners in *general* terms about management options (see later section) before referring the case.

Components of a behavioral history. A "cut to the chase" behavioral history for a problem clearly related to fear should identify precisely what the dog is doing and exactly what stimuli trigger the behaviors (and which do not). When attempting to identify the basis for an anxiety-related problem, many additional questions about the dog's previous history, his training, his current environment, and so forth are required. It's necessary to know as much as you can about the case because you must attempt to identify the source of the anxiety, which is not always easy or even possible. In other words, the details of what the dog is doing and what is triggering the behavior must be as precise as possible, as the following sections will demonstrate. Here are some of the questions you should ask to elicit meaningful, detailed information.

Description of the dog, description of the behavior.
- How old is the dog?
- What breed is the dog?
- Is she spayed/he neutered?
  Usually, these questions are not relevant to identifying the triggers for the fear or its manifestations, but it is always a good idea to obtain the signalment (i.e., age, breed, and gender).
- Can the owner describe, in detail, exactly what the dog does?
  For illustrative purposes here and in later passages, I'll use four typical scenarios: (1) fear of men, (2) fear of thunderstorms, (3) fear of hot-air balloons, and (4) fear of children. Using these four sample scenarios, the owner may say:
  1. "If a male approaches her, she immediately backs up. If he says something to her or reaches toward her, she backs away even more, barks, and will sometimes even urinate. Her ears go back, her tail is tucked, and she's kind of crouched down. If he continues to move toward her, she'll leave the room. She doesn't growl or show her teeth."
  2. "When it starts to rain or get windy, she begins to pace a little and pant. When it thunders, she shakes, pants, and tries to sit in my lap."
  3. "When she sees a balloon a little way off, she starts barking at it. As it gets

closer, she'll start shaking and either claw at the door to get inside or, if that doesn't work, start digging to try to get under the patio."

4. "When any of the visiting kids start moving toward him, with the exception of one little neighbor girl who is very quiet and calm, he'll put his head down, pull his ears back, take a few steps back, and start growling."

Description of dog's daily routine, environment, and behavior patterns.

- Where was the dog obtained?
- What is known about the dog's socialization history?
- Do any of the dog's relatives have similar fear-related problems?
- Has the dog always been fearful, even as a puppy?
- When did the fearful behavior first start?
- Have any changes occurred in the dog's environment? If yes, does the beginning of the problem correlate with any of these changes?
- Has the fearful or anxious behavior gotten worse, better, or stayed the same?
- Describe the dog's personality or temperament. Is it timid and shy?
- Where does the dog spend most of his time?
- When is the dog exposed to the fear-producing event?
- How often is the dog exposed to the fear-producing event?
- Can the dog's environment be modified to prevent this exposure?
- Is the dog being harshly treated by someone on an ongoing basis?
- Is the owner using punishment incorrectly or to excess?
- Describe a typical day for the dog.
- Is the dog crated or confined consistently for much of the day?
- How does the dog get along with other animals in the family? Are there conflicts between animals in the family?

Specifics about the occurrence of the problem behavior.

- Describe variations of the fearful situations in which the dog is least afraid, when is he most afraid, and when he isn't afraid. Perhaps the most recent (say, the last three) incidents may be most helpful. This is another way of pinning the owner down on what exactly the dog is responding to. Asking the question in this way also helps identify the behavioral starting point. Within the sample scenarios, you may learn, for example, that:
  1. "She does best with males in the family, she's gotten better with some friends or relatives who come over frequently, she's better if visiting men just ignore her. But if any other male just talks to her or approaches her, she's afraid. She does worst when a male she's never met before tries to walk right up to her, talk to her, and put his hand out to pet her."
  2. "She's best when I'm home with her during a storm, she's better if the thunder is a rumble rather than a loud crack, she's better when the storm is shorter, and she's a little better if we're in the basement and the TV is on kind of loud. She's worst when she's by herself, especially if she's outside, and if the storm goes on for longer times before it thunders—she seems to get more wound up."
  3. "She does best if there's just one balloon relatively far away and it's not making noise. Sometimes, if it's just one balloon at a distance, she's not too bad. She does worst the more balloons there are, the closer they are, and the more they use their heaters that make that whooshing sound."

4. "He does best with our kids and with the one quiet little girl in the neighborhood and a little better with older children. He's also better if they are sitting down playing and he can just come up and sniff them and leave. He does worst if they make any sudden moves toward him, if they try to pet him as soon as they come in the house, and when he meets a child for the first time."

Owners' attempts at problem resolution and the dog's response.
- Has the dog been scolded or punished for the behavior?
- Has the dog been forced to experience what he is afraid of (e.g., put on a sit-stay while a child comes up and pets him)?
- Has the owner attempted to reassure the dog? If so, how (e.g., holding, petting, cuddling, etc.)? How did the dog respond—was he calmer or more fearful (both in that particular situation as well as in later behavior)?
- Has any medication been tried?
- How has the problem been affected by these and any other attempts at resolution?

Differential results of the behavioral history. When you finish a behavioral history for a fear-related problem, you should be able to identify the specifics of the type of fear the dog is exhibiting. You should know exactly what the dog is afraid of and what he is doing in many varying contexts that involve the feared event. You should know what characteristics of the different situations make the dog more or less fearful. You should know when he is the most fearful and what version of the feared event will elicit very little, if any, fear. This information provides you what you need to know to complete the first three steps in the implementation of a counterconditioning and desensitization treatment plan (Box 11.5). The goals of this plan and how they can be accomplished will be discussed in a later section, but let's see how our four examples differ from each other in these first three preliminary steps from Box 11.5.

Step 1. Evaluate all the characteristics of the stimulus or situation that influence the animal's response.
- Scenario 1:
  — Whether the man is familiar or unfamiliar to the dog
  — What the man does (attempts to interact or ignores the dog)
  — Whether physical characteristics of the man are important (we don't know)
- Scenario 2:
  — How long the storm has been going on prior to the thunder
  — Whether or not thunder occurs
  — Whether or not the owner is home
  — Where in the house the dog is during the storm
  — What the thunder sounds like
- Scenario 3:
  — How many balloons are present
  — If the balloons make the whooshing sound
  — How far away the balloons are
- Scenario 4:
  — The age of the children (older children are easier)
  — What the children do (immediately approach the dog, ignore her, sit down before attempting to interact with her)
  — Whether the children are family members or familiar or unfamiliar visitors
  — Whether physical characteristics of the children are important (we don't know)

Box 11.5 Guidelines for implementing counterconditioning and systematic desensitization procedures

1. **Evaluate all the characteristics of the stimulus or situation that influence the animal's response.** Examples are distance; loudness; speed; characteristics of people, such as age, gender, or size; behavior of animals or people, such as approaching or attempting to interact with the dog; and environmental factors, such as inside, outside, familiar, or unfamiliar environments.

2. **Determine the importance of these characteristics relative to each other.** Make a prioritized list of the characteristics, from most to least relevant.

3. **Determine the behavioral starting point.** Determine what contexts or interactions the animal can tolerate without exhibiting the fearful behavior. These contexts will contain some or all of the relevant characteristics presented to the animal at subthreshold levels. In other words, the behavioral starting point is the easiest version of the situation the dog can tolerate.

4. **Use the prioritized list to create "practice" situations.** This means exposing the dog to the modified and controlled versions of the feared situation or stimulus, while pairing them with an enjoyable event for the animal, such as receiving food, toys, or petting. The feared stimulus should predict the occurrence of the pleasant one. Each stimulus intensity should be repeated until a clear behavior change has been observed (the dog anticipates the toy, tidbit, or attention rather than acting afraid).

5. **Intensify each characteristic individually, not simultaneously.** The characteristics that are manipulated first are those that are less relevant to the animal. When one characteristic is made more difficult (from chapter example, man reaching toward dog), another characteristic may initially need to be made less difficult (increase distance between person and dog).

6. **Increase stimulus intensities gradually.** Begin at the behavioral starting point, and from there, devise intermediate situations composed of increasingly difficult intensities of each characteristic. Finish with the most difficult situations that approximate "real" ones. Progression to the next level of intensity should be accomplished without eliciting undesirable behavior. If such behavior does occur, decrease the size of the incremental increases and repeat additional practice sessions at less intense levels.

7. **Remember that implementing these procedures inconsistently, haphazardly, too rapidly, or otherwise incorrectly can exacerbate the problem or at least be ineffective.** Correct implementation of these procedures requires planning and a knowledge of theory.

Step 2. Determine the importance of these characteristics relative to each other. Rank them from most to least important. A ranking of these characteristics for each scenario follows:

- Scenario 1:
    — The man's behavior (if he ignores the dog, what he does to try to interact with her)
    — Whether the man is familiar or unfamiliar to the dog
- Scenario 2:
    — Whether it thunders
    — The type of thunder
    — If the owner is home or not
    — The relative ranking of the length of the storm and where in the house the dog is needs to be clarified
- Scenario 3:
    — The animal's distance from the balloons
    — Whether the balloons whoosh
    — The number of balloons
- Scenario 4:
    — Whether or not the child is familiar to the dog
    — The behavior of the child
    — The age of the child

Step 3. Determine the behavioral starting point. This is the easiest version of all relevant characteristics; no fear should be elicited.

- Scenario 1: familiar men ignoring her
- Scenario 2: a brief storm without thunder, with the dog in the basement and the owner home
- Scenario 3: one balloon, at a distance, without any whooshing sound
- Scenario 4: quiet, familiar, older children

Creating these behavioral starting points to which the dog should be exposed, as you can see, may be very easy or very difficult.

5. Discuss Ways to Manage or Control the Behavior over the Short or Long Term

Managing fear-related problems almost always means controlling the environment to minimize the dog's exposure to the fear or anxiety producing situation or using medication to decrease the dog's reaction to the feared stimulus. Owners often already know what situations the dog can be in and not be afraid; if not, you may need to help people identify them, based on the behavioral history. For more information about medication, see chapter 18.

6. Explain the Goals of an Appropriate Behavior Modification Plan

If CCSD is to be used in treatment, the goal is to change the dog's "attitude" or initial reaction to the feared event. If the feared stimulus becomes associated with a good thing, it will no longer elicit fear. The steps in a CCSD program are listed in Box 11.5. Examples of these steps using our four scenarios follow.

Counterconditioning and desensitization.

Steps 4, 5, and 6. Use the prioritized list to create "practice" situations. Intensify each characteristic individually, not simultaneously. Increase stimulus intensities gradually. Pair each situation with an enjoyable event.

- Scenario 1:
  — Familiar men ignoring the dog while tossing her a tidbit. This continues until the dog anticipates the tidbit when familiar men appear.
  — The previous step is repeated with unfamiliar men ignoring the dog.
  — The first step is repeated with familiar men approaching but not petting the dog.
  — The first step is repeated with unfamiliar men approaching but not petting the dog.
  — The first step is repeated with familiar men petting the dog.
  — The first step is repeated with unfamiliar men petting the dog.

  A more precise gradient of the man's behavior will likely be needed (approaching the dog, reaching the hand toward the dog just a few inches from a distance as though to pet her, etc.). Each step may require many repetitions until the dog is able to tolerate petting from unfamiliar males.

- Scenario 2:
  — During a brief storm without thunder, the owner plays a favorite game (e.g., fetch) with the dog in the basement. As soon as the storm ends, so does the game. This continues until the dog heads for the basement at the sign of a storm, ready to play fetch.
  — The previous step is repeated with storms containing brief, rumbling thunder (not loud cracks).
  — The first step is repeated with storms containing a few cracks of thunder.

  Obviously, it is not possible to control thunderstorms to meet specifications, which is one reason why thunder phobias are so difficult to work with. Audiotapes or CDs must be used, but as mentioned previously, not all dogs respond to simulated sounds of thunder. Rather than changing the environment to create the incremental steps, medication in graduating doses can be used to decrease and control the dog's anxiety (see chapter 18).

- Scenario 3:
  — As soon as the dog sees one balloon at a distance that is not making any whooshing sound, the owner initiates a game of fetch or offers the dog tidbits periodically until the balloon is no longer in sight. This continues until, on seeing a balloon, the dog is ready to play fetch or looks to the owner for a tidbit.
  — The previous step is repeated with several balloons in the air at a distance.
  — The first step is repeated with one balloon making a whooshing sound at a distance.
  — The first step is repeated with more balloons at a distance making whooshing sounds.

  This is another set of circumstances that cannot, of course, be controlled; consequently, medication may be helpful if exposure to hot-air balloons can't be prevented during the behavioral modification process.

- Scenario 4:
  — Older children whom the dog knows, sitting quietly, gently toss tidbits to the

dog. This continues until, on seeing a familiar child of this age, the dog begins looking for a tidbit and displays friendly or at least tolerant behavior toward the child.

— Repeat the previous step with familiar *younger* children, sitting quietly.

— The first step is repeated with familiar older children, *approaching the dog*.

— The first step is repeated with *unfamiliar* older children, sitting quietly.

— The first step is repeated with familiar younger children, approaching the dog.

— The first step is repeated with unfamiliar younger children, approaching the dog.

Another type of increment that will need to be included involves the actual behavior of the children. This example only mentions approaching the dog; having the children pet her, play with her, and engage in rambunctious play among themselves in the dog's presence are all examples of additional increments.

Owners usually need a significant amount of coaching and instruction to work through a counterconditioning and desensitization plan successfully. They often have a difficult time devising the increments, they use increments that are too large (taking giant steps instead of baby steps), and they do not do a sufficient number of repetitions at each step. In other words, they generally attempt to do too much too fast. If you are going to direct a problem-resolution plan, you must be able to deal with these potential trouble spots.

During the initial consultation, it may be overwhelming to owners to hear about all the steps involved in a CCSD program, and it also requires too much time for you to explain them at this point. Instead, you may want to give the owners examples of initial practice sessions and have them contact you at a later time for follow-up so you can assess their progress and provide details for the next steps in the program.

Owners must also be prepared to implement a CCSD plan in more than one location or environment. For example, if all the sessions with a thunderstorm tape take place in the family room, the dog may continue to be fearful while in the bedroom, so the CCSD steps should be practiced there as well. This is called generalizing to different environments.

Counterconditioning without desensitization. Sometimes, it may be difficult to sufficiently control the dog's environment so that her experiences with the fear- or anxiety-producing stimuli are limited to the incremental exposures required in desensitization. For instance, if the dog is afraid of the husband in the family, there is a limit as to how much desensitization can be used: We can't have the husband in the house only for brief times at first, then leaving and returning later for a little longer! In these situations, therefore, counterconditioning by itself may be necessary. This limitation may affect the success of the treatment.

Flooding. Flooding means continuously exposing the animal to the stimuli he is afraid of until the fear response is no longer elicited. A common example is strapping a saddle on a young horse and letting him buck until he quits doing so and stands quietly with the saddle on his back. On a practical basis, flooding is often not possible, and it can be potentially dangerous. Inappropriate attempts at socialization, discussed earlier in this chapter, can be thought of as incomplete flooding experiences (the dog leaves the situation before the fear dissipates).

With some stimuli, such as thunderstorms, it is simply not possible to make the storm continue until the dog's fear abates. If the dog displays the same reaction to an audiotape of thunder as he does to the storm, flooding could technically be possible. Generally, however, this is not the case. First, in my experience, many dogs do not respond to the tapes at all, and those who do tend to show a milder reaction to the tapes than to an actual storm. Second, the flooding process may require a very long time for the fearful behavior to stop. If a dog is afraid of a vacuum cleaner, the owner may need to vacuum for an entire day, for example! An owner needs to be prepared to set aside a potentially very large block of time to dedicate to a flooding process. Third, if the dog's fear is intense, chances are he will try to get away (escape) from the feared stimulus during flooding. Injury to the dog or to those attempting to prevent the escape is a strong possibility. If the dog successfully escapes or if the stimulus terminates while the dog is still afraid, the behavior will have been made significantly worse. Flooding is also stressful for the animal. Because of these logistical problems and potential dangers, flooding is not generally recommended as a treatment technique except in cases of very mild fears.

However, some behaviorists use a "modified" flooding technique in which they create easier versions of the feared situation (a tape of a thunderstorm, for example, or the incremental examples given previously), flood the dog beginning with the easiest version possible, and incrementally make the situations more difficult. I would not recommend attempting this if you are a novice in the field, as you can easily exacerbate the problem if you implement such a plan incorrectly or if something goes wrong.

Difficulties in treating anxiety-related problems. Anxious behaviors such as stereotypies (e.g., tail chasing) and self-injurious behaviors such as hair pulling or excessive licking can be very difficult to treat. Obviously, it is always important to thoroughly evaluate medical causes for these problems.

If the stimuli that trigger the problem can be clearly identified, a CCSD plan or other appropriate treatment measures can be implemented. For example, if a dog is anxious because of fighting problems with another family dog, this underlying problem should be addressed using the information from chapter 12. Unfortunately, in many cases, the triggering stimuli can't be identified.

In such cases, it may be helpful to suggest the owner begin keeping a behavioral log to attempt to identify what the anxious behavior might be correlated with. Another option is to treat the problem symptomatically, using appropriate medication (see chapter 18). These types of problems are often best referred to behavior specialists who may have more experience working with them.

Medication. Detailed information regarding medication can be found in chapter 18. There are several reasons why medication might be appropriate:
- It can be used as a management tool to prevent the dog from displaying fear-motivated behaviors that are problems for the owner, such as housesoiling or destructiveness.
- It can be used as a way of preventing the dog from being triggered into a fearful response, which would impede the progress of the counterconditioning and desensitization program.
- It can be used if the desensitization plan gets "stuck" or if incremental exposures are not possible.
- It can be used if there is no behavioral starting point because the dog's fear is so intense or generalized.

SUMMARY

Fear-related problems can often be treated successfully. However, attention to detail is one of the keys. It is possible to exacerbate problems by implementing behavior modification techniques incorrectly. If you are inexperienced with the techniques explained in this chapter, you may want to work with someone who is familiar with them before attempting to use them on your own.

REFERENCES

1. Voith, V.L., and P.L. Borchelt. 1996. Fears and phobias in companion animals. In *Readings in companion animal behavior*, ed. V.L. Voith and P.L. Borchelt, 140–51. Trenton, N.J.: Veterinary Learning Systems.

2. Scott, J.P., and J.L. Fuller. 1965. *Genetics and the social behavior of the dog.* Chicago: University of Chicago Press.

3. Murphree, O.D., R.A. Dykman, and J.E. Peters. 1967. Genetically-determined abnormal behavior in dogs: Results of behavioral tests. *Cond. Reflex.* 2:199–205.

4. Denny, M.R., ed. 1991. *Fear, avoidance and phobias.* Hillsdale, N.J.: Lawrence Erlbaum Associates.

5. Gray, J.A. 1987. *The psychology of fear and stress.* 2nd edition. New York: Cambridge University Press.

6. Gregory, R.L. 1987. *The Oxford companion to the mind.* New York: Oxford University Press.

7. McFarland, D., ed. 1987. *The Oxford companion to animal behaviour.* New York: Oxford University Press.

8. Rugaas, T. 1997. *On talking terms with dogs: Calming signals.* Kula, Hawaii: Legacy by Mail.

CHAPTER 12

Canine Aggression Problems

Aggression is a serious and complex topic, and despite its length this chapter only scratches the surface on the topic of aggression. You need to do additional reading before considering working with aggression cases. If you are already well versed in the literature, this chapter should help you organize your thoughts, and maybe it will give you some new ideas about educating clients and explaining treatment techniques.

This chapter will be organized somewhat similarly to the previous chapter on fears and phobias. There, I noted that the cause of a fear-motivated problem may be irrelevant to treatment; in this chapter, I would stress that the causes of aggressive behavior are poorly understood. There are probably genetic influences, biochemical factors, and environmental and experiential factors such as inadequate socialization, abuse, traumatic experiences, and inappropriate handling and training. At present, we are not often able to identify which of these factors causes a particular aggression problem. Given the current state of the art in treatment, then, having this knowledge has little effect on developing the treatment plan, with the possible exception of deciding if medication is appropriate (and if so, which one). Of course, if inappropriate handling or treatment is ongoing, it is necessary to know this so these patterns can be changed.

As more is learned about the factors influencing aggression, particularly the role of biochemical factors[1], how aggression is treated in the future may change. For now, we do need to know the *type* of aggression being displayed, to the degree possible. Knowing the type of aggression is helpful in making predictions about what the dog is likely to do in the future and in knowing what types of situations and eliciting stimuli need to be worked with in a treatment program. As in the case of fears and phobias, the treatment plan is actually based on the *type* of aggression rather than its cause.

Aggressive behavior is probably the most common problem seen by behaviorists across the country[2]. Dog bites, especially to children, have reached what some consider to be epidemic proportions. One report estimates that almost half of all school-age children have been bitten by a dog[3]. Dog bites have negative consequences not only for the victim but also for the dog owner and the dog himself[4]. Owners are at risk of being sued and losing their homeowner's insurance, and they may be the recipients of the ill will of the victims, their families, and neighbors. Dogs are often subjected to abusive and cruel treatment, and some are even permanently injured or killed in the name of resolving aggression problems. Their quality of life may be negatively affected if restrictions are put on their activities in order to protect others, and they may be euthanized if they cannot safely be kept as companion animals.

Given these serious and even dire potential consequences, aggression problems, more than any others, require that you be crystal clear in deciding what role you will play. Think about the following issues.

LIABILITY

First, consider your liability exposure. If you make recommendations to an owner about how to work with a dog's aggressive behavior and someone is bitten while following these recommendations, you may be at least partially liable for the injuries (see chapter 1). Second, if you observe aggressive behavior in an animal or become aware of an aggression problem from talking to an owner you may also be in a vulnerable position should a future lawsuit arise if you fail to warn the owner of the risk her dog presents.

In assessing what you want your role to be, you should consider a few worst-case scenarios. If a lawsuit involving a dog bite ever came to trial, could you testify with confidence that the recommendations you gave the owner were based on sound scientific information? Would your recommendations stand up to the scrutiny of a board-certified veterinary behaviorist or certified applied animal behaviorist testifying for the other side? On a more emotional level, how would you feel if someone was bitten or permanently disfigured or another animal was killed or injured while the dog owner was doing what you told her to do? This is scary stuff, I know, and it gives me second thoughts about working with aggression problems. In fact, I recently had a scare in this regard. One morning, I opened up the local newspaper to a headline about an 18-month-old baby being killed by the family dog. My first (selfish) thought was, "Oh God, I hope it's not one of my cases." As it turned out, it wasn't, but both an animal control agency and a dog trainer had been involved in this case prior to this tragic, fatal bite.

ATTITUDE

A second thing to consider is your attitude, reaction to, and beliefs about dogs who bite. If your primary attitude or beliefs about dealing with aggressive dogs are something along the lines of "I'll show him," "Someone needs to clean his clock," or "He's not going to get away with this with me," you may want to read this chapter thoroughly! As you'll see later, many aggression problems are based in fear, having nothing to do with control and dominance; moreover, physical punishments usually do more harm than good with most aggression problems. Perhaps the most serious flaw in such attitudes is that it doesn't matter at all what *you* can do with the dog. What matters is whether or not *the owner* can handle the dog. Your role is not to pit your strength or will against the dog but to help the owner by giving her appropriate, effective, and humane tools and methods to change the dog's behavior.

Another component to consider is how you react or behave around potentially dangerous dogs who may bite. Are you afraid and nervous? Do you have an angry, macho, "make my day" attitude as described earlier? Are you tentative or, alternatively, overconfident? I would describe an ideal attitude as *cautiously calm*. This means you:

- Respect the dog and his ability to hurt you without being overly fearful
- Have confidence in your ability to accurately observe, interpret, and react accordingly to the dog's body postures and other communication signals without being overconfident or feeling invincible ("I'm good with dogs—they won't bite me")
- Know what you can do to avoid being bitten or getting in a confrontation with the dog
- Know that purposely setting the dog up to show aggression so you can punish him is not acceptable

• Know when to back off if you don't think you can accurately interpret the dog's intentions or realize that he will bite if you persist

KNOWLEDGE

Your third consideration—something that is always important but especially so with aggression cases—is your knowledge of canine ethology and learning. You must be familiar with the ethological literature on aggression, not with the majority of the popular literature that attributes most all aggression to dominance problems. You must know the ins and outs of operant conditioning, classical conditioning, and counterconditioning and how to apply these concepts to an aggressive behavior problem.

Think about these issues as you read through this chapter to help you decide what your role should be and when, or whether, you should refer the case. These points are summarized in Box 12.1.

> **Box 12.1 Factors to consider in choosing your role in aggression cases**
>
> **Liability:** Are you prepared if a lawsuit is brought against you because a person or animal was injured while your recommendations were being implemented?
>
> **Attitude:** When working with dogs who may bite, is your attitude one of "cautious calm," as described in the text, and not "I'll show him," "I'm good with dogs, they won't bite me," or "I don't know what I'll do if he threatens me"?
>
> **Knowledge:** Do you have a strong grasp of canine ethology and animal learning as they relate to aggressive behavior? Could your recommendations stand up against the testimony of expert witnesses, such as a board-certified veterinary behaviorist or a certified applied animal behaviorist if, in the worst-case scenario, one of your dog bite cases ever went to court?

PROTOCOL

You'll notice a heavy emphasis on owner education throughout this protocol. Being an educator in an aggression case is just as important, if not more so, as being a problem solver.

1. Obtain a Description of the Problem Behavior

Somewhat surprisingly, it may be difficult to get an owner to provide a behavioral description of the dog's behavior. Despite repeated questioning, the owner may say, "Well, he just goes after him [another dog, the mail carrier]," "He goes ballistic," "She really gets vicious," or "He acts like he wants to kill him." As you know, none of these descriptions really tells us anything about what the dog is doing.

I'll often ask an owner to tell me exactly what the dog does and what he looks like when he's doing it. Remember from chapter 6 that obtaining a behavioral description means developing a mental picture of what the dog is doing. This is particularly important with aggression cases. You can also ask the owner to videotape the dog in situations in which the behavior is likely to occur. Depending on the type of aggression involved, the dog may not display it during the consultation.

I'll also ask the owner if the dog has actually bitten anyone. Despite using words like those mentioned earlier, often the answer is no; alternatively, the owner may say, "It was just a very inhibited bite that left no mark [or left a red mark]" or "The dog grabbed the person's clothes but didn't actually bite him." In the case of aggressive behavior toward other dogs, I'll ask if either dog has been injured and if so what the extent of the injuries were. Although sometimes injuries, even severe ones, were inflicted, more often than not, the owner reports that there were no injuries at all or maybe just a few superficial puncture wounds or nicked ears. *Keep in mind that describing the dog's behavior as aggressive is an interpretation, not a behavioral description* (see the following material).

Furthermore, the owner may focus only on the few seconds that the dog bit or threatened or when a fight erupted. A behavioral description should include what happened several minutes prior to the bite or fight and what all individuals did immediately afterward. You need to determine what the person was doing, what the other dog was doing, and what the dog doing the biting or initiating the fight was doing, as well as gather details about the environmental surroundings. Be sure to ask about any displacement behaviors that were seen prior to the bite (see chapter 11). Remember that displacement behaviors indicate a dog may be anxious, and they include lip licking, yawning, sniffing the ground, and grooming.

You should obtain behavioral descriptions of several different episodes to be sure you know what is happening. A complete behavioral history would require detailed descriptions of as many aggressive or threatening episodes as the owner can remember, as well as additional information about other behavior patterns. Several good examples of formats to use for behavioral histories or "aggression screening" forms are available[2, 5], and you should review these.

2. Evaluate Potential Medical Causes for the Problem Behavior

There are a host of possible illnesses, diseases, and other medical conditions that can influence a dog's aggressive behavior[5, 6, 7]. They range from anything causing physical discomfort that would make the dog irritable and grumpy (an abscessed tooth, itchy skin) to endocrine or neurological disorders. For this reason, I will not see an aggression case unless it has been referred by a veterinarian or the owner has taken the dog to the regular veterinarian for a thorough workup prior to the behavior consultation.

Veterinarians need to fulfill their responsibilities before referring the case by performing appropriate examinations and laboratory testing to evaluate and rule out, to the extent possible, medical causes for the aggressive behavior. Refer to the references previously cited.

I think most owners almost wish there was a medical cause for the behavior because they believe that a disease or illness causing the aggression could be cured but they are doubtful that the dog's basic behavior patterns can be changed. In my experience and based on the literature on dog aggression problems, rarely are these problems due to disease or illness.

3. Educate Owners About the Problem Behavior

Education is particularly important with aggression cases. There are so many myths and misconceptions and such a general lack of understanding about aggression that owners require a significant amount of education on the subject. Although not everyone wants or is qualified to treat aggression problems, everyone *can* be an educator. However, it is crucial that the information you give to owners be based on sound scientific findings; it must not perpetuate inaccurate information and myths.

Educate the owner about anthropomorphic and other misinterpretations. The terms *aggressive behavior* or *aggressive dog* tend to be used rather loosely, and there is a great deal of confusion as to what is encompassed by these terms. Even in the scientific literature, the definition of *aggression* varies. Dogs are categorized as "aggressive" without identifying the criteria for placing them in that category. Given that aggressive behavior is normal for all dogs, should every canine be labeled aggressive? If not, what does a dog have to do to be considered an "aggressive dog"? What is the difference between an "aggressive dog" and a "vicious dog"? Do behaviors such as growling, baring teeth, and lunging fall into the category of aggressive behavior?

Box 12.2 Glossary

Aggressive behaviors: behaviors that result in intentional harm to another individual. A continuum exists between threats and aggression. The point at which a "bite" produces harm (e.g., causing a red mark, a bruise, or an indentation on the skin) is subject to interpretation.

Agonistic behaviors: those behaviors that are associated with competitive interactions or social conflicts between animals. Included under this system are avoidance, appeasement, submissive, threatening, and aggressive behaviors.

Displacement behaviors: behaviors that occur out of context or are irrelevant to the situation. They can be triggered by conflict, they may be part of aggressive encounters, or they may occur when an animal is thwarted from achieving a goal. Examples of the more common displacement behaviors seen in dogs include lip licking, yawning, self- or auto grooming, and even sleeping.

Provocation: an interpretation of motivation that becomes confusing when both the animal's and the person's viewpoint are considered. People interact with dogs in ways they intend to be friendly and affectionate, but dogs may perceive their behavior as frightening or challenging. Hugging a dog is a classic example (see text).

Threatening behaviors: behaviors designed to intimidate, repel, or warn another individual to stay away. These behaviors are not meant to result in harm.

Vicious behavior: the everyday sense of this word has no behavioral meaning because from the animal's perspective, aggression is not a value-laden behavior. Behavioral criteria for viciousness might be:

- Aggressive behavior that is displayed in response to a wide variety of stimuli
- Aggressive behavior that occurs with little or no warning threats
- Aggressive behavior that is displayed at full intensity and not inhibited
- Aggressive behavior that is not easily stopped or inhibited

---

Behaviorists identify a behavioral system known as agonistic behavior[8] (see Box 12.2). Agonistic behaviors are those behaviors associated with social conflict between animals. Agonistic behaviors include:

Avoidance behaviors. When a dog is challenged or threatened, he may decide to get away from the situation. Whether a dog chooses to flee depends partially on his *perception* of whether this option is, indeed, available. If a dog is on a sit-stay or on leash or if his escape route is blocked by someone he is afraid of, he may not think that fleeing is an option. If he can't leave, he is forced into other choices.

Appeasement or submissive behaviors. The dog will exhibit these behaviors to turn off the threat or aggression being directed at him. They include body postures such as holding the ears down or back, holding the tail down or tucked, crouching, grinning submissively, and rolling over and exposing the inguinal area. The latter is sometimes accompanied by submissive urination. The animal may also avoid direct eye contact and try not to face the opponent by turning the body to the side. There are some technical differences between appeasement and submission[9] (see chapter 15), but for our purposes, we can consider them to have the same intent.

Threatening behaviors. These include growling, snarling, baring teeth, lunging, or inhibited biting (i.e., snapping), which does not harm the target, or victim. When dogs snap, they may or may not actually touch the victim. Threats can be either offensive or defensive (see later section). Their goal is to warn other individuals to stop what they are doing. Although a dog may or may not escalate threatening behavior to aggression, it should always be assumed that he will.

Aggression. By this definition, aggressive behaviors are intended to harm another individual and include biting, scratching, etc. Aggressive behaviors can be either offensively or defensively motivated. Threats and aggression are not discrete categories: Clearly, when a bite wound is severe enough to require stitches, the dog has shown aggression; when a dog snaps at another dog or person but makes minimal or no contact, that behavior is probably a threat. Somewhere between are snaps or bites that leave red marks or bruises or barely break the skin. Whether these are threats or aggression becomes a matter of terminology and interpretation.

People often believe they have avoided a bite by quickly withdrawing their hand or other body part or that they were able to pull the dog away before he bit. Although there are some exceptions, this is usually not the case. Human reflexes aren't that quick, and the dog has a head start because he knows his intentions before his owner or victim does in most cases. The fact is that in most inhibited or minor snaps or bites that don't result in injury, the dog did exactly what he intended to do. In other words, the dog did, indeed, have an opportunity to injure, but he chose not to do so. Let me give you an example.

Years ago, I was working with a cocker spaniel whom I misread. Overconfident about my ability to predict his behavior, I reached for him too quickly, and he growled and lunged for my hand. I did not jerk my hand back but held it perfectly still. The dog went all around my hand with his mouth for several seconds, growling and snarling the entire time. He left nothing but saliva. Had I attempted to pull my hand back, I might have believed that I avoided a bite through my own actions. The truth was, though, that he never intended to bite me: He had all the opportunity he wanted, but he chose to only threaten.

Thus, dogs have choices when confronted by threats or challenges. Some choose to leave, some choose to threaten in return, others choose to appease, and still others choose to aggress. These choices are depicted diagrammatically in Figure 12.1. Dogs can make a variety of choices, in any sequence, and they can make more than one choice in any given situation.

Aggression: Understandable versus acceptable. When aggressive behavior is elicited in response to environmental stimuli (as compared to neurological disease or other medical conditions, for example), the behavior is provoked from the dog's perspective. Provocation from a human perspective is usually evaluated based on the intent of the victim's behavior (e.g., attempt to be friendly versus teasing or hurting the animal). However, the dog may perceive the victim's

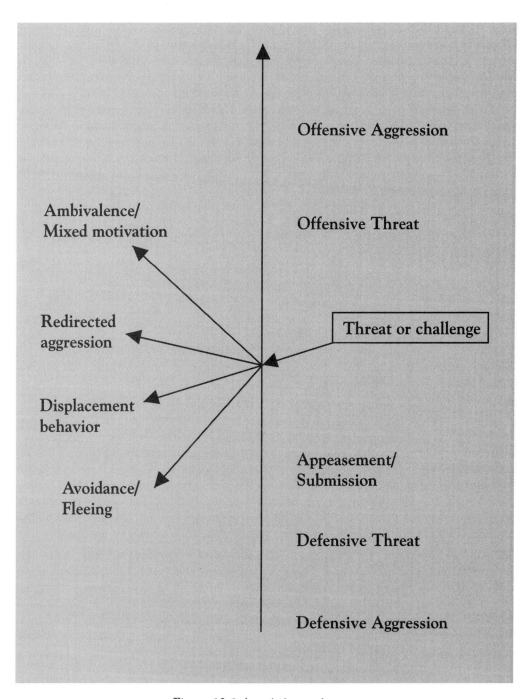

Figure 12.1 Agonistic continuum

Source: Adapted from a model used by Philip N. Lehner, Ph.D. Used by permission

Note: Agonistic behavior describes choices animals can make when confronted with a threat or challenge. In any situation, a dog can make more than one choice, and his choices can be in any order.

behavior differently than how it was intended. A common example is a child who hugs a dog in a display of affection. The dog may either be very frightened by this close contact and restraint or perceive the gesture as a dominance threat. From the dog's point of view, the aggression was provoked. However, because people do not expect dogs to bite when being hugged, it was an unprovoked attacked from the victim's point of view.

By the same token, dogs can aggressively guard their food and snap or bite when people approach too closely. Because owners are more likely to expect and understand this response, they may view the behavior as "instinctive" (which is not a helpful interpretation or explanation) and therefore provoked and even acceptable. Because the concept of provocation is confounded by anthropomorphic interpretations of animal behavior, it has limited value in assessing aggression cases. Provocation is a separate issue from categorizing the behavior as acceptable. In both cases described earlier and in almost all aggression directed toward people, even though the aggression is understandable, it is not acceptable.

A related issue arises when dogs bite or threaten their owners. This can devastate some people because they feel their dogs have betrayed them. Owners often tell me, "I thought he loved me, how could he turn on me this way?" What people fail to realize is that for a canid, agonistic behaviors, including threats and aggression, are a normal part of any generally affiliative relationship. Dogs can be very attached to their owners, just as wolves are attached to members of their social group, and still have conflicts and disputes that may escalate to threats or aggression. Owners often need to be educated about the understandable nature of their dog's behavior, even though it remains unacceptable. They need to know that their dogs can "love" them and still bite them before they can make a more informed decision about whether they want to work with the dog's behavior.

Jealousy. Owners often describe family dogs who are fighting with one another as being jealous of each other. An ethologic rather than this anthropomorphic interpretation is that there is an instability in the dominance hierarchy between the dogs (this will be discussed more fully in the section on types of aggression). An owner may use the same interpretation if her dog is threatening or biting another family member who shows affection to her or attempts to be in closer proximity to her than is the dog. I've had cases where the dog growls or snaps at one spouse or the other when they are dancing. These behaviors are not jealousy but are either dominance-related, protective, or attention-getting behaviors. Interpreting them as "jealousy" leads to the conclusion that the dog needs more attention, which can actually exacerbate the situation.

"Vicious" dogs. The lay use of the term *vicious* is loaded with malicious and evil connotations that have no bearing on animal behavior. The legal definitions of vicious behavior really have no meaning to behaviorists either. A "vicious dog" is defined in many animal ordinances along the lines of one who attacks another person or animal without provocation. We've already discussed the provocation issue, and "attack" is not a behavioral description and is open to interpretation. The term *vicious* could be operationalized into a behavioral definition by defining viciousness as[10]: aggressive behavior that (1) is displayed in response to a wide variety of stimuli, (2) occurs with little or no warning threats, (3) is displayed at full intensity and not inhibited, and (4) is not easily stopped or inhibited. A particular biting incident may also be categorized as vicious even if the behavior is not displayed in a wide variety of circumstances.

"Aggressive" breeds. Another issue that frequently arises is whether particular breeds are inherently dangerous, vicious, or aggressive. Although there are definitely differences between breeds in a variety of behaviors, it cannot be said that an individual member of any specific breed is predetermined to be a dangerous dog.

As I mentioned early in this chapter, aggressive behavior is influenced by numerous factors, many of which are still poorly understood. A statement such as, "Rottweilers, Akitas, German shepherds, or [fill in your breed of choice] are inherently vicious or dangerous" is a generalization that is simply inaccurate. Very complex behavior cannot be oversimplified in such a manner.

A more reasonable way to look at breed differences is to consider variations in the thresholds at which a particular behavior, such as aggression, can be elicited. Perhaps certain breeds of dogs, some of whom are in the working group, may, in general, have lower thresholds for aggressive behavior, but this does not mean they are destined to be dangerous and bite someone. When I respond to questions about these issues, I often tell owners to consider what the dog was bred to do. If the breed was bred to guard and protect (e.g., many working-group dogs) or to be intolerant of other dogs (e.g., most terriers), then chances are that certain types of threatening or aggressive behaviors will be more easily elicited from them; steps therefore need to be taken to discourage inappropriate displays of these behaviors. However, keep in mind that variations *within* a breed are significant, and perhaps they prevail over the degree of variation *between* breeds. I certainly see plenty of Labrador and golden retrievers who have bitten or threatened people or other animals, despite the fact that these breeds generally have gregarious, friendly temperaments.

With mixed-breed dogs, people have a tendency to focus on the potentially negative characteristics of one of the breeds in the mix. If a person has a chow-lab mix, for instance, the automatic worry is that the "aggressive tendencies" of the chow will prevail. Why would one assume that these tendencies would be more evident than the breed characteristics of the Labrador? Would a lab-chow mix be viewed differently? In the end, there is no way of knowing which breed characteristics of a mixed-breed dog will predominate. In fact, the animal may be a blend of characteristics that don't resemble the predominant characteristics of either breed.

Educate the owners about myths regarding problem solving and techniques to avoid. With certain notable exceptions[11], the popular literature on dog training has done dogs, their owners, and society a huge disservice in regard to canine aggression issues. There are three major areas in which misinformation is widespread:

Most aggressive and threatening behavior problems are related to dominance issues. As discussed in a later section on types of aggression, dominance is about the control of resources and social rank. How a dog responds to a stranger or visitor to the home has nothing to do with the dominance hierarchy between the dog and owner. In other words, territorial aggression—one of the reasons why dogs threaten visitors—has nothing to do with dominance aggression. Also, in my experience, most aggressive and threatening behavior that dogs display toward children is not a product of dominance but of fear. This can be determined by the contexts in which the aggression occurs and by the dog's body postures (see following).

What is relevant for these types of aggression problems is not the social ranking between dog and owner but the dog's reaction to the target of the aggression. I often tell owners, "It's not about *you*, it's about how the dog feels about the child [or visitor, etc.]. In other words, your being dominant over your dog is not going to make him less fearful of children or more accepting of people he perceives as territorial intruders." This idea will be discussed in more detail when the different types of aggressive behavior are defined later in the chapter.

The use of aversive procedures and physical force in dealing with aggression. Within the past 2 years, I have personally known of two cases in which puppies were killed in training classes by "corrections" for "aggression" and another case in which a dog was permanently blinded due to hypoxia (lack of oxygen to the brain) after being strung up (lifted off the ground by leash and collar, using a choke chain). I've also been contacted by numerous people who relate other stories of abusive techniques being used to show dogs "who's boss" and essentially beat them into submission. A dog who was beaten with a frying pan and another who was hit across the nose with a hard rubber hose are just two disturbing examples. (Under the guidelines for humane dog training, mentioned in chapter 1, these types of techniques would clearly be unacceptable.)

When I am reviewing any new dog-training or behavior book that comes on the market, the first thing I do is check out the section on aggression, for if any part of the book is going to be a problem, it will be that section. More than a few popular dog books recommend stringing dogs up (check this out the next time you are in the pet section of your favorite bookstore). In addition to the dangers of injury and death, inappropriate aversive procedures and physical force present several other problems.

First, it is well known from the learning theory literature that techniques that produce pain can also elicit aggression. When such techniques are applied to dogs who have already chosen threats or aggression over other options when challenged or threatened, it should be no surprise that such procedures elicit more aggressive behavior.

Second, in the case of dominance aggression, the dog has used threats and aggression successfully in the past to control resources and interactions with his owner. If an owner is advised to confront the dog with techniques such as scruff shakes and "alpha rolls," it should not be surprising that the dog escalates his behavior rather than becoming submissive. He already has a history of doing this!

Third, the common targets of dog aggression, such as children and visitors, are in no position to deliver any kind of punishment. Thus, punishment, in addition to its other drawbacks, can only be effective at getting the dog to inhibit the behavior when the owner is on hand to deliver it. Clearly, this is not practical.

This brings up the fourth and perhaps the most important point. The best that punishment can offer is to teach the dog to inhibit the aggression when he knows punishment will be delivered. It never teaches him how to be friendly to visitors, how to feel comfortable around children, how to willingly give up control to his owner, etc. If anything, punishment makes these interactions even more unpleasant for the dog than they already are, and therefore, it can exacerbate the problem. It is possible that punishment will teach the dog to inhibit one type of threatening or aggressive behavior (e.g., growls, snaps). However, because the dog is still motivated to be aggressive (he's still fearful of children, doesn't like visitors intruding on his territory, is intolerant of other dogs, etc.), he may well display another, more dangerous behavior (e.g., biting) in the future to avoid punishment but still be able to respond with the aggression he is motivated to exhibit.

Finally, there should be no justification required for the statement that injuring, maiming, or killing dogs while training them is intolerable. That is not dog training. It is cruelty and abuse.

I hope I have presented enough persuasive arguments to convince you that techniques that make use of physical force are not the answer to aggression problems (see Box 12.3). As you'll see in the later section on treatment, certain types of remote punishers *may* have a place in dealing with certain types of aggression but only if they are combined with procedures that teach the dog nonaggressive responses.

What contributes to dominance aggression problems. Many popular dog-training books stress the importance of the owner being dominant over the dog, and they often recommend brute force as the way to achieve dominance. Yet no scientific studies document that *any* training or handling procedures can prevent dominance aggression (see chapter 4). As mentioned before, the cause of any aggression problem is probably multifactorial. Consequently, it is highly unlikely that a simple set of handling procedures can prevent a problem that may well be caused by genetic and biochemical, as well as experiential, factors. There is also no evidence that "spoiling" a dog (allowing him on beds or other furniture, giving him treats, petting him on demand) contributes to aggression problems[12].

> **Box 12.3 Why physical force and procedures causing pain are not appropriate for working with aggression problems**
>
> - Pain can elicit further aggression and not only exacerbate the problem but also put the person delivering it at a greater risk of being bitten.
> - If the dog has responded with threats or aggression to less intense or even inadvertent challenges (such as direct eye contact or reaching for his collar), it can be expected that he will respond even more aggressively to more threatening confrontations. This will exacerbate the problem and again put the person delivering these procedures at risk of being bitten.
> - The targets of most dog bites are children. Children are in no position to deliver these kinds of consequences.
> - These techniques can never teach the dog how to be friendly or how not to feel threatened in the situations in which he is biting. In fact, these procedures will probably threaten him even more and exacerbate the problem.

It is often stated that playing tug-of-war games and allowing dogs on the bed or furniture are contributing causal factors to dominance aggression problems. A recent study, however, found no association between these practices and the occurrence of dominance aggression directed toward owners[13].

Some people advocate a number of other practices to suppress dominance problems, such as:

1. Waiting until after you eat your meal to feed your dog
2. Making the dog get up and move rather than walking around him
3. Not allowing your dog to demand attention from you by barking, nudging at you, or employing other annoying behaviors
4. Not allowing your dog to go through doors and gates ahead of you
5. Requiring your dog to make eye contact with you several times each day

Although some of these recommendations (3, 4) make sense in terms of having a well-behaved pet who isn't a nuisance, others (1, 2) may be matters of personal preference, and in my opinion, some (1, 2, 5) are totally irrelevant to preventing aggression. Certainly, I do not advocate letting the dog demand things from his owner, set his own limits, be a nuisance, and generally be out of control. However, I think it is important to differentiate between procedures that will produce an obedient dog who is pleasant to be with (such procedures are known) from ones that will prevent dominance aggression (such procedures aren't known). Another point to remember is that obedient dogs can still have problems with dominance or other types of aggression.

For an ethological perspective on eye contact (item 5), an interesting issue on its own, see

> **Box 12.4 An ethological view of eye contact**
>
> As you've learned previously, avoiding eye contact is a submissive behavior, and a direct, prolonged stare is an offensive threat. Encouraging your dog to pay attention to you is a worthy goal, but this should not be misapplied by encouraging your dog to stare at you and requiring her to look directly in your eyes for prolonged periods. You are, in effect, encouraging a behavior that is used as an offensive threat. If you want your dog to pay attention to you, pick a point for her to focus on, such as your chin, ear, or belt buckle, rather than looking directly in your eyes.
>
> If your dog avoids your eyes while you are staring at her, which most people do when they are trying to get the dog's attention, this is indicative of an appropriate deferential response; it should not be discouraged, nor should the dog be punished for not maintaining direct eye contact. Avoiding eye contact does not mean the dog is being "rebellious."

Box 12.4. Also refer to chapter 4 on problem prevention and the section on treatment goals later in this chapter for further discussion of these topics.

Educate the owner about realistic expectations. The owner of a dog who has threatened or bitten must take the problem seriously. He or she cannot excuse the behavior as a fluke, think it won't happen again, hope the dog will grow out of it, assume the dog was abused as a puppy, or chalk it up to the fact that the dog was just having a bad day. The owner must, as the first priority, take steps to ensure that people and other animals are protected from injury by the dog. For more details on this aspect of aggression problems, see later sections on management.

Steps should be taken immediately to address the problem, and owners almost always need professional help with canine aggression issues. Yet the existence of such a problem should not automatically condemn the dog to death.

If the target of the aggression is a child, the dog owner must be prepared to invest time and make changes to the dog's environment so that the animal is never left alone with children. Children who will be around the dog will also need to be educated about appropriate behaviors around dogs, at an age-specific level (see product list in appendix for an educational video). Children often put themselves at risk for being bitten without meaning to or without intending to antagonize the dog.

If the dog is aggressive toward another dog in the family, more often than not the problem is workable. If the aggression is directed toward nonfamily dogs, the outcome is more variable[14]. Such a dog may never be able to attend a doggie play group, for example, in an off-leash dog park.

Many dogs with aggression problems may need to be monitored or supervised in certain situations for the rest of their lives. Owners should recognize that some or all of the treatment procedures may be in effect for life. Given the dog's tendencies, they should view him as a high-maintenance pet, requiring more than the average amount of time, training, and supervision. Some aggressive behavior problems may be managed or resolved successfully in a home environment, but others may not.

The owners must recognize there are no guarantees that, even with treatment, their dog will never again bite or otherwise harm a person or another animal. Anyone who tells owners that he or she can "fix it" and guarantee the dog will never bite is, quite frankly, a charlatan (unless that individual is talking about euthanasia). Instead of seeking a nonexistent guarantee, the owners should enlist the help of a well-qualified behavior specialist to make a reasonable assessment of the degree of risk their dog presents.

Currently, no studies have identified the characteristics of an aggression problem that correlate with prognosis (i.e., with the successful resolution or management of the case), which means there is no good way to predict outcomes. One study that looked at factors correlated with the eventual euthanasia of aggressive dogs (thereby reflecting owners' decisions, not necessarily the success or failure of the treatment) found that owners were more likely to choose euthanasia for dogs who were larger, who delivered more severe bites, and whose behavior was less predictable.[15]. Box 12.5 contains a list of the factors that I believe you should discuss with owners when they are considering working with a canine aggression problem.

Box 12.5 Assessing risk: Factors to consider

As explained in the text, no studies have been done to correlate presenting characteristics of aggression problems with success of treatment. These recommendations are based on professional experience. There are always exceptions.

- Is this a long-standing problem, rather than a recent change in behavior?
- Is the aggression or threatening behavior generalized to many different stimuli or contexts?
- Is the behavior unpredictable—i.e., is it rarely possible to determine when the dog is likely to bite or threaten? (Is this true even after the owner has been educated about what to look for?)
- Does the behavior consist primarily of aggressive behavior that has caused injury, rather than threats or inhibited bites?
- Is it difficult to get the dog to stop or inhibit the behavior?
- Does the aggression or biting occur without observable warnings (e.g., tenseness, staring, growling, baring teeth, avoidance attempts, barking, or other threats) prior to the behavior?
- Are one or more family members afraid of the dog?
- Does the dog respond intensely to relatively minor triggers (i.e., does he have a "10" response to a "2" situation)?
- Is the family's lifestyle such that it is difficult to supervise the dog or control his environment (denying access to potential victims, muzzling in certain situations, etc.)?
- Is the family's commitment or ability to follow through with treatment recommendations questionable?

The more yes answers you have to these questions, the greater the risk the dog poses.

---

4. Recognize the Common Types of Aggressive and Threatening Behaviors

Before proceeding to management procedures or treatment goals, an understanding of various types of aggression is necessary. In general, threats and aggression can be either offensive or defensive in nature. The communication signals associated with these two motivations tend to be the opposite of one another.

An offensively threatening or aggressive dog can display some or all of the following body postures that make him appear larger and more intimidating:

- Tail up
- Ears up
- Stiff, straight-legged stance
- Piloerection (hackles up)
- Lips retracted vertically to show the canine teeth
- Often moving toward the threat
- Making direct eye contact

A defensively threatening or aggressive dog can assume some or all of the following more self-protective and fearful postures and behaviors:

- Tail down
- Ears down or back
- Dilated eyes
- Possible piloerection
- Partially crouched position, leaning away from the threat
- Remaining stationary or moving away from the approaching threat
- Avoiding eye contact

Many dogs show mixed motivations or are ambivalent, displaying both offensive and defensive elements in their behavior.

Within these two broad categories are many different types of aggression. The type is determined by the context in which it occurs, by the dog's behavior prior to and following the attack, and by the communication signals the dog displays. Sometimes, it's very difficult to categorize aggression more specifically than offensive or defensive. The behavioral descriptions of when the aggression occurs and the associated body postures often don't fit well into any of the classification schemes in the scientific literature on aggression. In addition, dogs may display more than one type of aggression, which contributes to the difficulty in categorization. (The more I work with dog aggression problems, the less satisfied I am with any of the classification schemes in the scientific literature.) Yet even if it's not possible to put a name to the type of aggression, at least a list should be made of all the contexts or eliciting stimuli for the behavior.

Determining the type of aggression is important in order to make predictions about what situations may trigger the behavior. Although I am referring to the categories of *aggression*, they also apply to different types of threatening behavior as well, as defined earlier. These categories include:

- Dominance
- Possessive
- Fear
- Territorial
- Protective
- Play
- Redirected
- Pain-elicited
- Maternal
- Idiopathic
- Predatory

Components of a behavioral history. Questions that will help you distinguish among these categories are divided in the following passages into several sections. You'll notice that some of these questions may overlap one another or that they seem to ask for the same information in a slightly different way. The reason for this is to help clarify what the owner is telling you. Sometimes, when obtaining a behavioral history, the answers to questions may seem to contradict each other. Asking questions in slightly different ways helps you to clear up these inconsistencies and be more confident that you have an accurate picture of what's going on. In addition, as mentioned in previous chapters, the owner's answers to the questions influence what other questions need to be asked.

If the problem involves aggression between dogs, obtain all of the behavioral history information on both dogs, if they are in the same family. If the problem involves a nonfamily dog, try to obtain at least all of the information in the first section that follows.

Description of the dog, description of the behavior.
- What breed is the dog?
- How old is the dog?
- Is she spayed/he neutered?
- What specific agonistic behaviors is the dog displaying? (Have the owner describe them in detail. Ask what is the dog doing?)
- What body postures does the dog exhibit during an aggressive or threatening episode? (Ask this question if the answer to preceding question does not completely describe what the dog looks like during an episode; elicit additional details about his body postures such as tail and ear carriage, whether the eyes are dilated, etc. Then consider whether these fit the pattern of an offensive, defensive or mixed [or ambivalent] posture.)
- If the dog has made contact with a person or animal's body during a threatening or aggressive episode, what was the result—e.g., torn clothes, bruised skin, red mark, puncture wound, stitches required, etc.?
- Have the owner describe all threatening or aggressive incidents, in chronological order if possible. Ask the owner to include a description of the setting or surroundings immediately prior to each incident, the incident itself (including the details asked for in the preceding questions), and what happened immediately after each incident (what the owner did, what other people or dogs did, what the victim did, what the problem dog did).

Description of the dog's daily routine, environment, and behavior patterns.
- Is the dog taken for frequent walks around the neighborhood along the same route? How does the dog behave on walks (is he happy, excited, on patrol, alert, watchful, fearful, barking, repeatedly urine marking, etc.)?
- How does a typical day for the dog go (including the feeding routine, where the dog sleeps, etc.)?
- Is the dog outside in the yard with opportunities to threaten or bark at passersby or other dogs? How frequently does this happen? What kind of fence surrounds the yard?
- What kinds of games or toys does the dog enjoy? How does he play?
- Has the dog been to obedience classes? If so, how did he react to the people and other dogs? What kinds of training techniques were used (e.g., food reinforcement, negative reinforcement, choke chains, pinch collars)? How did he perform?

- When and from where was the dog obtained? What is known about the dog's early history, including his socialization history? Do any known relatives have similar problems?
- How often is the dog required to perform simple commands such as sit, down, and stay? Under what circumstances? How does the dog respond to these commands (e.g., obeys willingly, slow to respond, acts aggressive or threatening, etc.)? What does the owner do if the dog doesn't respond?
- How does the dog react to visitors to the home?
- How does the dog react at the veterinary clinic, the boarding kennel, and the grooming shop?
- How does the dog react to unfamiliar dogs?
- If there are multiple animals in the family, how does the dog get along with them?
- If the problem involves fighting between family dogs, how long have they lived together?
- How were the dogs originally introduced to each other?
- What is the owner's opinion about which dog is "the boss"? What is the basis for this opinion? (Ask the owner to describe specific competitive interactions and their outcomes, such as who can control toys, favorite sleeping places, and priority access to the owner.)
- Does "who's the boss" vary based on context?
- Has "who's the boss" changed recently?
- Do the owners allow one dog to control the behavior of the other dog—e.g., take toys away, intimidate (through body postures) the other dog to move from a favorite resting place, push the other dog out of the way to get closer to the owner, etc.?
- Does one dog in the family clearly defer to or act submissive to the other dog? How does the submissive dog communicate this? How does the dominant dog react?
- Is this submissive dog being attacked despite her subordinate position?

Specifics about the occurrence of the problem behavior.
- Is the behavior shown *only* toward unfamiliar people or other dogs?
- Is the behavior only shown toward family members, including family dogs, or toward individuals whom the dog sees frequently and is very familiar with?
- Is the behavior shown toward both family and nonfamily members (dogs and people)? Is the behavior in these cases the same or different (e.g., does the dog bite family members but growl at visitors)?
- Does the behavior occur only on the owner's property, in the car, or in other familiar areas where dog spends time (e.g., a familiar walking route)?
- Does the dog lunge toward people or other dogs? Does he shy or back away? Does he do both? If so, in what sequence?
- Will the dog chase the person or other dog? Are these individuals walking, running, or playing? If people are being chased, are they skateboarders, joggers, bicyclists, etc.?
- Does the behavior occur only when the dog is with the owner or another family dog and an unfamiliar individual (human or dog) approaches? If yes, does this occur both on and off what the dog views as "his" property? Will the behavior

occur regardless of whether the owner or other family dogs are present?

- Does the behavior occur when the dog is on his own (off leash on a walk, by himself in the yard, etc.) and another person or dog approaches?
- Is the dog a nursing mother with puppies?
- If so, does the behavior occur only when a person or other dog approaches the puppies or the nest area?
- Does the behavior occur when an individual (person or dog)
  — Stares at the dog?
  — Attempts to take away an object the dog possesses?
  — Attempts to take away only certain objects, such as something the dog shouldn't have (such as "stolen" tissues or socks)?
  — Walks by the dog when he has possession of an object?
  — Approaches or gets too close to the food dish while the dog is eating?
  — Touches the dog while he is eating?
  — Attempts to pick up an object that is lying near the dog?
  — Walks by the dog when he is resting? Disturbs or moves the dog while he is resting? Does this occur only in certain resting locations, such as a bed or couch?
  — Jostles or gets too close to the dog in confined areas, such as walking down a hallway?
  — Attempts to interact with the dog when he is under or behind something, such as a table or couch?
- Does the dog have episodes in which he vocalizes or otherwise acts as if he's in pain?
- Does the behavior occur during play?
- Does the behavior occur when the dog is prevented or thwarted from biting or threatening another individual?
- Does the behavior occur when a visitor
  — Rings the doorbell?
  — Enters the house or yard (person or other dog)?
  — Gets up and moves around after being seated in the house?
  — Walks toward the dog or attempts to pet him?
  — Approaches or touches a family member (person or other dog)?
  — Leaves the house?
  — Turns and moves away from the dog (person or other dog)?
- When (how long ago) was the first aggressive or threatening episode? What were the circumstances? How has the problem behavior changed since it first began?
- How old was the dog when the problem started?
- Was the dog intact at that time?
- Is the dog threatening or aggressive to unfamiliar people, such as invited visitors to the home, delivery people, or mail carriers?
- Does the behavior occur when a person (identify if familiar/family member or unfamiliar/visitor)
  — Reaches to touch or pull on the dog's neck or collar, put a leash or head halter on the dog?

— Is attempting to punish the dog? What type of punishment is used? Is the punishment contingent or noncontingent (after the fact) on the dog's behavior? Is the punishment causing physical pain?
— Attempts to restrain the dog in any way, including hugging?
— Attempts to pick up the dog?
— Attempts to wipe feet, clip nails, brush or bathe the dog or do any other kind of grooming?
— Pets the dog?
— Hits or raises a hand or arm as though to hit the dog?
— Attempts to touch certain parts of the dog's body?
— Hugs or shows affection toward another family member (person or other dog)?
- Are any family members afraid of the dog or afraid to do certain things with or to the dog?
- Is the behavior shown toward unfamiliar dogs (i.e., nonfamily dogs)?
- What seems to trigger fights between dogs in the family?
- Do the fights occur only in high-arousal situations, such as greeting the owner or running to the door when the doorbell rings?
- How have the fights ended? Did one dog give in, one dog terminate the attack, one or both dogs have to be pulled away, etc.? If the latter, did either struggle to continue the attack?
- Is the dog biting or killing small animals, such as cats, birds, rabbits, and ferrets?

Owners' attempts at problem resolution and the dog's response.
- Has the owner attempted to punish the behavior? If so, how? What was the dog's response?
- Has medication been used?
- Has the dog's daily routine or his normal activity been modified because of the problem? If so, how?
- What have the owners done immediately after an aggressive or threatening incident?
- What do they do if they believe an episode is impending?
- Have the owners interfered or reprimanded one family dog for harmless threats (e.g., growling, posturing) directed toward another family dog?
- What else has been tried to resolve the problem? What have the results been?

Differential results of the behavioral history. Answers to these questions will reveal the following information, depending on the type of aggression:

Dominance aggression. There are many definitions of dominance aggression. The more I work with aggression cases, the more difficult it is to define this category. I will define it here as an offensive type of aggression seen in competitive interactions over control of resources or in response to what the dog perceives as dominant or challenging body postures, which could indicate a threat to his social status. Dominance aggression can be displayed toward either people or other dogs; however, it is generally displayed only toward individuals with whom the dog has developed a social relationship. This means it is usually directed at family members (human or dog). It is generally not shown toward people or other dogs the dog does not know well.

If the aggression is displayed only when the dog's possession of objects such as food, toys, space, etc., is threatened, without the status component, it may be defined as possessive aggression (see following). With dogs in the same family, the owner can be viewed as a possession that the dogs will compete over to gain priority access. Examples of human and dog behavior that can trigger this possessive or competitive component of the problem are given in Box 12.6.

Box 12.6 Examples of human and canine behaviors that may trigger dominance aggression

Following are some behaviors that may trigger dominance aggression related to control of resources or competitive interactions. This is not an all-inclusive list.

- Attempting to take anything away from the dog, including toys, chewies, and "stolen" objects such as discarded tissues
- Approaching too close to an object, such as a toy, that is near the dog
- Moving the dog while he is resting, with the intent of "controlling" the location
- Assuming a position next to the dog on furniture
- Having another family dog approach the owner or get between the problem dog and the owner
- Passing too close to the dog's food bowl or sometimes just entering the room it is in
- Being in close quarters and competing for space, as in hallways or doorways
- Being in high-arousal situations, such as rushing to greet the owner or visitors to the home (dog-to-dog aggression)

Dominance aggression is also triggered when the dog is the recipient of what he perceives to be dominant behaviors from another animal or person or if these individuals fail to display the proper appeasement behavior in response to dominant behavior from him. Examples of human behavior that could trigger dominance aggression are given in Box 12.7.

Box 12.7 Examples of human behavior that may trigger dominance aggression

Following are some behaviors that may trigger dominance aggression related to social status and perceived dominant or threatening gestures. This is not an all-inclusive list.

- Reaching for the collar
- Putting on the collar, including a head collar
- Petting on the head
- Hugging or kissing the dog
- Disturbing the dog while he is resting
- Requiring the dog to move from a resting place
- Reaching for the dog while he is under a table, chair, etc.
- Attempting punishment (saying no, shaking a finger at the dog)
- Positioning or commanding the dog to lie down, roll over, or even sit
- Stepping or leaning over the dog
- Attempting to restrain the dog in such situations as grooming, nail clipping, giving a bath, and wiping or removing something from his feet
- Picking up the dog
- Making eye contact

Dominance aggression toward other family dogs is usually caused by some sort of instability in the dominance hierarchy. Dominance between dogs is context-specific. For instance, one dog may be able to control the favorite resting place, but another dog can control access to toys. In some relationships, the same dog may be dominant across contexts. Problems arise when one dog's dominant position has in some way been undermined. Examples of initiating events for fights between family dogs caused by dominance problems are given in Box 12.8. Fights can also occur during high-arousal situations, such as when the doorbell rings or when dogs are racing to the door to go outside or greet owners. I've also had several cases in which one dog bit another family dog immediately after being shocked by an antibark collar. In these kinds of cases, other dominance instabilities in the relationship are often not apparent.

> **Box 12.8 Examples of contributing causes or initiating events for "canine rivalry" problems**
>
> Following are some causes of aggression problems between family dogs due to dominance aggression.
>
> - Owners have attempted to treat both dogs equally without supporting the ability of one dog to control resources (such as toys) or to control the other dog's behavior in competitive contexts (such as pushing in closest to the owner for petting)
> - Owners have not allowed the dominant dog to display normal ritualized behaviors and threats to establish or maintain a dominant position (e.g., growling, muzzle grabbing, standing over, mounting, etc.)
> - Introduction of new dog to household or loss of a resident dog
> - Reintroduction of a resident dog after an absence (usually prolonged but sometimes as little as several hours)
> - Resident dog reaching the age of sexual maturity (even if neutered)
> - Previously dominant dog aging or being ill
> - One or more resident dogs being sexually intact

There are dogs who, when greeting unfamiliar dogs, use very dominant, challenging body postures (see previous description of offensive postures). If the other dog assumes a subordinate role and displays the appropriate appeasement postures, the greeting may stay friendly. If, however, the second dog challenges back, the problem dog may initiate a fight. I am categorizing this as another form of dominance aggression by assuming that the dogs are attempting to establish a social relationship. This scenario doesn't quite fit the generally accepted assumption that dominance aggression occurs only between individuals who have an existing social relationship. However, it fits even less well in any of the other categories (an example of the somewhat arbitrary nature of classification!).

The age of onset of dominance aggression directed toward people is most commonly reported as between 1 and 2 years of age and is more common in males than females[12]. Owners often describe their dogs as having "Jekyll and Hyde" personalities, getting a "funny look" in their eyes right before the aggressive display, or acting "sorry" afterward. However, in fights between family dogs, which are presumed to be related to dominance, one study showed that females were more likely to initiate the aggression[14].

It would be expected that because dominance is about control and social status, the aggressive dog would display offensive body postures. However, I've seen aggression cases in which, though the context would indicate dominance aggression, the dog's body postures were more defensive. This could be the result of a mixed motivation. If owners have previously attempted to punish the dog, his body postures could have become more defensive over time because he is anticipating punishment. The dog would thus react to both the competitive nature of the interaction as well as the threat of punishment. This is another example of why careful questioning of the owner and observations of the dog are essential in diagnosing aggression cases.

By now, you should appreciate the complexities of dominance aggression and realize the inadvisability of taking a "quick fix" or "show him who's boss" approach.

Possessive aggression. Possessive aggression occurs when an animal is in possession of food, toys, or other valued resources and does not want to relinquish them. (Keep in mind that owners can be viewed as possessions, as can resting and sleeping places such as the dog's crate, favorite chair, dog bed, etc.) This may happen when the objects are merely near the dog (not necessarily in his mouth) and an individual (either person or dog) tries to pick them up or even just gets too close to them. As described previously, this is sometimes thought of as a subcategory of dominance aggression. However, dogs may show possessive aggression without other signs of dominance aggression. They may direct this behavior toward other dogs, cats or other animals (less often), or people. Possessive aggression may be associated with either defensive or offensive postures.

Fear aggression. This is a defensive type of aggression that occurs when the dog perceives its physical safety is threatened or when his "critical distance" (personal space) is invaded. It can be displayed in response to anything the dog is afraid of, ranging from someone reaching to pet him to the approach of another dog to someone raising a hand as if to strike the dog. In the popular literature, an animal displaying this type of aggression is referred to as a "fear-biter." Fearfully aggressive or threatening animals will not generally chase their opponent or continue their behavior once the opponent has retreated outside the critical distance or stopped the threatening behavior.

Fear-motivated aggression is associated with defensive body postures. It is not uncommon for there to be a component of fear or defensive behavior combined with other types of aggression. People often don't realize that a dog can be fearful and aggressive at the same time. I often hear, "I don't think he was really being aggressive, I think he was just afraid." Such a statement suggests that the individual equates aggression with offensive behavior.

I have seen many cases of fear-related aggression or other types of defensively motivated aggression misdiagnosed as dominance aggression. This often happens in cases where the aggression has occurred when the dog is being hugged, reached for to be petted, restrained, or approached by another dog. Although these could be contexts in which dominance aggression is displayed, careful questioning of the owner should reveal defensive body postures and often descriptions of avoidance, appeasement, or even displacement behaviors exhibited by the dog prior to the aggressive episode. There will be an absence of any behavior that would indicate a dominance problem, such as difficulty moving the dog while resting and other reactions listed in Boxes 12.6 to 12.8.

Fear-motivated aggression—not dominance aggression—is the most common type of aggression I see. Dogs in animal shelters and at veterinary clinics are far more likely to display fear-motivated aggression than dominance aggression. Remember that dominance aggression is usually not displayed toward people with whom the dog does not have a social relationship.

Territorial aggression. Territorial aggression occurs when a dog is defending its home area against intruders (or those he *perceives* to be intruders), either human or animal. The doorbell is a significant trigger for this kind of aggression. It can also occur in response to a visitor entering the dog's yard or passing by or reaching into the car. Delivery people and mail carriers are common triggers for this behavior. Territorial aggression is so easily reinforced because, from the dogs' perspective, their behavior causes people or other dogs to leave (in other words, it works for the them).

A dog's sense of territory may extend well beyond the legal limits of an owner's property to areas that the dog visits frequently. Thus, territorial aggression can also be the motivation for dogs threatening and lunging at other dogs and people when being walked on a familiar route (which the dog has come to perceive as "his"). When meeting people or other dogs away from what he perceives to be his territory, the dog is friendly. The behavior occurs regardless of whether the owner is present. Territorial aggression may be associated with either defensive or offensive postures.

Protective aggression. Protective aggression occurs when an animal is defending one or more members of its social group (human or canine) from a *perceived* threat. Some authorities include maternal aggression in this category. Others view territorial aggression as a special type of protective aggression that includes the protection of a home or breeding area[2]. However, if categorized separately, territorial and protective aggression can be distinguished from one another because the latter has to do with the presence of the dog's social group and can occur off the dog's territory.

Owners frequently misinterpret other types of aggression as protective aggression. They will often assume the dog's behavior is protective if the behavior occurs when a person or other dog approaches the dog and owner when they are together. In many of these cases, however, the dog's behavior is motivated by fear and the dog is actually attempting to keep someone away from himself, not his owner. It's more of a "keep out of my personal space" behavior in these cases, not a protective behavior. To classify aggression or threats as protective, I look for behavior from the approaching person or animal that the dog could perceive as a threat—someone reaching toward the owner to shake hands (I never shake hands at the door with people when I'm seeing an aggressive case), give a hug, or hand over a package; wrestling games between family members; or other dogs running up or jumping up on the owner in greeting. A dog may also display protective aggression directed toward the owner when he or she is attempting to punish another family dog.

If protective behavior is the motivation, the dog will usually be positioned in front of the owner or other family dog but possibly alongside instead (although I've heard people erroneously describe the dog as being protective when, in fact, he is hiding behind them!). Protective aggression may be associated with either defensive or offensive postures. Problems with protective aggression, at least in my practice, are much less common than problems with dominance, fear, territorial, and possessive aggression.

Another misconception about both territorial and protective aggression is that higher-ranking animals are more protective and territorial. Although objective data on this have never been gathered on dogs, there is no evidence of this in research on other species (primates, wolves)[16]. Once again, dominance has nothing to do with territoriality and protectiveness.

Play aggression. The term *play aggression* is really an oxymoron. Play is not intended to harm, but aggression is. However, the term is functional in describing either injuries or threats that occur *during* play. The play behaviors of most predatory species are similar to their predatory behaviors and involve pouncing, stalking, chasing, shaking, biting, etc. Playful aggression is seen most frequently in puppies and young adult dogs, but it can also occur in older adults who never learned any limits of play or from whom rough play has been encouraged. Bites often do not break the skin, although they can be painful because of the sharpness of the young animal's teeth. A variety of body postures can be seen during play-motivated aggression, and the determination of play as a cause for the behavior must be made based on the context, occurrence of playful postures (such as the play bow), and ruling out other types of aggression.

Redirected aggression. Redirected aggression is aggressive behavior that is directed toward an individual (a person or another animal) who did not trigger the initial aggressive response. It usually occurs when an animal is prevented or blocked from directing the threat or aggression to its primary target. The original trigger for the aggression is often a territorial or fear motivation. A classic example is two dogs in a backyard reacting to a dog walking down the sidewalk. They can't get to the dog on the sidewalk, so one turns and attacks the other. Another example would be a dog who is threatening other dogs in an obedience class as they pass by and then turns and snaps at his owner. A third example would be a dog who is fighting with another dog and bites a person who is intervening in the fight. Dogs typically do not redirect to subordinates[17], so potential dominance problems should be thoroughly evaluated if a dog is displaying redirected aggression to its owner. Redirected aggression may be associated with either defensive or offensive postures.

Pain-elicited aggression. Pain-elicited aggression is a defensive aggression in response to physical pain or discomfort; it is classified under fearful aggression by some. Pain stemming from punishment is classified either in this category or under fearful aggression. Mild attempts at punishment (e.g., a verbal no) can also be associated with dominance aggression. Pain-elicited aggression is seen only in response to painful stimulation or, sometimes, what the dog anticipates will be painful. For example, if the dog has had an ear infection and handling or medicating the ears has been painful, future attempts to touch or manipulate his ears may produce an aggressive response.

Maternal aggression. Maternal aggression is a defensive type of aggression displayed when the female perceives her offspring are threatened. This can be triggered just by having an unfamiliar person or even a family member or another family dog walk into the room. There is no evidence that dogs who show maternal aggression are more likely to have other types of aggression problems once the puppies are weaned.

Idiopathic aggression. Idiopathic aggression is an unpredictable type of aggression that is not well understood. It often involves very intense, unpredictable aggressive responses in reaction to relatively mild stimuli[18]. The contexts in which the behavior occurs often are similar to those that might trigger dominance aggression, but the dog's response seems to be out of all proportion to the situation[19]. Owners sometimes say the dog acts confused, doesn't seem to know where he is, or gets a glazed look in his eye. The latter has also been described in some cases of dominance aggression, but some authors believe that the presence of this characteristic would place it in the idiopathic category[5]. This form of aggression has been referred to by a variety of anthropomorphic terms, including *rage*[19] and *mental lapse syndrome*[20]. It is not known whether there is associated pathology in the nervous system or if the behavior is the result of epilepsy[5, 18]. Certain breeds may be predisposed to this problem, including Bernese mountain dogs, English cocker spaniels, springer spaniels, St. Bernards, Doberman pinschers, and German shepherds[18, 21]. My personal experience would add Lhaso apsos to this list.

Predatory aggression. Many behaviorists do not consider predatory aggression to be aggression at all because it is not a social conflict behavior. The goal of predation is to obtain food or at least to kill the prey. It is not displayed in relation to social conflicts and may be seen more commonly in groups of dogs rather than individuals. True predatory behavior is usually not accompanied by threatening behavior, such as vocalizing, snarling, baring teeth, etc. When dogs kill birds, cats, and other small animals, this is probably predatory behavior.

When dogs chase bicyclists or joggers, however, this may not be predatory behavior but territorial behavior, in some cases also involving a fear component[22]. The dog may display territorial behavior only toward fast-moving stimuli and not people walking because the faster movement creates a stronger eliciting stimulus. Herding behavior is predatory behavior arrested before the onset of the final killing attack, and therefore, it would also not be classified as aggressive behavior[23].

True predatory attacks on people are rare, but of the fatal attacks by dogs or groups of dogs on children or babies, many are the result of predatory behavior[24]. Dogs may view infants not as small people but as small mammals and therefore prey.

5. Discuss Ways to Manage or Control the Behavior over the Short or Long Term

The most important aspect in the management of an aggression problem is keeping people and other animals safe from the threatening or aggressive behavior of the dog. This may involve environmental management, preventing the behavior from being triggered, or successfully getting the dog to inhibit the behavior under some conditions. Remember that management techniques do not change the dog's response from aggressive to nonaggressive.

General management procedures—no behavioral diagnosis. Few recommendations can be safely given regarding aggressive behavior without establishing a behavioral diagnosis or at least developing a comprehensive list of triggering stimuli or contexts obtained in the behavioral history. Without a diagnosis, you simply cannot know what is triggering the aggression. Consequently, the aggression must be viewed as unpredictable until sufficient information can be obtained to categorize the aggression and make predictions about what triggers the dog. If you do not have the time or expertise to arrive at a behavioral diagnosis or obtain the list of triggers, you should refer the case. You should also tell the owner to keep the dog away from people and other animals he may bite; if this is not possible, the dog should be muzzled.

Although muzzling the dog and restricting his activities are good recommendations to keep people and other animals safe, they are not good long-range recommendations in terms of the dog's quality of life or affecting the problem behavior in a positive manner. That's why your better option is to refer the case to a behavior specialist with experience in handling aggression cases. Of course, if you are a veterinarian, you should first evaluate the dog's medical status, and other professionals should refer the owner to the veterinarian and a behaviorist, as well.

Management procedures based on a diagnosis.

Dominance. Management for dominance aggression would mean avoiding those interactions that trigger the aggression. For owners, this means not confronting the dog and ceasing all physical or interactive punishment. It might also mean not attempting to take items away, avoiding dominant signals directed at the dog, or any other type of interaction that might trigger the aggression. If these stimuli cannot be predicted with certainty, the dog may need to be muzzled when interacting with family members.

For dominance problems between family dogs, management may entail avoiding stimuli that trigger a competitive interaction, such as not giving the dogs rawhides or other highly prized items or separating them when rawhides are available. It may also mean housing the dogs separately until professional help can be enlisted or muzzling one or both if they must be together. One or both dogs may also be kept on leash when the owner is home if the fights have occurred in the owner's presence. Actually, many fights between resident dogs occur *only* in the owner's presence, so the dogs can safely be left alone together in some cases. *You must have a thorough behavior history and be confident in this conclusion before you make this recommendation. Put bluntly, you do not want the owner coming home to a dead or injured dog because you told her it was okay to leave them alone together.*

For dominance problems involving greeting unfamiliar dogs, one management option is to keep the family dog away from other dogs temporarily. If this is not possible, the dog should not be allowed to run loose, since the owner would have no control over the animal's behavior should another dog appear. Although tight leash restraint can make these problems worse, at least a loose leash or long line should be used so the dog can be removed from the situation if necessary. A muzzle won't change the behavior, but it will prevent other dogs from being injured.

Management may also involve the use of medication (see chapter 18).

Possessive. If the possessive aggression predictably occurs over certain objects, such as rawhides, do not allow the dog to have access to them in the short term. If this is not possible because of the nature of the object or if "mistakes" occur, do not confront the dog or attempt to take the object away. Instead, substitute another behavior—call the dog into the kitchen for a treat, get the leash out and take the dog for a short walk, call the dog to go for a ride in the car, etc. This approach does not reinforce the possessive behavior because the dog has been required to perform intervening behaviors (come, sit, etc.) prior to the positive consequences. If a walk or ride is promised, however, the owner must follow through (even briefly); otherwise the dog may quickly learn that this is just a ploy and refuse to leave the object.

Fear. As with any other fear-motivated problem, management of fear-based aggression means not allowing the dog to experience the stimuli that trigger the fear (see chapter 11) and therefore the aggression. Medication can be used to manage the dog's behavior over the short term, as well (see chapter 18).

Territorial. Managing territorial aggression means (you guessed it!) not putting the dog in situations that trigger the behavior. How this is done will depend on the context in which the behavior occurs. It may mean modifying the dog's regular walking route and substituting unfamiliar locations she doesn't consider hers. It may mean crating her in the car so she can't see people or other dogs or maybe not taking her at all if crating does not prevent the behavior. A doggie seat belt, which is a harness that attaches to the car's seat belt, prevents the dog from lunging at the windows, pacing, or jumping around in the car.

The dog may need to be left inside during the day rather than being allowed to threaten people or dogs walking by the yard. Management may mean not letting other dogs visit the home temporarily, and confinement when visitors are expected or when the doorbell rings. Many dogs are very accepting of and friendly toward people once they are in the house and seated, so in such a case, the dog could be released from confinement at that point. The doorbell can be disconnected temporarily if this is helpful in decreasing the intensity of the dog's response and making him more manageable.

Some territorial responses can be managed by putting the dog on leash when answering the door. Having the dog sit and stay manages the problem by not allowing him to charge the door, although it does not, by itself, decrease his motivation to do so.

Protective. Discourage behaviors from people or other dogs that could trigger protective aggression. For example, suspend family wrestling games temporarily, or don't shake hands with strangers in the dog's presence. Another management option would be for the owner to approach other people and dogs rather than waiting for their approach. If the pet's behavior is triggered by the approach of other dogs, don't allow other dogs to visit, try changing the dog's walking route or time to decrease the probability of encountering loose dogs, or don't allow other dogs to approach in an uncontrolled manner.

Play. The dog should not be allowed to engage in those types of behavior that trigger play aggression. Play only fetching games, perhaps, but no wrestling or tug-of-war if the latter present problems.

Redirected. Redirected aggression may be difficult to manage because it sometimes is impossible to prevent situations that trigger the initial aggressive response. If, in a multidog family, the redirected behavior is occurring in reaction to another dog walking by, the family dogs may need to be outside one at a time, or one or both might be kept inside during the day in the owner's absence. If the problem is occurring in an obedience class, the dog could be given private lessons or be worked in class at a greater distance from the other dogs until the problem resolves.

Pain-elicited. This is an easy one, right? Don't cause the dog pain! If the pain is due to an injury, disease, or illness, the veterinarian should be consulted for proper treatment and pain medication, if needed. The dog may need to be muzzled when administering medical treatments.

Maternal. Maternal aggression is usually self-resolving once the puppies are weaned and gone. In the meantime, people and other dogs who trigger the behavior should not be allowed near the dam. If this includes all family members to the point that no one can care for the dog, a problem-resolution approach will be necessary. Another option would be to try to call the dam away from the puppies before approaching her, feeding her, etc.

Idiopathic. By definition, the reason for this behavior is not understood and the behavior is unpredictable, so it may be very difficult to manage idiopathic aggression. The dog may need to be muzzled, or his interactions with people he is likely to bite may need to be severely limited. Medication is sometimes used as either a management or a treatment option (see chapter 18).

Predatory. Managing a predatory problem is best done by not allowing the dog to be either off leash or unsupervised, which would give him the chance to chase and kill small mammals. Alternatively, he could be muzzled. If predatory behavior toward people, especially children, is suspected, professional help should be sought immediately and the dog should be muzzled and on leash if he can't be confined away from children. Euthanasia may need to be considered.

6. Explain the Goals of an Appropriate Behavior Modification Plan

There is one overriding goal in the treatment of any aggression problem—the safety of all individuals involved. This must be accomplished by whatever means are necessary. A muzzle is often required, particularly when treatment has progressed to the point of putting a person or other animal within biting range.

Euthanasia is always a consideration in aggression cases. Often, however, owners need to try treatment before they make a decision about euthanasia. There is a fine line between making sure owners recognize the risks, doing your best to prevent someone from being hurt, and at the same time understanding the wishes of the owners in terms of trying to work with the problem before deciding to order the death of their pet. There is no one, best option that fits every case; each situation must be evaluated individually. More information about talking to people regarding euthanasia can be found in chapter 17.

In chapter 6, I said that explaining the goals of a behavior modification plan may or may not include the actual treatment procedures. At this step in the protocol for an aggression case, you must decide if it is appropriate for you to be a problem solver. Make sure you have thought through the knowledge, liability, and attitude issues that were discussed at the beginning of this chapter. If you've jumped to this section to find out what to do about a particular case, go back and read the beginning of the chapter before you proceed along a problem-resolution path. The decision to work with an aggression case should not be made lightly. Both you and the owner need to proceed with realistic expectations of the risks involved. Counterconditioning and systematic desensitization (CCSD) are frequently used with aggression cases, so you should be very knowledgeable and experienced in these techniques. An example of a hypothetical, partial CCSD program is given in Box 12.9.

Box 12.9 Example of a hypothetical, partial counterconditioning and desensitization plan for a fear-motivated aggression problem

This is not a "cookbook" recipe for the problem because the characteristics of the situation and how they are manipulated are completely dependent on the specifics of each case. **See chapter 11 for a review of the CCSD protocol.**

In this hypothetical case, the problem dog is growling, air snapping, and sometimes showing his teeth when a variety of people approach or attempt to interact with him. Factors that could influence the behavior of such a dog are used in the examples that follow.

1. **Evaluate all the characteristics of the stimulus or situation that influence the animal's response.**
   A list of possibilities might be:

   - How close the person is to the dog—the farther away, the less fearful
   - Gender of the person—the dog is more afraid of men than women
   - Adult or child—the dog is more afraid of adults than children
   - What the person looks like or wears—hats and beards elicit more fear
   - The person's behavior—the dog is less afraid when the person ignores him, more afraid if the person tries to touch him

2. **Determine the importance of these characteristics relative to each other, from most to least important.**

   1. Distance
   2. Person's behavior
   3. Adult or child
   4. Gender
   5. What the person looks like or wears

3. **Determine the behavioral starting point (a situation involving these characteristics in which the aggression is not elicited).**
   The easiest situation would feature a female child, not wearing a hat, at a distance, ignoring the dog. Another dog could have a different behavioral starting point—an adult female wearing a hat, at a distance, softly talking to the dog. The starting point is different in each case.

   (Box continues)

4. **Use the prioritized list to create "practice" situations. These consist of exposing the dog to the modified and controlled versions of the problem situation while pairing these experiences with enjoyable stimuli for the dog, such as food, toys, petting, etc.**

1. Female child, not wearing a hat, at a distance, ignoring the dog (although the dog is aware of her), owner gives dog a tidbit
2. Female child, wearing a hat, at a distance, ignoring the dog (although the dog is aware of her), owner gives dog a tidbit
3. Repeat step 1 with a male child
4. Repeat step 1 with a female adult
5. Repeat step 1 with the female child reaching toward the dog as though to pet him
6. Repeat step 1 with the female child closer to the dog (perhaps close enough to drop a treat on the ground near his feet) but otherwise ignoring him
7. Male child, wearing a hat, at a distance, ignoring the dog

Continue progressing by increasing the intensity of each characteristic one at a time. **Many repetitions of each step may be required before a behavior change is seen.** Variations of each characteristic will also be necessary, such as hats, beards, and glasses for the differences in clothing and appearance or reaching to pet the dog, leaning over him, or talking to him for the differences in the person's behavior.

5. **Each characteristic should be intensified individually, not simultaneously.**
The characteristics that are manipulated first are those that are less relevant to the dog. When one characteristic is made more difficult (e.g., adding a hat), another characteristic may temporarily need to be made less difficult (e.g., switching from adult to child). Refer to the examples in the previous step.

6. **Stimulus intensities should be increased gradually.**
For example, adding a hat could meaning starting first with a close-fitting cap and gradually increasing the size to a wide-brimmed, floppy hat (assuming that the dog is more afraid of larger hats). Decreasing distance might mean doing so literally one step at a time. Each version of the practice situation should be repeated until the dog is anticipating a pleasant outcome (e.g., looking for a tidbit) and his body postures and behavior are relaxed and friendly, without any sign of threats or aggression.

Owners also need to know that there is no set answer as to how long treatment will take. People often ask me, "How far am I supposed to get this week?" My answer is, "However far you get." You need to explain to owners that they do not progress to the next step in a treatment plan until they have seen the desired behavior change(s) in their dog at the current step. As discussed in the *realistic expectations* section, some treatment and management procedures may be lifelong.

Dominance.

Dominance aggression toward people. One of the goals in working with dominance aggression is to restructure the dominance hierarchy between owner and dog. This is not done through confrontational techniques (scruff shakes, alpha rolls) or physical force (hanging the dog). Instead, the interactional patterns between owner and dog are changed so that the owner does not provide things on demand for the dog. The dog always has to relinquish some degree of control to obtain what she wants from the owner (this is similar to the "nothing in life is free" concept mentioned in chapter 4). The starting point for these changes will be determined by the specifics of the case. The changes must be made in small increments, so that they can be successfully accomplished one by one. For example, if a dog refuses to lie down on command before being petted, trying to force the issue may result in a confrontation. However, the dog may willingly shake hands or sit (especially if a food reinforcer is used), so this would be the behavioral starting point; obeying the down command might be several incremental steps away. Positive reinforcement is always used in this process. A head halter (such as a Gentle Leader) can be very helpful in the treatment of dominance aggression (see product appendix), but care must be taken when the collar is put on because in some dogs, this can trigger a bite, snap, or other threatening behavior.

Another common goal is to teach the dog to enjoy accepting dominant gestures from the owner (reaching for the collar, wiping feet, whatever the triggering stimuli) or relinquishing control of important resources (toys, food, space, etc.) by using CCSD procedures. This is somewhat similar to the prevention approach discussed in chapter 4, although with existing problems, the incremental steps in desensitization are crucial. Punishment, confrontations, and situations in which the dog can reasonably be expected to "win" (e.g., retain possession of a rawhide because the owner can't take it away without being bitten) should be avoided during treatment. Drug therapy is somewhat controversial in any aggression case, but it may be helpful[1, 5] (see chapter 18). Many of the references listed at the end of the chapter provide more information on dominance aggression.

Dominance aggression toward other family dogs ("canine rivalry"). In this case, the treatment goals are to stabilize the dominance hierarchy among the dogs by supporting the dominant dog's position and also eliciting and reinforcing subordinate or submissive behavior from the other dogs. The dominant dog receives preferential treatment (gets fed first, petted first, etc.), and the other dogs are reinforced for waiting, as well as for assuming more subordinate postures (such as lying down) in the presence of the dominant dog. Which dog is dominant may depend on the context, as previously explained. Thus, one dog's dominance may be supported by feeding him first if this dog can control access to the food, but another dog may be supported in his ability to take a toy away. It is very important to obtain sufficient information in the behavioral history to know whose dominance should be supported when; the problem could worsen if the wrong choices are made.

Counterconditioning and desensitization procedures may also be necessary, especially if the dogs must be reintroduced to one another after being housed separately, so that they expect good things to happen as a consequence of being in each other's presence.

Dominance when greeting unfamiliar dogs. The goal of treatment is to elicit and reinforce more subordinate behaviors and postures from the dog when he greets or meets other dogs and for him to do the same in response to dominant behaviors and postures from the unfamiliar dog. This can be accomplished by using desensitization combined with either counterconditioning or counter-commanding or both. I find this a very difficult problem to treat for two reasons. First, desensitization requires setting up scenarios with very submissive dogs and gradually progressing to dogs who show more dominant behaviors during greetings. Finding and recruiting this continuum of dogs can be quite difficult logistically. Second, experience has taught me that it is very difficult to teach a dog to change his MO (method of operation) from one of challenging for dominance to accepting a subordinate role. Perhaps the second problem is a function of the former because it is difficult to arrange the scenarios necessary for successful treatment. This problem can, at times, be tackled under somewhat controlled conditions (e.g., with the dog on leash or near the owner so that the pace of the approach and greetings are managed), but most of my clients want success when their dogs are 30 feet ahead of them on a hiking trail and another off-leash dog appears. *That* is a challenge. A "Jolly Routine" (see chapter 4) may also be useful.

Possessive. The goal in treating possessive problems is to countercondition the dog by teaching him that relinquishment of objects causes wonderful things to happen (that is, that it is more rewarding to give up possessions than to retain them). In the case of food guarding, he should learn that having a person come near his food is not a bad thing but a desired event because it is associated with positive consequences, such as finding a piece of steak in his bowl. In the process, he should learn that people come to give, not take away. Put another way, his attitude should change from "stay away" to "please, somebody, walk near my food bowl."

It is almost always necessary to use desensitization in conjunction with counterconditioning. This means that the process might be started by tossing the piece of steak from a distance so that the aggression is not elicited and gradually moving closer. As with any CCSD program, the goal is to progress so gradually that the aggression is not elicited. Thus, it is important to identify the behavioral starting point—the version of the problem scenario in which the dog can be approached without eliciting a growl. This also means, in the short term, avoiding situations that elicit the aggression, as was discussed in the section on management. Refer to Box 12.9 for an example of a CCSD plan involving aggression. (Chapter 11 has additional examples.) Possessive aggression can be a component of dominance aggression, so the behavioral history should thoroughly evaluate this possibility.

Fear. As with any fear-related problem, CCSD techniques are used to change the dog's fearful response to one of calm tolerance. With fear-motivated problems, the dog uses threats and aggression to keep people or other animals away from him or to deter them from interacting with him in certain ways. Through the use of CCSD, the dog changes his attitude and associates these individuals with good things, so that the fear (and therefore the aggression) is no longer elicited. Food and toys are probably the most common stimuli used to create these positive associations. Countercommanding may also be helpful but not if used without CCSD. A hierarchy of the characteristics of interactions and of individuals (dog or human) that trigger the aggressive response must be determined in order to implement a desensitization program. (See chapter 11 and Box 12.9 for examples.)

Management procedures should also be implemented in the meantime because each time an aggressive or threatening response is triggered, it will significantly interfere with the dog learning the new associations. Fear- or defensive-motivated aggression is one situation in which medication may be very helpful in the short term (see chapter 18). However, if the aggression has an offensive component (i.e., mixed motivation), reducing the fear with medication may actually increase the potential for an offensively motivated bite[25].

Territorial. The goal in treating territorial aggression is to change the dog's perceptions. Rather than viewing people or other dogs in his territory as intruders, he is counterconditioned to view them as individuals he welcomes because their presence is associated with good things for him. (See the discussion of territorial barking in chapter 10.) Desensitization will need to be part of the treatment process. Countercommanding (having the dog be under more control by sitting, etc., rather than lunging, for example) may also be helpful if used in conjunction with CCSD. The judicious use of punishment (usually remote, such as an airhorn) to stop an aggressive response may be needed if the dog's threshold for the behavior is exceeded. Ideally, however, if the desensitization process is implemented correctly, the aggression will not be elicited.

Management procedures are usually needed during treatment, as well, because aggressive displays interfere with behavior change. Most behaviorists have not found medication helpful with territorial aggression[25]. However, one study found that with a subset of territorially aggressive dogs who were also fearful, reducing dietary protein levels did help[26].

Protective. Once again, the goal of a treatment program for protective aggression is to change the dog's expectations about what it means to have individuals (human or canine) approach his social group. Instead of perceiving individuals as potential threats, he should be counterconditioned and desensitized to anticipate and associate great things with their presence. The dog needs to learn that the behaviors he is seeing as threatening are not only innocuous but also predictive of good things for him. For example, if the dog has snapped at someone attempting to hug his owner, situations involving an easier version of the hug can be set up. Perhaps a person could act as though she were going to hug the owner but from a distance. At the same time, she would toss a tasty piece of steak toward the dog. The dog should not be threatened by this easier version of the problem situation, so he will be watching quietly while receiving his steak. Using many repetitions, this situation is incrementally made more like the actual situation of a person hugging the owner. Remember, though, that countercommanding can be helpful in gaining more control over the dog, but it is not a substitute for changing his motivation to be protective through counterconditioning.

Play. Play aggression is usually a pretty easy problem to treat. First, management procedures are very helpful because they keep the dog from engaging in the type of play that triggers the aggression. Tug-of-war and wrestling games are the common types of play that need to be temporarily avoided because they trigger the behavior. If more appropriate forms of play, such as fetch, still trigger the behavior, then negative punishment can be applied. This means taking away the dog's opportunity to play (ending the game) when the dog grabs or nips at the person. Remote punishment in the form of a blast from an air horn or an ultrasonic device, a squirt from a water bottle, or even a spray of citronella may also be appropriate to inhibit the behavior. The dog should then be given the opportunity to engage in appropriate play. Interactive procedures (scruff shaking, hitting, even verbal scolding) usually exacerbate the problem, either by exciting the dog into additional out-of-control play or by creating fear-related or other types of aggression problems.

Redirected. The goal of working with redirected aggression is to identify the triggering event and the type of aggression elicited and then to use the appropriate techniques to work with the dog's response to this event. If the aggression is being redirected to the owner, a thorough behavioral history should be obtained to determine if there is a dominance aggression problem, as well.

Pain-elicited. Theoretically, the goal of treatment procedures for pain-elicited aggression would be to help the dog tolerate pain without showing aggression. In one sense, this is not appropriate, as teaching a dog to tolerate unnecessary pain (e.g., pain delivered through punishment) is not a legitimate goal. However, in contexts in which medication or medical treatments cause pain (e.g., putting drops in infected ears, changing bandages, or administering physical therapy), treating the aggressive response is reasonable. This would best be done through CCSD techniques. An example of a starting point would be to barely touch the ears (without eliciting any pain) at times when they did not need to be treated and pairing this with a positive outcome, such as a tasty tidbit. Of course, if pain is unavoidable when the ears must be medicated, this will delay the counterconditioning process because touching the ears still causes pain. If the required medical treatment occurs more frequently than the counterconditioning sessions, little progress will be made.

Nail clipping is another context in which pain-elicited aggression can be triggered if the dog's nail have been quicked in the past. This may be a more reasonable scenario for using a CCSD program because many practice repetitions can be done before the real nail clipping must be done.

Maternal. CCSD techniques are the most appropriate treatments. Habituation (repeatedly having a person in the vicinity of the dam and puppies with no unpleasant outcomes) may be helpful. Management may suffice in many cases until the puppies are weaned.

Idiopathic. By nature, idiopathic aggression is not a very treatable problem, but management may be considered. Medication is also an option[5, 18, 19]. However, experts agree that euthanasia is the only option in some cases.

Predatory. Predatory aggression can be extremely difficult to work with. Management by keeping the dog on leash or fenced may be the best approach if the problem occurs when the dog is running loose. The dog could also be muzzled, but he will still have the potential to injure small animals by pawing or pinning them. Countercommanding or conditioning can be tried, but usually the dog is so motivated to engage in the predatory behavior that it is very difficult to find a way to reinforce a competing behavior.

Although controversial, the use of a remote-controlled shock collar may be an option when the behavior is directed toward animals. The collar should *not* be used as a punishment for the predation but rather in an avoidance paradigm: The dog is first taught to come when called using any kind of positive techniques, and shock is added later as a negative reinforcer. Only when the "coming when called" response is utterly reliable should the dog be exposed to situations that could trigger the predatory behavior. An incremental approach should be taken, starting with mild triggers. The shock should be used to induce the dog to choose coming when called over predation. The crucial point is that prior training has been done on the coming-when-called response, completely out of any context that would elicit predatory behavior. However, because this is a very complex procedure and shock is easily misused or abused, this technique should be implemented *only* by a behavior specialist who has an absolutely rock-solid understanding of the learning principles involved; he or she must also have impeccable timing. I have never used this technique, and were I to use it, I would work closely with colleagues who have employed it successfully. Remote-controlled shock collars of this nature, in my opinion, do not belong in the hands of the general public. A remote-controlled collar using citronella (see product appendix) is, I believe, more humane, but for some dogs, the citronella may not be sufficiently aversive to inhibit the predatory behavior.

If a dog has shown predatory behavior toward a person and has injured the individual, strict supervision and management is imperative. In these cases, euthanasia may be necessary to keep the community safe from a dog who truly presents a serious danger to people.

SUMMARY

Clearly, aggression problems are complicated and risky, and both you and the owners must give serious thought to the difficulties they entail before embarking on treatment. Given the frequency with which dog bites occur in this country, much more research must be done in understanding aggression problems and developing better ways to prevent and treat them. Not only do we need to work to protect people from dangerous dogs, we also need to protect dogs from outdated information and abusive procedures that have been used far too frequently in the name of training and treatment.

REFERENCES

1. Reisner, I.R. 1997. Assessment, management and prognosis of canine dominance-related aggression. *Vet. Clinics of North Amer. [Small Anim. Pract.]* 27 (3):479–796.

2. Borchelt, P.L., and V.L. Voith. 1996. Aggressive behavior in dogs and cats. In *Readings in companion animal behavior*, ed. V.L. Voith and P.L. Borchelt, 217–9. Trenton, N.J.: Veterinary Learning Systems.

3. Beck, A.M., and B.A. Jones. 1985. Unreported dog bites in children. *Public Health Reports* 100:315–21, as cited in J.M. Cornwell, 1997, Dog bite prevention: Responsible pet ownership and animal safety, JAVMA 210:1147–8.

4. Hunthausen, W. 1997. Effects of aggressive behavior on canine welfare. JAVMA 210:1134–6.

5. Overall, K.L. 1997. *Clinical behavioral medicine for small animals*. New York: Mosby.

6. Towell, T.L., and L.G. Shell. 1997. Endocrinopathies that affect the central nervous system of cats and dogs. In *Readings in companion animal behavior*, ed. V.L. Voith and P.L. Borchelt, 116–21. Trenton, N.J.: Veterinary Learning Systems.

7. Reisner, I. 1997. The pathophysiologic basis of behavior problems. *Vet. Clinics of North Amer. [Small Anim. Pract.]* 21 (2):207–24.

8. Drickamer, L.C., and S.H. Vessey. 1991. *Animal behavior*. 3rd edition. Dubuque, Iowa: William C. Brown.

9. Immelmann, K., and C. Beer. 1989. *A dictionary of ethology*. Cambridge, Mass.: Harvard University Press.

10. Lehner, P.L., Ph.D. 1998. Personal telephone communication, March.

11. Weston, D., and R. Ross. 1992. *Dog problems: The gentle modern cure*. New York: Howell Book House.

12. Borchelt, P.L., and V.L. Voith. 1996. Dominance aggression in dogs. In *Readings in companion animal behavior*, ed. V.L. Voith and P.L. Borchelt, 230–9. Trenton, N.J.: Veterinary Learning Systems.

13. Goodloe, L. 1997. Issues in description and measurement of temperament in companion dogs. In *Readings in companion animal behavior*, ed. V.L. Voith and P.L. Borchelt, 32–9. Trenton, N.J.: Veterinary Learning Systems.

14. Sherman, C.K., I.R. Reisner, L.A. Taliaferro, and K.A. Houpt. 1996. Characteristics, treatment, and outcome of 99 cases of aggression between dogs. *Appl. Anim. Beh. Sci.* 47:31–108.

15. Reisner, I.R., N.E. Hollis, and K.A. Houpt. 1994. Risk-factors for behavior related euthanasia among dominant aggressive dogs: 110 cases (1989–1992). *JAVMA* 205:855–63.

16. Wilson, E.O. 1975. *Sociobiology: The new synthesis*. Cambridge, Mass.: Belknap Press of Harvard University Press.

17. Voith, V.L. 1996. Communication and miscommunication between people and dogs. Presentation at American Veterinary Medical Association (AVMA) 133rd Annual Meeting, Louisville, Ky., July.

18. Hart, B.L., and L.A. Hart. 1985. *Canine and feline behavioral therapy*. Philadelphia: Lea and Febiger.

19. O'Farrell, V. 1992. *Manual of canine behaviour*. Shurdington, Cheltenham, Gloucestershire, United Kingdom: British Small Animal Veterinary Association.

20. Beaver, B.V. 1980. Mental lapse aggression syndrome. *J. Am. Anim. Hosp. Assoc.* 16 (6):937–93.

21. Voith, V.L. 1989. Behavioral disorders. In *Textbook of veterinary internal medicine*, ed. J.S. Ettinger, 227–40. Philadelphia: W.B. Saunders.

22. Askew, H.R. 1996. *Treatment of behavior problems in dogs and cats*. Cambridge, Mass.: Blackwell Science.

23. Coppinger, R., and R. Schneider. 1995. Evolution of working dogs. In *The domestic dog: Its evolution, behaviour, and interaction with people*, ed. J. Serpell, 21–50. New York: Cambridge University Press.

24. Borchelt, P.L., R. Lockwood, A.M. Beck, and V.L. Voith. 1983. Attacks by packs of dogs involving predation on human beings. *Public Health Reports* 98:54–66.

25. Marder, A.R. 1997. Psychotropic drugs and behavioral therapy. *Vet. Clinics of North Amer. [Small Anim. Pract.]* 21 (2):329–42.

26. Dodman, N.H., I.R. Reisner, L. Shuster, W. Rand, U.A. Luescher, I. Robinson, and K.A. Houpt. 1992. Effect of dietary protein content on behavior in dogs. *JAVMA* 208:376–9.

CHAPTER 13

Elimination and
Urine-Marking Problems in Cats

E limination outside of the litterbox and urine marking are two of the most common behavior problems in cats. They are also the most common behavioral reasons why cats are surrendered to animal shelters[1,2]. A conservative estimate is that at least 10 percent of the population of companion cats exhibit an elimination problem at some point in their lives[3]. A good deal of confusion exists regarding why cats do not use their litterboxes consistently and what should be done to resolve these problems. These can be summarized into four primary categories of mistaken impressions:

- Anthropomorphic interpretations for the behavior, such as: "He's mad at me," "She's trying to tell me something," or "He's obviously upset about something." Elimination outside of the litterbox is *not* motivated by spite or revenge.
- The belief that confinement will help solve the problem. Cat owners are often told to restrict the cat to a small room with food, water, and a litterbox for anywhere from days to months. In reality, this only prevents the cat from having the opportunity to housesoil. As you'll see later in this chapter, if nothing else is done to address the cause of the problem, the soiling continues in virtually all cases as soon as the cat is released from confinement.
- The inappropriate or ineffective use of medication. Veterinarians too often suggest psychotropic medications without arriving at a behavioral diagnosis or for causes for which medication is unlikely to be helpful (such as surface and location preferences). Veterinarians are often motivated to try medication or other approaches because clients are threatening to have the cat euthanized unless a quick fix is found. Refer to chapter 2 on communication skills for some responses you can use to avoid this quick-fix trap.
- Jumping to the conclusion that elimination problems are behavioral without first evaluating potential medical causes.

If an elimination or marking problem is approached with such perspectives in mind, none of which is likely to resolve the problem, the cat's quality of life and perhaps even his life itself is literally put at risk. To be sure, some owners are committed to working through the problem no matter how long it takes or what damage the cat does to their house, but most owners lose patience if the problem doesn't improve quickly. If the problem becomes chronic, the pet often ends up at a shelter or becomes an outdoor-only cat. Owners also frequently resort to using punishments that are delivered inappropriately, are too often severe, and rarely have any positive effect on the problem. If the owner is mad and disappointed about the cat's behavior and therefore gives him less time and attention or resorts to excessive confinement, the cat will be stressed and his quality of life may be diminished.

Thus, it's important to start a relevant treatment program early in the course of the problem. In general, the longer elimination out of the box or urine marking continues to occur, the more likely these behaviors are to become habitual and the more difficult they are to change. There are exceptions, of course. I had a case about 5 years ago of a beautiful Birman male who had not used the litterbox reliably in over 2 years. We made some very relevant changes to the litterbox, and the problem was resolved in two weeks. The important point here is that this case was treated successfully because an accurate behavioral diagnosis was made. If you aren't going to be able to take the case to the point of establishing a solid diagnosis, you should educate the owner and refer the case. It's not fair to your reputation, to the owner, or to the cat to take a "try this, try that" approach.

PROTOCOL

Because there are so many possible reasons for cat elimination problems, each step of the protocol must address a number of issues.

1. Obtain a Description of the Problem Behavior

As with dog elimination problems, owners often use vague or euphemistic language to describe such problems in their cats: "He's going all over the house," "He's making in the dining room" (I still don't understand how *making* came to mean elimination!), "She's leaving little presents for us in the living room when she's mad about something." Owners may also start by saying their cat is spraying or marking. Your first job, then, is to decipher these descriptions. Do *not* take comments about marking at face value. A surprisingly large number of cat owners who call me describe any urination out of the litterbox as either marking or spraying. It's your job to decide whether the behavior is elimination or marking.

A behavioral description starts with determining if the cat is urinating, defecating, or both. The next step is to obtain a good description of the cat's body posture. This is probably not as important with a defecation problem as it is with urination: The posture cats use for defecation is pretty standard, but they can deposit urine from either a squatting or standing posture, depending on their motivation. There is no evidence that domestic cats use feces as a marking behavior[4,5]. In the domestic cat[6] and other cat species, feces may be buried less often when deposited outside the home area and can instead be deposited in conspicuous, elevated locations[7,8]. Whether this is evidence of defecation as a marking behavior in the domestic cat is not known[9].

Owners do not always limit their use of the word *spraying* to describe a cat who, from a standing position, backs up against a vertical surface, raises his tail, and releases urine. They may use the word when the cat is actually squatting on the floor to urinate. Therefore, you need to find out whether the cat is squatting or standing. If you ask this question, an owner might respond somewhat angrily, "Well, I don't know, I never see him do it!" If your next question is, "Tell me where you find the urine," you may get answers like, "In the dining room." Try a more direct approach: "Are you finding urine on horizontal surfaces, such as the carpet, countertops, or couch cushions (it's best to give specific examples), or are you finding it on vertical surfaces like walls, drapes, or the backs of chairs?" Usually, at this point, you'll get a meaningful answer. Urine deposited on vertical surfaces is the result of spraying; that on horizontal surfaces is usually a symptom of an inappropriate urination problem. However, cats can occasionally mark from a squatting position[10].

It's a little more difficult when people describe a location such as just above the baseboards on the wall. If you picture this, most cats would need to be half squatting and half standing to leave urine at that particular height. Consequently, I might pose the question, "Are you finding the urine on the wall at 'standing cat height' or lower?" You will also need to find out what the cat's normal posture for urination is. There are a few rare cats who routinely stand up when urinating or assume sort of a half squat. (My husband and I once had a cat who assumed this latter posture rather than a full squat due to an arthritic hip.)

With a multicat household, it's important to determine which cat is doing the soiling. To help with this, a veterinarian can give fluorescein, a harmless dye, either by injection (Fluorescite Injection 10 percent, 0.3mL subcutaneously) or orally (0.5 mL of the same solution)[11, 12]. The dye, which does not stain carpeting, causes the urine to fluoresce blue for 24 hours under an ultraviolet light. Alternatively, cats can be confined sequentially to determine which one is doing the soiling.

2. Evaluate Potential Medical Causes for the Problem Behavior

Once I've asked whether urine or feces is involved, the next question I'll ask the owner is if the cat has been seen by a veterinarian recently (within the past 2 weeks) *specifically for this problem*. If the problem involves urination, I also ask if a urinalysis has been done. If the answer to either question is no, I am very reluctant to work on the case. One of my major complaints is with clinics where a technician (or anyone who answers the telephone) refers cases without a veterinarian ever being consulted. If a veterinarian has referred the case without seeing the cat or doing a urinalysis, I'll usually see the animal because I assume that the veterinarian has a valid reason for doing so. However, I'll often remind owners, via their instructions, and veterinarians, via my follow-up letter, that they may want to give more thought to medical causes if the problem is not being resolved.

I remember a case I did agree to take on even though the animal had been referred by a clinic staffer without first having the veterinarian see the cat. While taking a behavioral history and asking the owner about a typical day in the life of the cat, it occurred to me the cat was urinating and drinking far more than normal. I voiced my concerns to both the owner and the veterinarian. When, as a result, the case was worked up by the veterinarian, it was discovered that the cat was diabetic. After that experience, I became much more adamant about getting direct referrals from the veterinarian, and this veterinarian also changed his policy about how behavior cases were referred.

As all veterinarians know, a dizzying list of potential medical conditions can influence a cat's elimination habits[13]. While writing this chapter, I was working with a cat who had been diagnosed with irritable bowel syndrome by the referring veterinarian. This medical problem was being managed, but the cat continued to both defecate and, more frequently, urinate, outside the box. We couldn't think why there would be a connection between the bowel problem and the inappropriate urination, apart from the cat not feeling well in general. The owner and I made a variety of changes to the box and even tried a program of positive reinforcement, but after 3 weeks, the problem was only slightly better. However, during a medical follow-up, the cat was diagnosed with lymphoma. This serves to illustrate that with chronic elimination problems, any of a host of factors may be in play.

In recent years, more has been written about feline lower urinary tract disease (FLUTD) or interstitial cystitis[14, 15, 16]. Veterinarians should refer to this and other literature when evaluating possible medical causes for recurrent inappropriate urination behavior. In addition to the basic medical texts, there are a number of good references for veterinarians to consult regarding medical workups for feline elimination problems[17, 18].

Nonveterinarians should not be overzealous in their rush to work with an elimination case until the cat has been evaluated by a veterinarian. Think about what you would want if your own cat was not using the litterbox reliably. You wouldn't want to jeopardize her health—or your best chance of solving the problem—by ignoring medical factors. In dealing with owners, it may be necessary to point out that cats often don't act ill even when they are, and without getting a veterinary examination first, a behavioral consultation could be a waste of time and money. Refer to chapter 6 for additional suggestions to convince reluctant owners that a visit to the veterinarian is necessary prior to a behavior consultation.

3. Educate Owners About the Problem Behavior

Educate the owners about anthropomorphic and other misinterpretations. Inappropriate elimination in both cats and dogs is the one behavior that most consistently evokes anthropomorphic explanations. Some owners strongly believe that elimination or marking is an act of spite or revenge, with the message being, "I'll show you!" The inaccuracy of this interpretation is revealed by considering that, unlike humans, neither cats nor dogs view the products of elimination as particularly distasteful. Dogs, in fact, often eat feces, although this behavior is not often seen in cats, (probably because of their habit of burying their waste). Moreover, cats and other species will take urine into their vomeronasal organ (VNO), through their oral cavity, in a behavior known as *flehmen* because urine has communicative value[18]. These behaviors (eating feces and drawing urine into the nose and mouth) are obviously outside the realm of human experience!

Attributing elimination problems to spite and revenge assumes some fairly sophisticated logic on the part of the animal, plus a willingness to bear noncontingent (after-the-fact) punishment, which we already know animals don't understand. Many owners don't think logically about this issue, however; rather, they look at the matter from a very human perspective: "I'd have to really hate someone a lot to poop or pee on his bed, so therefore, since my cat did that, he must either hate me or be really mad about something." You may need to dissuade them from this way of thinking before they are ready to consider appropriate treatment for the pet.

The other anthropomorphic slant that some owners take on cat elimination or marking problems is that the behavior is a form of cat-to-human communication: "He must be trying to tell me something." In fact, urine *can* serve a communicative function, but not in the way that owners think it does. Although urine itself, because of its odor and chemical composition, has communicative value, owners view *the act of urination* as being communicative. Such misconceptions are fostered by faulty information in the literature, such as an article entitled "A Messy Cry for Help," which erroneously states that *"indiscriminate defecation is a cat's way of telling you there's something wrong* [italics added]"[19]. Once again, a lot of cognitive assumptions are made on behalf of cats, but when thought through logically, they are just too much of a stretch:

> "My litterbox is dirty. I don't like a dirty litterbox. How do I get a cleaner litterbox? My owner ["Mom"] cleans my litterbox. Mom doesn't like poop outside the litterbox. If I poop somewhere else, Mom will be mad. If Mom is mad, she'll know something's wrong with me. She'll know that if she cleans my litterbox, I won't poop somewhere else anymore."

Does this make sense to you? From a learning standpoint, this progression assumes that defecation outside the box would be reinforced with a clean litterbox. Based on what we know about the timing of positive reinforcement, this connection is an impossibility. Beyond that, if inappropriate defecation is reinforced, it should occur more, not less, often.

Although it is not an anthropomorphic interpretation, the belief that declawed cats are more likely to have litterbox problems still exists. This issue has already been addressed in chapter 5, but to summarize it, there is simply no evidence at this point to suggest that declawing predisposes cats to ongoing litterbox problems. I have, to be sure, seen cats who have not used the litterbox reliably for a week or two immediately following a declaw procedure. The cause, however, has nothing to do with a persistent connection between declawing and inappropriate elimination. Rather, the behavior occurs not only because the cat's feet are tender but also because the veterinarian has likely recommended using only shredded newspaper in the litterbox. This sudden shift in substrate is not acceptable to many cats and probably influences their decision to go elsewhere until the regular litter is returned. On a few occasions, I've seen cats for whom this change in litterbox habits seems to have become a litterbox aversion because of the change in substrate, combined with a secondary surface preference problem (e.g., the cat found she liked carpet better). In most cases, these problems have been easily resolved, and some veterinarians do not recommend using a different type of litter after declawing but suggest continuing to use whatever the cat is accustomed to[20].

Educate the owners about myths regarding problem solving and techniques to avoid. As mentioned at the beginning of this chapter, confining the cat is too often thought to have a beneficial effect on a litterbox problem. This belief probably stems from the (appropriate) importance given to confining a dog who is not yet housetrained when he can't be supervised. Confinement does nothing more than prevent the animal from having an opportunity to housesoil. It does nothing to address the cause of the problem. Furthermore, if the cat uses the litterbox when confined, as many do, this behavior should not be misinterpreted: Since many litterbox problems are related to the development of surface and location preferences for areas other than the litterbox, this just means that when his preferred area is not available, he is making do with the litterbox. In some litter or litterbox aversion cases, the cat won't use the box even when confined. That means that in the cat's hierarchy of acceptable places for elimination, the box is at rock bottom.

Confinement for relatively brief periods can make some sense. Some behaviorists recommend confining the cat for 30 minutes or so around the time she most often defecates or urinates. (Some owners know their cats well enough to determine when the cat is likely to eliminate, but others wouldn't have a clue.) Restricting the cat's access to certain areas of the house for a time might help to break the "habit" of eliminating in those locations. However, continuous, relatively long-term confinement (days to weeks or longer), without any other type of intervention, is bound to be useless.

Punishment also has limited value in working with cat elimination problems. None of the criteria for effective punishment can easily be met (especially consistency and immediacy—see chapter 3), and punishment does nothing to address the cause of the problem. Interactive attempts at punishment, such as hitting the cat or rubbing his nose in the mess, are never appropriate. Remote punishment when the cat is caught eliminating outside the box, such as using a loud noise or tossing a pillow at the cat, can effectively interrupt that occurrence and even discourage elimination at that particular location. However, the cat will generally just choose another location and still not use the box unless the cause of the problem is addressed. The same holds true for spraying behavior.

Making random changes to the litterbox without having a clear rationale for doing so is also ineffective and can actually exacerbate the problem. Owners, either on their own or on the advice of someone else, often start trying a variety of litters, moving the box to different locations, or experimenting with covers or different boxes. Unless this is done as the result of a planned intervention and for a specific reason, this can often make the problem worse because now the litterbox location and characteristics are *always* changing. Inconsistency does not solve litterbox problems.

A related misconception is the idea that making changes to the litterbox can help resolve a urine-marking problem. I have encountered numerous cat owners who have been advised to try all kinds of different litterbox arrangements when their cats are spraying. The critical point here is that elimination habits have nothing to do with marking behavior, so forget about litterbox details if the problem is urine marking.

Owners often try to block the cat's access to soiled locations by moving furniture or putting other items in her way. What most often happens, in turn, is that the cat picks a new spot. Occasionally, she will use the box for awhile, but usually she will revert back to soiling somewhere else because the reason for the soiling has not been addressed.

Educate the owners about realistic expectations. I often receive calls from frantic cat owners who make such statements as, "If he does this one more time, we're going to have to get rid of him." Although they may have tolerated an elimination or marking problem for weeks, months, or years, all of a sudden it becomes intolerable because of some unrelated circumstance, such as the purchase of a new carpet, a move to a new house, an attempt to sell the current house, or the fact that the baby has reached the crawling stage. I tell such owners that the vast majority of elimination problems respond to treatment but that, since the problem did not develop overnight, they also should not expect an overnight cure. This is another reason why elimination cases should be dealt with *appropriately* as soon as they occur. Many of these owners also state they have "tried everything." Often, the help they've obtained has been of a "try this, try that" nature, and they probably sincerely believe they've tried everything. But no one has helped them take a *systematic* approach to the problem. Halfhearted attempts at resolution and random suggestions are unlikely to be successful.

Many things exacerbate the problem or at least aren't helpful, so the next question is what *should* be done? Before that question can be answered, the cause for the problem must be determined.

4. Identify the Behavioral Cause of the Problem

Assuming that medical causes for the behavior have been evaluated and ruled out, there are a number of behavioral causes for cat elimination problems. Although these causes are listed separately here, it is extremely common for inappropriate elimination to have multiple causes. The common causes include:

- Surface preference
- Location preference
- Litter or litterbox aversions
- Conflicts between family cats
- Separation anxiety
- Fear or anxiety
- Olfactory cues
- Urine marking (which is *not* an elimination problem)

Components of a behavioral history. To determine which of these potential causes is at work in any given case, you will need to ask a series of detailed questions. If you do not have the time to do so and if you have already educated owners appropriately, using information from the previous section, then you should either discuss general management options, refer the case, or do both.

The answers to the following questions, which are divided into several categories, will help you distinguish among these causes. Getting answers to the questions on this list does not substitute for obtaining a complete behavioral history. A complete history relies on the feedback from the owner. In other words, the owner's answers to the questions influence what other questions need to be asked.

Two examples of forms that can be used to guide you in taking a behavioral history for a feline elimination problem are given in Boxes 13.1 and 13.2. Keep in mind that these are to be

---

Box 13.1 An example of a summary form for feline elimination problems

CHECKLIST FOR A BEHAVIORAL HISTORY ON A CAT ELIMINATION PROBLEM

This form does not include questions pertaining to urine marking.

Circle all appropriate responses.

Type of Problem: urination   defecation

Vet Check? When? YES, date _____ result_____ NO

Description of Litterbox(es):
1. **Substrate:** brand-name clay   generic clay   clumping   newspaper   pellets
   soil/sand   scented? Y N   other_____
2. **Number of boxes:** 1   2   3   4   more   (number of cats: 1   2   3   4   more)
3. **Covered (C) or uncovered (U):** Box # 1___   2___   3___   4___   5___
4. **Liners? (Y, N):** Box # 1___   2___   3___   4___   5___
5. **Depth of litter:** <1"   1–2"   2–3"   3–4"   >4"

Location of Litterbox(es) (put number in each blank):
1. main floor___   upstairs___   downstairs___   basement (finished, unfinished)___
      other_____
2. bedroom___   dining room___   kitchen___   den/family room___
   laundry room___   bathroom___   living room___
3. **Location in room(s):** near wall___   in corner___   under/behind
   furniture/objects___   out in open___   other_____
4. **Cat's food, bed, or scratching post near box?** YES   NO
5. **Strong scents near box (room deodorizer, etc.)?** YES   NO

(Box continues)

Litterbox Cleaning Procedures:
1. **Frequency of removing feces:** don't remove   several times/week
   every other day   1/day   2/day   more often
2. **Frequency of litter changes:**
   Clay: once/day   every other day   2/week   1/week   every 2 weeks
   other_____
   Clumping: don't change—just remove clumps and add   several times/day
   1/day   every other day   2/week   1/week   every 2 weeks   other_____
3. **Frequency of washing box:** don't wash   1/week   every other week
   1/month   2/month   other_____

Cat's Behavior in Box:
covers urine   covers feces   scratches in litter prior to elimination
scratches surroundings before or after   "misses" box   hangs off edge
shakes feet   runs away   vocalizes   doesn't bury or scratch   other_____

Number of Other Animals:
dogs____   cats_____   other_____

Relationships Among Pets:
Friendly relationships between: _____
Agonistic relationships between:_____
Neutral relationships between: _____
Other: _____

Texture of Soiled Surfaces:
Soft: carpet   throw rugs   clothing   bedding   furniture   towels
other_____
Slick: tile   linoleum   tub/sink   counters   plastic   vinyl   wood   cement
Other:_____

Location(s) of Most Commonly Soiled Surface:
1. main floor   upstairs   downstairs   unfinished basement   other_____
2. bedroom   dining room   kitchen   den/family room   laundry room
   bathroom   living room
3. **Relationship to box:** next to box   same floor as box   same room as box
4. **Location in room(s):** near wall   in corner   under furniture/objects
   out in open   other_____

Location(s) of Other Soiled Surfaces:
1. main floor   upstairs   downstairs   unfinished basement   other_____
2. bedroom   dining room   kitchen   den/family room   laundry room
   bathroom   living room
3. **Relationship to box:** next to box   same floor as box   same room as box
4. **Location in room(s):** near wall   in corner   under/behind furniture/objects
   out in open   other_____   (Box continues)

When Does Soiling Occur:
unknown   only when owner gone   mornings   afternoons   evenings   nights

Owner's Responses to Problem:
Type of punishment _____
Modifications to box _____

_____
Products used to clean soiled areas _____
Modifications to soiled areas _____
Other _____

Source: Developed and copyrighted by Suzanne Hetts, Ph.D., and Daniel Q. Estep, Ph.D., Certified
Applied Animal Behaviorists, Animal Behavior Associates, Inc., Littleton, CO. Used by permission.

Box 13.2 An example of a summary form for feline elimination problems

CLIENT QUESTIONNAIRE REGARDING HOUSE-SOILING

1. Describe the problem: squat/spray

2. Relevant early history: stray? shelter?

3. Description of current litterboxes:

       Location

       Type of box

       Type and depth of substrate

       Cleaning procedures (or scooping)—frequency?

4. Cat's behavior in the litterbox?

       digs, scratches?

       shakes feet?

       perches on side?

       frequent misses?

5. If allowed outside—preferred substrate?

6. Relationship with other animals in house?

7. Description of problem:

       when it began

       when and where it occurs

       frequency of occurrence

       progression of problem

       owner's attempt at resolution

8. Treatment:

Source: Provided courtesy of Paige Garnett, DVM, Care Animal Hospital, P.C., Arvada, CO 80005.
Reproduced by permission.

used as guidelines or summaries and do not necessarily constitute all of the information required for a complete behavioral history.

Description of the cat, description of the behavior.
- How old is the cat?
- Is the cat male/female? Is she spayed/he neutered?
- What breed is the cat?
- Is the cat declawed? If yes, when was she declawed?
- Is the cat urinating, defecating, or both?
- What posture is the cat in when urinating? (Distinguish between squatting and standing up; see the section on describing the behavior for more information.)

Specific details about all litterboxes and their locations.
- How many boxes are in the house? Has the number changed recently?
- What kind of boxes are used (regular rectangle, high sides, self-cleaning, oversized, smaller substitute, etc.)?
- Are they covered? If yes, with what kind of cover?
- Are liners used?
- What kind of litter is used, including the brand name and type (clumping, clay, etc.)?
- Has the type or brand of litter been changed recently?
- Is the litter scented or unscented?
- How deep is the litter in each box?
- How often are feces and clumps scooped from the box?
- How often is the litter changed?
- How often are the boxes washed? What is used to wash the boxes?
- Are any room deodorizers used in or near the boxes?
- Where are the boxes located—in what room (describe the room in detail), where in the room, on what surface in the room (carpet, tile, wood flooring, etc.)?
- Has the location of the boxes changed recently?
- Has anything about the characteristics of the boxes or their locations, including the surrounding environment, changed recently?
- Are the boxes all located in the same room or adjacent to each other (a row of litterboxes)?
- Does the cat have clear visibility of what might be approaching him while he is in the litterbox?
- Is the cat able to leave the litterbox in a different direction from a person or animal who is approaching the box?
- What is the traffic pattern in the litterbox area (are family members frequently in and out of the room, does no one ever spend time in the room, etc.)?
- Are any large appliances (furnace, etc.) located near the box?
- What route must the cat take to access the litterbox—e.g., barriers, obstacles, and surfaces to be negotiated (look for any problem factors).

Description of cat's daily routine, environment, and behavior patterns.
- Is the cat allowed outside? If yes, how often, is he supervised, how long is he outside, and where does he go when outside?

- Does the cat eliminate outside? If yes, where (include location and type of surface)?
- Does the cat have a cat door?
- What other pets are in the house? Provide species, breed, age, and gender.
- How does the "problem" cat get along with each of these other animals? Provide detailed descriptions: Do they sleep together? Do they avoid one another? Will they play? Who initiates the play? If the play involves chasing, does who is the "chasee" and the "chaser" alternate? Does any animal seem afraid of any other?
- Have any of these animals harassed the "problem" cat while she was in the litterbox?
- Describe the cat's personality—confident, timid, shy, fearful, friendly, etc.
- Does the cat hide a lot or seem afraid to wander around the house?
- How attached is the cat to the owner? Does he seem to be overly attached?
- Where does the cat generally sleep?
- Where does the cat like to spend his time when inside the house?
- Where is the cat's food and water kept?
- What kind of feeding schedule is the cat on?
- What does the cat eat?
- Where is the cat's scratching post?
- Is the cat's environment fairly consistent, or are guests or other people frequently staying for a few days and then leaving (children home from college for the weekend, etc.)?
- Have any new pets joined the household either recently or about the time the elimination or urine-marking problem began?
- Are stray cats commonly seen in the neighborhood? Do these cats come into the owner's yard? Does the "problem" cat have contact with these animals when she is outside? Can she see them from inside the house?
- Does the cat have any specific fears or phobias?
- Does the cat pester to go outside? Is she often denied access to the outside?
- How does the cat behave in the litterbox?
   — Does he stand all the way in the litter or place any feet on the side of the litterbox?
   — Does he assume a full squat? Does he partially stand? Does he do both?
   — Does he bury his waste? Does he shake his paws or run from the box when finished?
   — Does he vocalize while eliminating?
   — Is there any evidence of straining, soft stools, diarrhea, or blood in either the urine or the feces?
   — Does the cat scratch outside the box after eliminating?
   — Will the cat use the box while the owner is nearby?
- If there are multiple cats in the family, do all cats use all litterboxes, or does one or more preferentially or exclusively use one particular litterbox?

Specifics about the occurrence of the problem behavior.
- When did the problem start?
- What happened with the first occurrence of the behavior? How long ago and where did it happen? What did the cat do? What did the owner do?

- What detailed descriptions can be given of all the locations the cat has eliminated or sprayed? Include the room, where specifically in the room, what type of surface, and any nearby odors. (Look for similarities and differences, for example: similarities in texture, such as all soft surfaces—carpet, beds, etc.—or all slick surfaces—linoleum, bathtub, etc.; all in out-of-the-way places, under something, or in only one room, etc.)
- Are any of the soiled locations areas where the litterbox was previously located?
- If known, what was going on (what were the circumstances) immediately prior to the elimination or marking (in what context did the behavior occur)?
- What time of day or evening does the behavior typically occur?
- What is the frequency of the behavior now? What has the frequency been (if different from the current one) throughout the course of the problem?
- Is the behavior associated with the owner's overnight or longer absences from the house?
- Do any of the other pets in the house now have inappropriate elimination or marking problems? Have they in the past? Where have they soiled?
- Has the cat ever had a bad experience in the litterbox—e.g., being "ambushed" by another pet, frightened by a loud noise, or startled by the owner?
- Has the cat ever eliminated or sprayed while the owner was watching (i.e., in front of the owner)?

Owners' attempts at problem resolution and the cat's response.
- What has the owner used to clean the soiled areas? Have these been enzymatic products?
- What kinds of changes has the owner made to the litterbox? How has the cat responded to these changes? For example, if the owner moved the box to the soiled area, did the cat use it, go right next to it, soil in an entirely new area, etc.?
- Have any additional boxes been added? If so, what are their characteristics? Does the cat use any of them?
- Has any attempt at punishment been tried? If so, what? How has the cat responded?
- Has confinement been used? If so, how? How has the cat responded?

Differential results of the behavioral history. Keep in mind that the factor that initially causes a problem may not be the same as the factor(s) that maintain it. For example, as you'll see, a problem may start because of a litterbox aversion but be maintained because of a surface preference. Answers to the preceding questions will reveal the following information, depending on the cause of the problem:

Surface preference. When inappropriate elimination is due to a surface preference problem, the cat has decided that substrates or textures other than what is in the litterbox provide more desirable surfaces for elimination. Owners often have a hard time understanding this if the cat is still using the box inconsistently. Preference, however, is not necessarily an all-or-nothing concept. Sometimes the litterbox will do for elimination, sometimes it won't. If a cat is confined and does not have access to her preferred surface, she may use the box reliably. However, as soon as she is free to move around the house, she typically goes back to her preferred surface. This is why confinement *by itself* isn't helpful in problem resolution.

Cats' preferences are influenced by early experience, but they can change later in life for reasons that often are not fully understood. Based on several preference studies, finer-grained and softer substrates seem to be preferred by most cats[3]. Furthermore, surface preference problems can sometimes develop secondarily to litterbox aversions. For example, a cat could begin eliminating on carpet if the box is not kept clean. Then, even after the owner changes his maintenance procedures and provides a cleaner box, the cat may continue to eliminate on carpet, as this has become her preferred substrate.

In most (but not all) surface preference cases, the soiled areas are all of similar texture. Cats most often choose soft surfaces, such as beds, carpets, and piles of clothes or towels on the floor. Less frequently, they prefer slick surfaces, such as linoleum, tile, counter tops, bathtubs, etc.

In surface preference cases, when the owner moves the box to where the cat is eliminating, typically the cat goes right next to the box or in another area with the same or similar surface. If the owner changes the texture of the area by covering it with foil or some other material, usually the cat goes right next to the covered area. Surface and location preference problems often occur together.

Location preference. When inappropriate elimination is due to a location preference problem, the cat has decided that areas other than where the litterbox is located are more desirable for elimination. With a strict location preference, the type of surface doesn't matter. In other words, if the owner covers the soiled area with foil or plastic or moves the litterbox to the soiled place, the cat will eliminate on whatever substrate is provided, including the litterbox. In my experience, that rarely happens. Usually, the cat then eliminates right next to the box, foil, or plastic. This indicates that the surface or texture is the cat's primary consideration but that there is a secondary location preference, as the cat is attempting to stay as close as possible to the soiled location.

If the cat is confined away from her preferred location, she may use the box. If she does not, then this indicates that the litterbox location is her last choice or that a litterbox aversion may exist.

Location problems sometimes occur after an owner abruptly relocates the litterbox. The cat goes to the area where the litterbox used to be and eliminates there because that is the "elimination location"! Something undesirable about the location of the litterbox may also contribute to the cat choosing another area. A location may be undesirable if it:

- Has too much activity or high traffic
- Has only one way in and out of the box, making it easier for another animal to "trap" the cat in the box (an example would be a box located in a shower stall)
- Does not provide the cat with the ability to see on all sides, allowing another animal to approach and startle her in the box (which can also happen with covered boxes)
- Is isolated and possibly cold, not well lit, with a cold floor the cat must walk across, and so out of the way that it is not part of the house the cat would frequent (e.g., an unfinished basement that is never used or a garage)
- Has unpredictable noises, such as sounds from a furnace or washer, occurring there

Location may be particularly important if there are other pets in the house. If the cat cannot see other animals approaching or, as in the shower stall example, if he cannot leave the box without going toward an approaching animal, he may decide not to use the box[21]. Putting multiple litterboxes right next to one another only provides one functional location. Two cats may not be comfortable using the litterbox area at the same time, as this might require them to be adjacent to one another while eliminating.

For more discussion on location factors, see chapter 5.

Litter or litterbox aversions. Aversions can develop for any number of reasons. In feline elimination problems, the aversion can be to the litter or to the entire box. Any kind of bad, frightening, or startling experience in the box can be a trigger for an aversion. Consequently, some aversion problems could be classified as fear or anxiety problems or placed in the animal-conflict category. If a cat is ambushed in the box by another cat, an aversion can develop. If the cat experiences pain or discomfort when eliminating in the box, an aversion can be the result. In fact, painful elimination can result in a classically conditioned aversion (wherein the box predicts pain). Aversions may also develop if the box is consistently dirty, so the owners should be asked about the cleaning routines used when you are taking the behavioral history. Litterbox aversions can occur if the box is too small or if the sides too high (for a small kitten), and litter aversions can develop if the litter is too deep, dusty, or has a strong scent. In sum, there are all kinds of possibilities for trouble!

A clear sign of a litter or litterbox aversion is when the cat eliminates right next to the box: Something is not acceptable about that box. You should also suspect that a litter aversion has developed if the cat is not burying his waste (although some cats never bury their waste but never have inappropriate elimination problems), if he does not want to step in the litter and perches on the side of the box instead, or if he shakes his paws excessively to remove the litter after exiting the box. In addition, surface and location preferences often develop secondarily to litterbox aversions.

A cat with a litter or litterbox aversion often won't use the box when confined (although if the aversion is mild, he may), and if the owner moves the box to the soiled area, the cat will not use it.

Conflicts between family cats. Such conflicts can be an indirect cause of a litterbox problem. Fortunately, it is very clear to owners when their cats aren't getting along. They will often describe threatening behavior from one or more cats; one cat being afraid of another to the point of hiding and not moving freely around the house; one cat often lying in wait for another; chasing and harassment; yowling or swatting matches; and full-blown fights (see chapter 15 on feline aggression for more information). These conflicts can result in inappropriate elimination problems because:

- One cat is being harassed and threatened while in the box
- One cat is simply too afraid to go to the litterbox location
- Using the box makes a cat vulnerable to attack or harassment (even if it has yet to happen) because his visibility and means of escape are limited when he's in the box (this overlaps with a location problem)

An example of this last situation happened with my own cats when we had a covered box located in an unused shower stall. Tipper, our older female cat, used this box almost exclusively. Shortly after we obtained Buffett, a young male, Tipper began urinating on a throw rug in front of the toilet. One day, we discovered Buffett lying in wait for Tipper at the bathroom door as she exited the litterbox. It was immediately clear that by eliminating on the rug, rather than being sequestered in the covered box, she was able to see Buffett if he approached and could exit the bathroom and avoid being ambushed. Removing the cover on the box solved the problem.

The number of cats in the household can influence elimination behavior if there are fewer boxes than there are cats, which means that each cat does not have access to a box at all times. If multiple boxes are all lined up side by side, this creates only one functional litterbox location, and a second cat may not feel comfortable using a box if another cat is using the adjacent one.

There is the occasional cat who will not eliminate in a box that has been used by another cat. Some owners attempt to provide individual boxes for the exclusive use of each cat in the house, but rarely does it work out as planned. Usually, all the cats use all the boxes, at least to some degree. Diagnosing a problem of litterbox avoidance involving use by other cats requires a very detailed, careful questioning of the owner. Often, cats may need to be separated from each other temporarily to provide additional information. Yet doing so may not provide diagnostic information because separating the cats also removes the opportunity for social conflicts, which are more likely the cause of the problem. In the behavioral history, look for consistent use of the box *only* when it has just been cleaned or *only* when it has not been used by another cat.

Separation anxiety. Separation anxiety in cats is rare. When it does occur, it is usually in reaction to owner absences that are longer than a workday[10]. I don't recall ever having a feline separation anxiety case manifest through inappropriate elimination that was the result of normal, workday owner absences. I have had cases, though, in which the cat housesoiled in association with the owner's frequent overnight or longer absences. Indeed, some cats with separation anxiety react to the sight of a suitcase. Some express their anxiousness by meowing or pacing; others may even eliminate in the suitcase (this could be a marking behavior, so it must be differentiated from an elimination problem). There is variation in terms of just when the housesoiling starts relative to the owner's departure. In some cases, it occurs if the owner is away just overnight, but more often, it seems to require at least a two-day absence.

Before jumping to a diagnosis of separation anxiety (which, again, is quite rare—I've had maybe four or five cases in 15 years of practice), you must rule out the possibility that the cat is housesoiling because the litterbox is not being kept as clean as normal when the owner is absent. Also look for signs that the cat is very attached to the owner—e.g., following the owner around the house or preferring to be in the owner's presence rather than napping in a quiet place as most cats do. It may also be valuable to have the owner keep a log of the occurrence of the behavior. Like many others, the owners may have selective memories and make connections between events when they really don't exist. A log will help to verify (or refute) the connection. Inappropriate elimination due to separation anxiety can occur in almost any location, but some cats do choose items or areas with a strong scent of the owner, such as clothes or the bed.

Fear or anxiety. Anytime a cat is afraid to move comfortably around in his environment, the potential for inappropriate elimination exists. However, certain fear-related problems are more commonly associated with litterbox problems. One example involves the owner's use of non-contingent punishment. I've had a few cases in which the owner was using punishment after the fact for other misbehaviors, such as destructive scratching. Whenever the owner discovered damage, he would rush over, grab the cat, take her to the "evidence," and scream at her. With good reason, the cat began hiding out and eliminating close by in order to minimize her chances of being found by her owner.

If a cat is frightened while using the litterbox, an inappropriate elimination problem can result. This is a relative common problem when boxes are located in the basement, where noises from nearby appliances (such as the furnace or water heater) can bother the animal. In one case, the owner had gotten into the habit of picking up the cat to wash her face (she had feline acne) as she exited the litterbox in the laundry room. Not surprisingly, the cat started eliminating elsewhere.

A third common example of a fear-related problems is seen when a family dog is chasing and harassing the cat. Not only is the cat not at ease moving around the house, she also senses that being in the litterbox puts her in an even more vulnerable position, as it is hard to run from a dog when she's in the middle of "doing her business."

Fear-related litterbox problems are also common in cats new to the house who are still frightened and not comfortable in their environment.

Olfactory cues. If other pets have housesoiled, additional animals may be attracted to the same spot, creating a perpetual problem. Unless the source of the odor is other animals, odor cues can't initiate a problem; they can only maintain it (i.e., the cat's own odor won't be there until she soils, so something else attracted her to the spot). I believe olfactory cues from other animals more likely trigger urine marking rather than elimination.

Urine marking (not an elimination problem). Cats urine mark primarily to make other cats aware of their presence and to establish or maintain territorial boundaries. Thus, marking behavior occurs whenever the cat *perceives* there is some threat to the integrity of his territory. The introduction of a new cat to the family, the presence of free-roaming cats outside, and ongoing social conflicts between cats in the family are probably the most common triggers. However, even human visitors to the home, unfamiliar odors, or the introduction of anything new to the home (carpet, furniture, etc.) can also trigger urine marking. Both males and females spray, although the behavior is much more common in males, especially if they are intact.

Marking can also occur in high-arousal situations unrelated to territorial behavior. Cats seem to spray as a frustration behavior[17, 22]. Case histories typically reveal that spraying occurs when the cat has been denied access to the outside, when the owner fails to provide social interaction (petting, attention, or play) on demand, or when the cat has become frustrated or is prevented from doing something. Food or diet restriction has also been associated with spraying behavior[23, 24] (see Box 13.3). When frustration is the motivation for spraying, owners often interpret the behavior as an expression of spite or revenge. However, there is a difference between frustration and revenge: The former is merely a reaction to the situation (just as people swear or hit things when they are frustrated); the latter implies a malicious intent, which is an anthropomorphic interpretation.

Urine marking typically involves spraying behavior in which the cat, in a standing position, backs up against a vertical object, raises his tail, and releases urine. Usually, the amounts are

---

Box 13.3 Spraying related to diet and frustration

"Snowy," a 5-year-old castrated male DSH [domestic shorthair], had begun spraying 8 months prior to the in-home visit. There were two other cats in the family, a 6-month-old spayed female and Snowy's neutered male littermate. Most of the spraying occurred in the kitchen, where the female cat was fed. At about the time the spraying began, Snowy and his littermate's diet was changed to RD [a high-fiber diet], and they were fed in the hallway or dining room. The female cat was fed in the kitchen and continued to eat CD [a urinary-prescription diet] or kitten food, much more palatable diets. After the female finished eating, the owner would put a lid on the food bowl and leave it on the floor. Snowy would often try to take the lid off. Food restriction was suspected as the motivation to spray in the kitchen, so the RD was left out for all three cats in the hallway. The female cat was supplemented with CD only at night in the daughter's bedroom, where Snowy was not present, and the food was then put away in a cabinet. The kitchen floor was cleaned with bleach. By the time of follow-up at 1 and 3 weeks, spraying had ceased.

Source: A. Marder, 1992, Feline behavior problems related to diet, *Animal Behavior Consultant Newsletter* 9 (4):1–2.

relatively small, at least in comparison to a full bladder of urine, and the marking normally occurs in several consistent locations. Marking from a squatting position has been reported by females in estrus and at other times as well[10]. When the cat squats and deposits urine consistently on items that have a strong scent of the owner, such as the bed or clothes, a marking problem may exist. This must be differentiated from urination caused by a surface or location preference or separation anxiety by the context in which it occurs, the eliciting stimuli, the amount of urine (usually marking involves smaller amounts), and other pertinent details revealed in a complete behavioral history.

5. Discuss Ways to Manage or Control the Behavior over the Short or Long Term

As mentioned in previous chapters, management procedures can be discussed in a very general way if you have not determined the cause for the problem by asking detailed questions, or they can be given based on the cause. Remember, as well, that managing the problem is not necessarily the same thing as resolving it.

General management procedures—no behavioral diagnosis. Without a behavioral diagnosis, about the only recommendation you can offer to manage the elimination problem is to deny the cat the opportunity to eliminate outside the litterbox. This usually means either some sort of confinement or close supervision of the cat. For short periods (for instance, to manage the problem while waiting for help), confinement may be acceptable, but it should not be regarded as a long-term management procedure. If you are a veterinarian, you should not use psychotropic medication as a management tool without having a behavioral diagnosis, as medication may be irrelevant to the problem.

Thus, without a diagnosis, you are almost stuck in one of the inappropriate frames of reference discussed at the beginning of the chapter. The conclusion then and now is that you are better off educating the owner about the prevalent misconceptions mentioned at the beginning of this chapter and then referring the case if you cannot or do not want to proceed to diagnose the problem yourself. Although an in-home visit is the ideal way to approach this problem and gather full information, an elimination problem *can* be handled via a telephone consultation, and there are a number of board-certified veterinary behaviorists and certified applied animal behaviorists who offer telephone consulting services. Consequently, any clinic or shelter can always find someone to whom to refer such cases.

If the cat is urine marking and the triggering stimuli can be identified, management entails protecting him from exposure to these stimuli. Urine-marking problems can sometimes be managed with psychotropic medication, as well (see chapter 18).

Management procedures based on a diagnosis.

Surface preference. Managing an elimination problem caused by a surface preference means denying the cat access to the surfaces on which she may soil. This can be accomplished by covering the surface (such as carpeting) with another material (such as plastic) that the cat will not eliminate on. However, because it is usually impossible to cover all similar surfaces (an owner can't put plastic over all the carpet in the house), confinement is also necessary. Too often, though, people believe these management steps are a way to resolve the problem. They are not. These procedures should only be used over the short term, and a problem-resolution approach should be taken to address the underlying cause.

Location preference. Managing location preferences is very similar to managing surface preferences: The cat cannot be allowed access to the locations she has soiled. This either means confining her or restricting access by closing doors leading to the soiled areas. (Unfortunately, baby gates don't work with cats!) Alternatively, the problem can be managed by putting the box at the preferred location, even if it is in the middle of the dining room. I consider this a management approach: The cat's behavior has not changed but has only been accommodated, and the owner is unlikely to agree to permanently leaving the box in that location. Thus, additional resolution techniques will be necessary.

Litter or litterbox aversions. Whether management techniques can be successful with litter and litterbox aversion problems depends on the severity of the aversion. With relatively mild aversions, cats will use the litterbox if they are confined and have no other choice. If the aversion is severe, however, the cat will still avoid the box even if confined. In the latter case, taking a management approach may not be possible, and the focus should therefore be on problem resolution. Further, whenever confinement must be used to manage a problem, it should be viewed as a short-term approach until assistance can be obtained to resolve the problem.

Conflicts between family cats. To manage elimination problems caused by conflict between cats in the same household, the cats may need to be separated. The soiling cat will need to feel safe approaching and using the litterbox, so if he has taken to hiding and not moving around his environment, a litterbox may need to be located, at least temporarily, in an area where he *is* comfortable.

Separation anxiety. Elimination problems caused by separation anxiety can be tough to manage and treat. Luckily, such cases are not that common. Antianxiety medication may be an effective management tool, but it must be administered in the owner's absence, requiring some sort of in-home care for the cat—and many cats will not be thrilled about being medicated by someone they don't know well. Alternatively, the cat could be boarded in the owner's absence.

Fear or anxiety. Management of a fear- or anxiety-based elimination problem can be accomplished by keeping the cat away from the things she fears. Sometimes, this is practical, but at other times, it is not. If a cat is new to the household and has become overwhelmed with too many unfamiliar things, confining her for a few days in a smaller part of the house, such as a bedroom, may help (see the section on problem prevention in chapter 5). In other situations, the short-term use of antianxiety medication may be helpful (see chapter18).

Olfactory cues. Management of an elimination problem tied to olfactory cues might involve restricting the cat's access to the soiled locations. A pungent, masking odor (such as oil of wintergreen) could also be used. However, the litterbox should not be anywhere in the area, for this unpleasant odor will carry to the box as well and possibly result in an aversion problem. Reducing the odors through the use of enzymatic products (see product appendix) is best.

Urine marking (not an elimination problem). If the triggers for the urine marking can be identified, the cat should not be exposed to these stimuli. If the trigger is the presence of outdoor cats, the problem can be managed by keeping him indoors or blocking his view of the outside from the windows. In some cases, making the marked areas less appealing (see later section on this topic) may inhibit or actually stop the behavior, but more often than not, the cat will just choose a new place to mark if the motivation to do so has not been decreased.

If the spraying is a frustration behavior, changing the cat's environment to prevent the frustration reaction will manage the problem (see Box 13.3). It may, however, be more helpful to change the cat's reaction to these events, which is discussed in the section on treatment.

Several medications that have been used to successfully manage spraying and urine-marking problems are discussed in chapter 18. In my experience, many chronic spraying problems are managed, but they aren't always resolved.

Ways to make soiled areas less attractive. This aspect of problem management does nothing to address the cause of the problem, and if nothing else is done, the cat will likely choose another location to soil. Use these procedures only in conjunction with a complete management or resolution plan. There are 4 major strategies to employ in this regard:

- Change the texture, using:
  — Double-sided sticky tape
  — Vinyl carpet runner with the pointy-side up
  — Sandpaper
  — Newspaper
  — Contact paper
  — Aluminum foil
  — Water in bathtubs or sinks if these are the soiled areas
- Use pungent odors (*the odor should be associated only with the soiled area and not permeate the entire house, especially not the litterbox area*):
  — Citrus odors
  — Floral odors
  — Menthol
  — Oil of wintergreen
  — Most anything that is intense, such as perfumes (but not ones used by members of the family)
- Make being in the area aversive, using:
  — Balloons that will pop if disturbed
  — Snappy Trainers (see product appendix)
  — Motion detectors that make a loud noise or activate flashing lights if triggered (see product appendix)
  — An electrified mat that delivers a static shock (like we've all received) when touched (see product appendix)
- Change the significance of the area
  — Leave toys in the area or engage in frequent, interactive play with the cat in the soiled area
  — Leave a few sprigs of catnip in the area
  — Leave small treats or kibble in the area (this, of course, depends on the climate or if other animals are in the house)

6. Explain the Goals of an Appropriate Behavior Modification Plan

As mentioned earlier, litterbox problems often have multiple causes, as the following scenario illustrates:

> A box with a cover is located in the basement, just around the corner from the stairs. The litter is a generic brand of clay, about 4 inches deep. The cat, one of two in the family, has started eliminating (both urinating and defecating) on the carpeted landing on the stairs to the basement.

There could be several contributing factors to the litterbox problem in this scenario. An aversion may be involved because the litter is probably too deep for the cat's liking and it is made of large-particle clay. A surface preference may be involved because the cat now prefers using the soft carpet. Conflicts between the cats may be involved because it is easy for one to ambush the other from around the corner—the cat in the covered box cannot see who is lying in wait. A

Box 13.4 Example of a form summarizing client recommendations

RECOMMENDATIONS TO CLIENT

This form does not include recommendations pertaining to urine marking.

1. Suspect medical or not ruled out—take to vet: YES   NO

2. Change location of box to: _____

3. Change number of boxes to: _____

4. Change substrate to: clumping soil/sand brand-name clay other_____

5. Change depth to: 1–2" 1" (prefer slick surface) other_____

6. Change cleaning schedule to: _____

7. Change cleaning procedures to: _____

8. Change surface/texture under box to: _____

9. Add a cover? YES   NO   **remove a cover?** YES   NO

10. Remove liner? YES   NO   **use a liner to make cleaning easier?** YES   NO

11. Modify soiled areas:
   a. Clean with enzyme products   other_____
   b. Change texture: sticky tape plastic newspaper foil Scat Mat carpet runner
      other_____
   c. Change significance: food   toys   catnip   scratch post
      other_____
   d. Change odor: perfumes   room deodorizers   muscle rubs   other_____
   e. Make aversive: balloons   Snappy Trainers   other_____

12. Improve relationship between pets by: _____

_____

_____

_____

*Source:*Developed and copyrighted by Suzanne Hetts, Ph.D., and Daniel Q. Estep, Ph.D., Certified Applied Animal Behaviorists, Animal Behavior Associates, Inc., Littleton, CO. Used by permission.

location preference may be involved because from a spot on the landing, the soiling cat can see who is approaching from all directions and can dash either up or down the stairs to escape.

As this scenario shows, litterbox problems can, indeed, be complicated. Depending on your point of view, they can be a challenge (something like solving a puzzle), a mystery, or a nightmare—or a combination of all three.

Box 13.4 provides an example of a way to briefly summarize treatment recommendations made to clients in this regard.

Surface preference. The goal in treating a surface preference problem is to either modify the material used in the litterbox so that it provides for the cat's preferences or modify the cat's preferences so that the litterbox material once again becomes the preferred surface for elimination. The soiled areas also need to be made less appealing (see previous section). With a strict surface preference, the goal is to change the substrate (litter) in the box so that the texture is more like that of the soiled areas. Most often, that means making the litter feel softer by switching to a fine-grained, clumping litter. Occasionally, using a carpet remnant in the box is effective. If the cat prefers slick, smooth surfaces, the litter can be made very shallow, newspaper can be tried, or an empty box can be provided. If the cat eliminates outdoors, surfaces similar to what he uses there (such as potting soil, a small piece of sod, or decorative bark) can be put in the box and litter can be gradually added later.

For both surface and location preference problems, a good behavioral history is a must. My approach is to identify all the characteristics of the litterbox and the surrounding area, identify the characteristics of the soiled areas, and then determine how they are different. The differences give insight to the cat's preferences and what the soiled areas provide that the litterbox does not. The next step is to modify the litterbox and surrounding area to provide the same preferred characteristics that the soiled areas offer.

Many litterbox problems involve surface preferences, but as the prior scenario illustrates, there are often other factors involved simultaneously.

Location preference. The treatment goals with location preference problems are essentially the same as those for problems related to surface preferences: change the location of the litterbox to meet the cat's preferences or modify the cat's preferences so that another location becomes acceptable. Common mistakes owners make in selecting a location include:

- Locating the box in a high-traffic area
- Putting the box in such an out-of-the-way place that the cat is reluctant to use it
- Making access to the box difficult (e.g., if the cat has to jump up on a storage table, into a bathtub, or squeeze into a closet)
- Placing the box so the cat cannot see who is approaching while she is using it
- Positioning it where the cat can leave the box from only one direction, making ambush by another pet likely

Look for these mistakes in the existing litterbox location, and see if the soiled areas the cat has chosen instead avoid these pitfalls. Avoid these mistakes in choosing a new location for the box or modify the existing location so the mistakes are corrected. There can, of course, be other, idiosyncratic reasons why any particular cat finds the location of her litterbox unacceptable, and these must be identified through the behavioral history. The soiled locations should also be made less attractive (see previous section). Chapter 5 offers more information about litterbox locations.

Litter or litterbox aversions. The first step in treatment is to identify the reason for the aversion. Earlier, a variety of examples were given on how aversions can develop. If the aversion is to the litter, then the type, depth, or cleanliness (or all three features) of the litter must be changed. If the aversion is to the box because it is too small, too large, covered, etc., then these characteristics must be modified. If the cat has developed an aversion due to a frightening experience, the litterbox may need to be relocated (e.g., if the box has been too near noisy appliances). In the case of classically conditioned aversions (in which the litterbox is associated with pain or other bad experience), it is sometimes necessary to provide a new box that is as different as possible from the old one, so that the cues that elicit the aversion are no longer present. With some aversion problems, positive reinforcement for using the box can be helpful. Finally, remember that aversions are almost always associated with some other cause for the elimination problem, most often secondary location and surface preferences.

Conflicts between family cats. The treatment goal for a conflict-based problem is straightforward—improve the relationship between the cats. Of course, this may be easier said than done. For assistance in achieving this goal, refer to chapter 15. In addition, location of the box can be crucial in these cases. Cats need to feel safe in the box and not vulnerable to attack, harassment, or surprise. Thus, it is important for the cat to be able to either see what is approaching from all sides or be protected on some sides (e.g., in a box located in a corner against a wall with an unobstructed view of the area in front of the box). It is also important that the cat be able to exit the box in a direction away from a cat who is approaching. For example, if another cat is approaching from the front, the cat in the box can exit to the side, at a 90° angle. There should also be as many boxes as there are cats (some experts recommend the number of cats plus one), and they should be placed in different locations.

Separation anxiety. Elimination problems caused by separation anxiety are probably best resolved using counterconditioning, whereby the cat learns to associate the owner's absence with good things (see chapter 7). Most cats only react to overnight or longer absences, so a desensitization component is very impractical. It may be possible and helpful to habituate the cat to departure cues such as suitcases, packing, etc., by bringing out the suitcases and not leaving. These cues can also be paired with tasty treats if a counterconditioning approach is used. This should decrease the anxious reaction to some degree, but antianxiety medication may need to be part of a treatment plan, as well. I had one case in which Feliway was helpful (see product appendix), but the effectiveness of this product is still controversial (see the section on urine marking).

Fear or anxiety. The first step in treating a fear- or anxiety-based elimination problem is to identify what the cat fears. If the fear-producing event is coming from the owner, such as noncontingent punishment, then you must, of course, instruct the owner to cease such actions. If there is something about the location of the box that is frightening the cat, move the box. If the cat is new to the house and is generally fearful, refer to the introduction procedures under problem prevention in chapter 5. Counterconditioning and desensitization techniques can then be implemented, if appropriate (see chapters 3, 11, and 16). Feliway is a possibility as well (see the section on urine marking). If you cannot identify the fear-eliciting stimulus, either the problem has been misdiagnosed, the owners need to do some detective work, or you should refer the case.

Olfactory cues. Olfactory cues are most often contributing factors to an elimination problem rather than the sole, initiating cause. Although it is important to deodorize soiled areas, other steps must be taken, as discussed in the rest of this chapter, to address the underlying cause of the behavior. Even if a cat was attracted to an area because of soiling from another animal, it is very likely that surface or location preferences have subsequently developed, and these must be addressed.

Most every professional in our field has a favorite deodorizing product. In general, products that use enzymes to degrade the organic material (urine and feces) work well. Other products attempt to inhibit bacterial growth arising from the organic material, which also contributes to the odor. I have not found vinegar or spray-on products designed for carpet spot-cleaning to be very effective deodorizers, but the latter can be helpful in removing the stains from urine or feces.

A great review of products is provided by Melese[12], and a list of various types of deodorizing products I have found useful is provided at the end of this book.

Urine marking (*not an elimination problem*). The goals in treating a marking problem, which may also include management techniques, include:

- Removing the triggering stimuli or events from the cat's environment. If the problem is a reaction to free-roaming neighborhood cats, their presence should be discouraged or the cat's awareness of them should be minimized by closing window shades or curtains or even blocking his view out the window with pieces of cardboard or other opaque materials. Although people are often reluctant to take action when they know the roaming cats' owners, I encourage clients to talk to their neighbors personally about keeping their pets either indoors or on their own property. This is not a popular message for some cat owners, so the next step may have to be convincing the loose cats that it is not fun to be on the client's property by using some type of deterrent. Commercially available odor deterrents are ineffective. Motion detectors that produce loud noises or flashing lights or even turn on a garden hose can be helpful to discourage roaming cats (see product appendix). In extreme cases, you can consider recommending that the client rent a humane trap from the local humane society and either take the free-roaming cat to the shelter or back to the owner. Warn the client of the ramifications to the cat (which may be euthanasia at the shelter should the animal not be reclaimed), as well as to neighborly relations, if this option is chosen. If the marking is caused by problems between family cats, these conflicts must be resolved (see chapter 15). An interesting case history involving a cat's frustration related to diet restrictions that triggered spraying can be found in Box 13.3.
- Changing the cat's reaction to the triggering stimuli using counterconditioning. For example, when the spraying cat sees other cats through the window, he can be immediately presented with a treat, a toy to chase, or any other pleasant activity that will decrease his arousal. Consistency will be a problem with this approach. If the marking occurs in response to houseguests, then tidbits, toys, or catnip could be placed near the door to the guest's room.
- Making the marked areas less attractive (see previous section)
- Restricting the cat's access to the marked areas
- Using an effective deodorizing product (see previous section and product appendix)
- Using medication to decrease the cat's motivation to mark (see chapter 18). Medication is best used in conjunction with a behavior modification plan, not as a replacement for one. A relatively new product mentioned earlier is Feliway, a synthetic analog of the cat's facial pheromones. Developed in France, it is based on a theoretical concept that cats will not urine mark on objects that are scented with these facial pheromones[25]. The pheromones are also purported to have calming effects on cats who are in unfamiliar or stressful environments, such as animal shelters and veterinary clinics. Thus, Feliway is sprayed on prominent objects in the environment and on urine-marked areas. Although high success rates have been reported[26, 27], my personal experience with the product has not produced the same degree of success. I think it is reasonable to try the product, but I don't think it should be relied on as the sole intervention.

SUMMARY

Cat elimination and marking problems are very common, and they result in the death of many cats who are surrendered to shelters or euthanized in veterinary clinics. Consequently, these problems should be taken very seriously as soon as the owner reports them. A good medical workup is a must, followed by a thorough behavioral history and subsequent behavior modification plan. If you cannot complete these procedures, the case should be referred in a timely manner to someone who can. Relying only on medication or confinement is not sufficient and puts the cat at risk for losing his home or even his life.

REFERENCES

1. Patronek, G.J., L.T. Glickman, A.M. Beck, G.P. McCabe, and C. Ecker. 1996. Risk factors for relinquishment of cats to an animal shelter. *JAVMA* 209:582–8.

2. Salman, M.D., J.G. New, J.M. Scarlett, P.H. Kass, R. Ruch-Gallie, and S. Hetts. 1998. Human and animal factors related to the relinquishment of dogs and cats in 12 selected animal shelters in the United States. *Appl. Anim. Wel. Sci.* 1 (3):207–26.

3. Borchelt, P.L. 1991. Cat elimination behavior problems. *Vet. Clinics of North Amer. [Small Anim. Pract.]* 21 (2):257–64.

4. Beaver, B.V. 1992. *Feline behavior: A guide for veterinarians.* Philadelphia: W.B. Saunders.

5. Leyhausen, P. 1979. *Cat behavior.* New York: Garland STPM Press.

6. Liberg, O. 1980. Spacing patterns in a population of rural free roaming domestic cats. *Oikos* 35:336–49.

7. Schaller, G. 1967. *The deer and the tiger.* Chicago: University of Chicago Press.

8. Hornocker, M.G. 1969. Winter territoriality in mountain lions. *J. Wildl. Mgmt.* 33:457–64.

9. Bateson, P., and D.C. Turner. 1988. Questions about cats. In *The domestic cat: The biology of its behaviour,* ed. D.C. Turner and P. Bateson, 193–201. New York: Cambridge University Press.

10. Borchelt, P.L., and V.L. Voith. 1996. Elimination behavior problems in cats. In *Readings in companion animal behavior,* ed. V.L. Voith and P.L. Borchelt, 179–90. Trenton, N.J.: Veterinary Learning Systems.

11. Hart, B.L., and M. Leedy. 1982. Identification of source of urine stains in multi-cat households. *JAVMA* 180:177–9.

12. Melese-d'Hospital, P. 1996. Eliminating urine odors in the home. In *Readings in companion animal behavior,* ed. V.L. Voith and P.L. Borchelt, 191–7. Trenton, N.J.: Veterinary Learning Systems.

13. Reisner, I. 1991. The pathophysiologic basis of behavior problems. *Vet. Clinics of North Amer. [Small Anim. Pract.]* 21 (2):207–24.

14. Buffington, C.A.T. 1994. Lower urinary tract disease in cats—New problems, new paradigms. *J. Nutr.* 124 (suppl.):2643S–51S.

15. Buffington, C.A.T., and D.F. Chew. 1995. Idiopathic lower urinary tract disease in cats—Is it interstitial cystitis? Presented at the American College of Veterinary Internal Medicine Conference, Lake Buena Vista, Fla.

16. Kruger, J.M., C.A. Osborne, and T. Kalkstein. 1998. Feline idiopathic lower urinary tract disease—Part 1: Truth and consequences. *Veterinary Proceedings*, vol. 12, pp. 401–2. Gainesville, Fla.: Eastern State Veterinary Association.

17. Cooper, L.L. 1997. Feline inappropriate elimination. *Vet. Clinics of North Amer. [Small Anim. Pract.]* 27 (3):569–600.

18. Hart, B.L. 1985. *The behavior of domestic animals*. New York: W.H. Freeman and Company.

19. Wilbourn, C. 1986. A messy cry for help. *Cat Fancy* 29:45–8.

20. Garnett, P., DVM. December. Personal communication, 1998.

21. Wright, J.C. 1994. *Is your cat crazy?* New York: Macmillan.

22. O'Farrell, V., and P. Neville. 1994. *Manual of feline behaviour*. Cheltenham, United Kingdom: British Small Animal Veterinary Association Publications.

23. Wright, J.C. 1992. Hunger induced feline inappropriate elimination. *Animal Behavior Consultant Newsletter* 9 (4):2–4.

24. Marder, A. 1992. Feline behavior problems related to diet. *Animal Behavior Consultant Newsletter* 9 (4):1–2.

25. Package insert from Feliway, Abbott Laboratories, North Chicago, Ill.

26. White, J.C., and D.S. Mills. 1997. Efficacy of synthetic feline facial pheromone (f 3) analogue (Feliway) for the treatment of chronic non-sexual urine spraying by the domestic cat. *Proc. of the First International Conference on Veterinary Behavioural Medicine*, p. 242. Potters Bar, Great Britain: Universities Federation for Animal Welfare.

27. Hunthausen, W. 1998. Evaluation of the use of a pheromone analogue (Feliway) to control urine marking in cats. *Newsletter of the AVSAB* 20:5–6.

CHAPTER 14

Feline Scratching and
Other Types of Destructive Behavior

I rarely see cases involving feline scratching and other destructive behaviors, though, on balance, the calls about destructive chewing probably outnumber those about scratching. I assume this is because such problems, particularly scratching, are easily resolved by the veterinarians or animal shelter personnel whom the owners contact for help; perhaps, too, owners choose to resolve scratching problems by declawing their cats.

Consequently, this chapter will be relatively short. In part, this is because preventing scratching problems is not very different from treating them, so much of the material on scratching has already been covered in chapter 5. In the case of some of the chewing behaviors, we simply do not have many treatment options because we know so little about what motivates the cat. Beyond scratching and chewing of objects, this chapter will address other annoying cat behaviors, such as jumping up on counters and climbing drapes.

PROTOCOL

Accomplishing each step in the protocol for a feline destructive problem is simpler than for other problems in the book.

1. Obtain a Description of the Problem Behavior

It is easy for owners to describe scratching and destructive behavior, but they may be less specific about what the cat is damaging. Obtain details about the location, texture, and position (horizontal, vertical, slanted, etc.) of the objects the cat is scratching. If the cat is chewing items, list and describe them. For climbing behaviors, find out exactly what surfaces or objects the cat is getting onto, when he is getting on them, and what he does when he gets there.

2. Evaluate Potential Medical Causes for the Problem Behavior

Although destructive chewing in kittens could be associated with teething, other potential medical conditions influencing these behaviors just don't come to mind. If pica (the ingestion of nonfood items) is involved, a medical workup would be appropriate, and it would be as important for ruling out ill effects from the behavior as for determining a cause of it. It has long been suggested that pica occurs due to some dietary insufficiency, but there are no data or other evidence to support this belief[1].

229

3. Educate Owners About the Problem Behavior

Educate the owners about anthropomorphic and other misinterpretations. Many people assume that cats behave destructively because they are mad and want to get back at their owners. Cats, however, don't think of chewing and scratching as destructive—I'm not sure they even have a concept of "destructive"! Simply put, cats chew and scratch things because they are cats—it's what cats do—and because chewing and scratching meet a behavioral need. The bottom line is that viewing the behavior as revengeful will not help solve the problem. Cat owners must discard these anthropomorphic beliefs so they won't hold a grudge against their pets and so they will be willing to accept treatment recommendations that don't include interactive punishment. Attributing destructive behavior to the cat challenging the owners' authority is also erroneous.

Educate the owners about myths regarding problem solving and techniques to avoid. As discussed in chapter 5, the goal in working with a scratching problem is not to prevent the cat from scratching but merely to direct the behavior onto appropriate objects. It is not helpful to take the cat to the scratching post and move his paws up and down on it. Doing this can actually be an unpleasant experience for the cat, and it may make it more likely that he'll avoid the object altogether. In sum, the cat does not have to be taught how to scratch; he merely needs to be provided with acceptable objects to use.

With many chewing behaviors, management will probably be a big part of the treatment. If a cat has the opportunity to chew on something appealing, he likely will do so unless a way to create a strong aversion to the item can be found. So, having the family pick up their socks, for example, may just be a necessary part of having a cat. Providing acceptable alternatives will also be important.

Punishment after the fact is not appropriate because it is not contingent on the cat's behavior (see chapters 3 and 5). Any kind of punishment severe enough to hurt the cat or provoke an aggressive response is also not appropriate. Remote punishment is best, when necessary, and will be discussed more in later passages.

Excessive confinement or relegating the cat to the outdoors are also options owners should avoid. Most owners seem to use these approaches as last resorts, so helping them solve problems in a timely fashion is important.

Educate the owners about realistic expectations. As I said in chapter 8 in regard to destructive behavior in dogs, new owners should be told to expect they will lose something of value as a result of owning a pet, whether canine or feline. When Buffett was a kitten, he raked a hole in the black mesh cover of a stereo speaker. This problem was easily resolved by placing a scratching post in front of the speaker, which he uses to this day.

Many cat owners seem to believe that if their pet is allowed outside, he won't need a scratching post inside because he can get all his scratching done in the great outdoors. (Incidentally, far too many people have a similarly erroneous belief about litterboxes!) This is not a realistic expectation. If a cat has the desire to scratch, he probably is not going to think, "Gee, I'd really like to scratch something now, but I'll wait for several hours until someone is home to let me out so I can scratch the tree." No, it is far more likely that the cat will walk to an appealing object nearby, whether that be the couch or the stereo speaker, and proceed to do just what he is motivated to do at that particular time. Therefore, appropriate scratching objects must be provided inside. Merely letting the cat have more access to the outside is not going to solve the problem.

It may well be unrealistic to think that a cat will never jump on a counter or table when the owner is not there to supervise her. Cats love to be up high, and they make use of the vertical space in their environment. One of my cat's favorite perches, for example, is on a ledge that runs along two walls in my kitchen, just below the ceiling. I store seldom used cooking equipment there, and from time to time, Buffett knocks something off as he roams around. If he chooses to get up there when I'm not home, I don't think anything short of a really painful experience would deter him. As with scratching, the goal with climbing is not to prevent the cat from doing it but to direct the behavior onto an acceptable object.

There is also no evidence that kittens' preferences in terms of what they like to scratch are determined by the queen. Certainly, early experience does influence a number of behaviors, including the ability to hunt, but just because a particular queen has acceptable scratching habits does not mean her kittens will, as well.

4. Identify the Behavioral Cause of the Problem

Before proceeding to management procedures or treatment goals, you must first have an understanding of the cause for the destructive behavior. Keep in mind that cats don't seem to be destructive for quite the same reasons dogs are. For example, dogs will often tear things up when they are frightened by noises such as thunder; a frightened cat, by contrast, is far more likely to quietly hide. If you have such a case, refer to chapter 16 on fear and anxiety in cats.

In my opinion, feline scratching can be a displacement behavior at times (refer to chapter 11) that is exhibited when cats are anxious or in conflict about something. The real problem, then, is the anxiety (not the scratching), which will be discussed in chapter 16.

Sometimes, destruction can inadvertently occur if a cat is running to hide and knocks an item off a shelf or scratches a surface as he digs in his claws for traction, but this is not an intended behavior. Cats will also often chew the leaves of houseplants. This is easily resolved by spraying the leaves with a bad-tasting product that is harmless to the plant (see product appendix) and growing a container of kitty greens (many types are available at pet stores). Also, be sure to check with the local poison control center about poisonous houseplants. I don't ever remember seeing a case of cat destructive behavior due to separation anxiety, which is one of the most common problems seen in dogs. Most feline destructiveness is just normal, species-typical behavior, although it may, of course, be annoying to cat owners.

The causes of destructive behavior to be discussed in this chapter are:

- Normal scratching behavior, which may be motivated by play, marking, stretching, greeting, or claw maintenance (see chapter 5)
- Play, investigative, and teething behavior (including scratching and other destructive behaviors)
- Attention-getting behavior
- Comfort seeking behavior (chewing, kneading, suckling)

Components of a behavioral history. Cat destructive behavior problems due to normal scratching and play are relatively easy to diagnose. Some of the other causes may be somewhat more difficult. If the behavior is due to normal scratching, it is important to characterize the cat's preferences, identify what attracts her to the damaged items, and determine if her behavioral needs for scratching are being met in other ways. The answers to the following questions will help you determine this and other causes of destructive problems. They are divided into several categories.

Description of the cat, description of the behavior.
- How old is the cat?

- What breed is the cat?
- Is she spayed/he neutered? (This is always good to know but may not help much in diagnosing reasons for destructive behavior.)
- What specifically is the cat doing? How is he damaging the items—scratching with his front claws, chewing or biting them, or using other means, such as suckling or climbing on things?
- What is the cat damaging?
  — List the items
  — Describe the textures of the items and where are they located
  — List as many examples as possible, in chronological order (to determine if the types of items the cat is destroying have changed over time)
- Is the kitten teething?
- Is the cat very calm and easygoing or very active, nervous, or playful?

Description of the cat's daily routine, environment, and behavior patterns.
- Does the cat frequently solicit the owner's attention and misbehave or pester if he is ignored?
- What kinds of toys does he have?
- How frequently does the cat have opportunities for play, including social play with the owner? How does the owner play with the cat?
- Is the cat a high-energy, active individual or content to be a couch potato? Is the cat nervous, easily excited, or easygoing?
- How does the cat get along with other pets in the family?
- Does the cat play with other animals in the house?
- How does he play—by himself, with other animals, and with people?
- Is the cat very reactive to either people or other animals she sees passing by the yard?
- Does the cat often become anxious or frightened about something (a new family pet, visitors coming in and going out, noises in the neighborhood)?
- What acceptable objects have been provided for the cat to scratch? Where are they located? What type of covering do they have? Are they horizontal, vertical, slanted, or oriented in some other direction?
- Does the cat have climbing posts or "cat condos" with high perches? Describe them, including where they are located.
- Is the cat allowed outside? What does she like to scratch or climb when outside?
- At what age was the cat weaned?
- Have there been any significant changes in the cat's routine, such as a move, changes in the family composition, etc.?

Specifics about the occurrence of the problem behavior.
- Does the destructive behavior occur only when the owner is not watching the cat or is away from home?
- Does it occur even when the owner is watching the cat?
- Does it occur only in the owner's presence? Does the cat turn the situation into a game?
- If the destruction is intermittent, is it correlated with times when the cat has less opportunity for play and physical exercise? If the owner doesn't know, suggest keeping a behavioral log or diary for a few weeks.
- How often, on average, is the behavior occurring (e.g., everyday, once a week, once a month)?

- When (what time of day) is the behavior occurring most often, or does it occur randomly, at any time?
- What is happening in the cat's environment immediately preceding a destructive episode?
- When did the behavior start? How long has it been going on?

Owners' attempts at problem resolution and the cat's response.
- Has the cat been confined and not allowed access to the items she is damaging? What were the results? How did the cat tolerate the confinement?
- Have any changes been made to the cat's scratching post?
- Has anything been done to make the damaged items less appealing?
- Has the cat been punished, either if caught in the act or not? If so, how?
- Has the cat been hit or verbally scolded?
- Has the cat been played with more or provided with additional toys?
- Has the cat been ignored more?
- Has the behavior improved, gotten worse, or stayed the same since the problem began?
- What other things have been attempted to resolve the problem? What were the results?

Differential results of the behavioral history. Answers to these questions will reveal the following information, depending on the cause of the problem:

Normal scratching behavior. Cats scratch for a variety of reasons, so they are likely to have different preferred locations based on their motivations to scratch. Some common examples include scratching near their sleeping or resting areas to stretch their legs; scratching near outside doors, windows, or preferred areas over which the family cats compete for access (e.g., a favorite window perch) to mark their territories; and scratching just about anywhere for claw maintenance and play. In addition, some cats seem to scratch when they are aroused or agitated for any reason, such as after a conflict with another family pet (this may be displacement behavior).

It's not that important to know why a cat has chosen a particular location. The key things are knowing that there *are* preferred locations and identifying the characteristics of the preferred items so that acceptable objects for scratching can be placed in those spots.

It is important to know what kind of texture the cat likes to scratch. Not all cats prefer loosely woven materials, as has been suggested[2,3]; some prefer to pick at knobby materials rather than raking their claws in longitudinal strokes. The behavioral history should, therefore, identify the individual cat's preferences and also reveal whether he prefers horizontal, vertical, or slanted objects.

Normal scratching can occur regardless of whether the owner is home or away. If interactive punishment has been used, the cat will likely scratch the off-limit items only when the owner is not nearby.

Play, investigative, and teething behavior. These behaviors are generally identified by describing the context in which they occur and observing playful body postures. A clearly defined play signal, similar to the play bow in dogs, has not been identified in cats (see chapter 5). Cats engaging in solitary play may run around vocalizing, acting as though they are chasing something or being chased, and then pouncing on and scratching an object. During the running-around phase, household items can be damaged inadvertently if they get in the cat's way, and cats will climb or jump on things during play bouts, as well. A cat can turn virtually anything into a toy—earrings, tubes of lip balm, makeup brushes, caps to pens, toilet paper that can be unrolled, or even 35-mm slides (I've lost a few that way!); as any cat owner knows, the list is endless. Cats may engage in problem play behaviors when they are alone or at night when the owners are asleep. Chewing on electrical cords, socks, pillows, etc., can be play or investigative behavior as well. Cats, like dogs, investigate objects with their mouths. Certain odors may stimulate chewing behavior: Buffett, for instance, likes to chew on all my swimming gear that smells of chlorine. Finally, kittens and young cats play more than older cats, and obviously, chewing by kittens may be related to teething.

Attention-getting behavior. I've given several examples in this book of how misbehavior can evolve into attention-getting behavior because it works for the animal. If the owner's attempts at punishment (yelling, chasing the cat away, etc.) are actually viewed as enjoyable attention by the animal, then the misbehaviors have been positively reinforced. (This is *not* negative reinforcement—if you don't remember why, check back in chapter 3.)

My cat Buffett frequently performs his climbing feats up to the kitchen ledge when my husband and I are sitting at the dining room table talking to each other and not paying attention to him. We have found that either ignoring him or just calling him down is much more effective than racing to get him, which only reinforces the behavior.

One of my volunteers at the animal shelter where I worked related a perfect personal example of attention-getting destructive behavior during a training session for our behavior help line. Her family's cat had developed a ritual with her husband. Every evening when her husband sat down in a bedroom chair to read, the cat would go to the back of the chair and scratch it. Her husband would leap up and yell at the cat, who would hightail it down the stairs with her husband in hot pursuit. Her husband would always give up the chase. Later in the evening, the cat would unobtrusively go back to the bedroom without the husband noticing, proceed to the back of the chair, and set off the whole sequence all over again. Interestingly, the cat never scratched this chair at any other time. Another example of attention-getting behavior is the cat who is confined in a room and scratches the door to get out.

The behavioral history should reveal these kinds of patterns if there is an attention-getting component to the problem.

Comfort seeking (chewing, kneading, suckling). Some of the very methodical chewing observed in cats may actually be comfort-seeking behavior. When engaged in this behavior, the cat will lie for quite some time with an object in his mouth (usually something soft, like a sock), repeatedly chewing it like a person absently chewing gum; he will also appear calm and relaxed. Similarly, cats will sometimes suck on the owner's hair, hands or feet or on the skin of other animals. I have a wonderful snapshot of a client's kitten suckling on the nipples of an Irish setter whose abdomen was shaved because she had just been spayed. Suckling problems are sometimes, but not always, associated with early weaning. Wool chewing, which seems to be more frequent in Siamese and Burmese cats[1,4], may fall into this category, as well. These behaviors are poorly understood, but it is my opinion they are comfort-seeking behaviors because they seem to have such a calming effect on the cats and because nothing is ingested. These problems are also often attributed to early weaning or being orphaned, but I have seen them displayed by cats who were known to have experienced neither. They may be a response to stressors in the cat's environment, such as a move, new pets in the family, etc. Sometimes, the wool or other chewed fabric is ingested, a behavior known as pica (eating of nonfood items). Pica has been attributed to a need for fiber[1] or lanolin[5], but this has never been proven. It has also been suggested the behaviors are associated with stressful events, such as a move to a new household[4]. The kneading of soft objects, which resembles the kitten's pressing on the mother's abdomen to release milk, may also be a comfort-seeking behavior.

5. Discuss Ways to Manage or Control the Behavior over the Short or Long Term

Short-term management of a destructive problem would mean not allowing the cat to have access to the things she is damaging. Longer-term management may be a part of treatment.

6. Explain the Goals of an Appropriate Behavior Modification Plan

With cat destructive behavior, management is often a part of treatment, so these aspects will be discussed concurrently.

Normal scratching behavior. To manage the problem, the cat's nails can be trimmed regularly to minimize any damage. Another management alternative is to use plastic caps that are attached to the cat's nails with an adhesive (see product appendix). They last from 4 to 6 weeks and prevent the cat from damaging the objects he scratches. They are now available, in a variety of colors, from veterinarians and other sources, including catalogs (see product appendix). The only trick is putting them on!

Treating a scratching problem is very similar to preventing one, and much of this information is discussed in chapter 5. The goals of treatment are to identify the cat's preferences, provide scratching objects that meet those preferences, and make the unacceptable items either less attractive or temporarily inaccessible.

Scratching posts should be located in the areas where the cat has been scratching inappropriately, placing them adjacent to the off-limit objects if possible. The posts should be covered with a material similar in texture to the fabrics for which the cat has displayed a preference. If the cat prefers to rake his claws down an object in long strokes, loosely woven fabrics that permit this should be provided. If he likes to pick with this claws, something like sisal would work well. Several objects for scratching should be available to him, and if he seems to like more than one texture, different textures should be offered in different locations.

Some of the scratching objects should be tall enough to allow the cat to extend to his full reach, especially if he has been scratching draperies or other long objects. Few commercially available products (except the tall cat condos) allow cats to reach this high, so owners may have to build their own.

The scratching objects should also have the orientation the cat seems to like—horizontal, vertical, slanted, or a combination thereof. The scratching post should be sturdy and not collapse, move, or fall over when the cat uses it. As discussed in chapter 5, owners tend to discard well-used scratching objects when they begin to look tattered and worn, so advise the client that such items are probably just the way the cat likes them! Mention, too, that eliminating a cat's favorite scratching object can cause him to scratch elsewhere, most likely on something inappropriate. Owners shouldn't discard the cat's favorite objects until the cat has accepted substitutes.

A cat can be encouraged to use the scratching object by scenting it with catnip or attaching a toy to the top that entices her to jump for it and hopefully scratch the post on the way down. My cat Buffett will scratch the post in response to my scratching it with my fingernails.

A number of strategies can be employed to make off-limit scratched objects less attractive. The first is to change their texture. The damaged objects can be covered with plastic, sandpaper, loose netting, double-sided sticky tape, or a piece of vinyl carpet runner with the pointy side out. Alternatively, the section of floor where the cat must stand to scratch the object can be made uninviting with similar materials or a vinyl mat that delivers a small, static shock when touched (see product appendix). If an acceptable object is located nearby, using unpleasant odors to make the off-limit item unappealing is not a good idea, as the odor may also permeate it, as well. The damaged objects can also be booby-trapped by using a variety of remote punishers (see product appendix). Booby traps, however, must be used carefully if an appropriate object is located nearby. The aversive event should occur *only* when the cat tries to scratch the inappropriate object, *not* when he approaches the general area because that would discourage use of the adjacent appropriate object, as well. Lastly, remote punishers can be used when the owner catches the cat scratching inappropriately. My favorite ones for this purpose are any of the ultrasonic devices (listed in the product appendix). G.M. Landsberg and W.L. Hunthausen provide a great review of remote devices[2,6] some of which are also mentioned in the appendix of this book.

Confinement is not very effective in resolving scratching problems, for the same reason it doesn't work for litterbox problems. Experience shows that as soon as the cat is released from confinement, he goes back to scratching the same objects. Confinement can, however, be a short-term management tool.

Declawing or tenectomy are other alternatives for dealing with destructive scratching, and the behavioral aspects were discussed in chapter 5. The latter procedure seems to produce less pain after surgery, but nail upkeep is a significant drawback[7]. Many behaviorists feel that declawing should only be used as a last resort, not as a prophylactic or preventative approach[8]. I tend to agree. Before we were married, my husband, Dan, had always had his cats declawed, so when we obtained Buffett, his first reaction was, "Let's just get him declawed when we have him neutered." I, on the other hand, had never had my cats declawed and was not enthusiastic about this approach. Dan agreed to wait on the declaw if I would agree to have it done if Buffett became a problem scratcher. I agreed. Seven years later, Buffett still has his claws. We used many of the techniques discussed in this chapter and in chapter 5 to prevent his scratching from becoming a problem, including tolerating some degree of damage.

Play, investigative, and teething behavior. Play-motivated destructive behavior can be addressed by providing the cat with more acceptable outlets and opportunities for play, cat-proofing the house, and, in the case of a kitten, supervision and a reasonable amount of tolerance until she grows up.

Owners may discover some unexpected benefits to living with a playful, investigative cat. When Buffett was a kitten, for instance, he forced me to pick up after myself. If I happened to take my earrings out at night and leave them lying on the kitchen table, chances were good that one would be missing in the morning. Some of the missing earrings turned up in out-of-the-way places to which Buffett had carried them, but I never did find all of them. (If we ever move, who knows what we'll find under the furniture!)

Cat-proofing the house is not an unreasonable request to make of owners. They would do it for a toddler, so why not for a cat? If inappropriate items can't be placed out of the cat's reach, it may be possible to booby-trap them (I've used Snappy Trainers successfully to keep Buffett out of my makeup box), and sheaths for electric cords and guards for toilet paper rolls can be obtained from pet supply catalogs.

Playful kittens and older cats need a variety of toys. Individual cats have preferences for how they like to play, but most like to bat around small objects, pounce and jump on pretend prey, chase things, and hide in covered areas. Toys should be provided that allow the cat to display each of these play patterns; among the best is the toy attached to a flexible rod that the owner can dangle and the cat can chase.

Because play can involve the investigation of novel objects, the owner should provide different items for the cat to explore every few days—boxes to crawl into, paper sacks to hide in, etc. Another alternative is to build an outdoor cat enclosure with branches to climb on and perches to sit on. This environmental enrichment approach gives the cat other ways to spend his time. If he is caught playing with something he shouldn't, redirect the behavior onto an appropriate toy.

Not much has been written about teething-related chewing in cats. I have seen kittens chewing on the edges of throw rugs, which I have usually attributed to teething. Providing kittens with acceptable items to chew is the best approach in such cases; some cats like rawhide pieces. Refer to the section on comfort-seeking chewing for more information.

Attention-getting behavior. Resolving attention-getting problems requires changing the interactional patterns that produce them. One option is to remove the positive reinforcement by ignoring the behavior. There are, however, a few problems with this approach: The behavior itself may also be reinforcing (e.g., it may feel good to scratch the chair even it if doesn't get the owner's attention), and ignoring the behavior may result in damage to household items. Furthermore, because the behavior is likely to get worse before it gets better (i.e., the cat might become more obnoxious before giving up, as discussed in chapter 3), the owner simply may not be able to outlast the cat.

If the cat can be encouraged to engage in an appropriate behavior to obtain the attention he wants, the ignoring approach will be more successful. For example, after we started requiring Buffett to come down from the ledge to get attention rather than racing into the kitchen to yell at him, his ledge climbing significantly decreased. This technique works even better when the cat can be intercepted as he is getting ready to be destructive (e.g., when I would see Buffett preparing to launch himself) and then engaged in a competing behavior.

Alternatively, the behavior can truly be punished using an appropriate, remote punisher, such as an ultrasonic device, a motion detector, etc. Any punishment must not involve the owner interacting with or even moving toward the cat.

Comfort-seeking behavior (chewing, kneading, suckling). Comfort-seeking behaviors can be somewhat tricky to deal with. If they are occurring in a young kitten, the behaviors will often stop as the animal matures. In other cases, one approach is to provide the cat with an acceptable object to chew, knead, or suckle. I had a case a few years ago of a cat who was chewing the corners of the cushions on the couch. We successfully handled this by substituting very small rawhide chew flips and covering the couch with plastic for awhile.

That case illustrates another component to resolution: making the chewed items less attractive. I believe this works best if an acceptable and appealing alternative can be found. Unfortunately, the bitter-tasting products that deter chewing in dogs don't work with cats because cats cannot taste bitterness[9], but hot substances, menthol, or eucalyptus oil[4] are other options. For taste aversion to be successful, every item the cat tries to chew for awhile must taste bad and he should not be able to predict, using odor cues, which items are treated and which are not. An alternative approach is to add an odor cue, such as perfume or potpourri, to the treated objects. This scent then becomes paired with the bad taste through classical conditioning, and all off-limit items can be scented without being treated with the aversive-tasting substance[1].

Environmental enrichment as discussed in the section on play, investigative, and teething behavior is also a possibility.

I don't like using punishment for these behaviors because they are so often related to stress[4,10]. Identifying the cause of the cat's stress (the stressor) and either eliminating it or helping the animal find other ways to cope with it is a better approach (information in chapter 16 may be helpful). If the target of the comfort-seeking behaviors is the owner, I would have the person get up and walk away from the cat as soon as the behavior starts (negative punishment) and establish other, acceptable interactional patterns between the cat and the owner. These often include play or petting, depending on the cat's personality. If the behaviors are directed toward objects, I would focus on providing acceptable alternatives.

SUMMARY

Dealing with feline destructive problems involves a significant amount of owner education and the use of management techniques in addition to problem-resolution approaches. Most of these problems are fairly easy to handle by providing for the cat's behavioral needs, judiciously using remote punishment when appropriate, and recognizing that some tolerance is required.

REFERENCES

1. Houpt, K.A. 1991. Feeding and drinking problems. *Vet. Clinics of North Amer. [Small Anim. Pract.]* 21 (2):281–98.

2. Landsberg, G.M. 1991. Feline scratching and destruction and the effects of declawing. *Vet. Clinics of North Amer. [Small Anim. Pract.]* 21 (2):265–79.

3. Hart, B.L. 1980. *Feline behavior: A practitioner monograph.* Culver City, Calif.: Veterinary Practice Publishing.

4. Bradshaw, J.W.S. 1992. *The behaviour of the domestic cat.* Wallingford, Oxon, United Kingdom: CAB International.

5. Beaver, B.V. 1992. *Feline behavior: A guide for veterinarians.* Philadelphia: W.B. Saunders.

6. Hunthausen, W.L., and G.M. Landsberg. 1995. *A practitioner's guide to pet behavior problems.* Denver, Colo.: AAHA Press.

7. Jankowski, A.J., D.C. Brown, J. Duval, T.P. Gregor, L.E. Strine, L.M. Ksiazek, and A.H. Ott. 1998. Comparison of effects of elective tenectomy or onychetomy in cats. *JAVMA* 213:370–3.

8. Overall, K.L. 1997. *Clinical behavioral medicine for small animals.* St. Louis: Mosby.

9. Kesel, L., DVM. 1995. Personal communication.

10. Wright, J.C. 1994. *Is your cat crazy?* New York: Macmillan.

CHAPTER 15

Feline Aggression Problems

Feline aggression problems are second only to housesoiling in terms of the frequency with which they are seen by animal behaviorists[1]. According to surveys of owners, cats are much more likely to direct aggressive behavior toward other cats than to people[2], but just how often they bite humans is unknown. Yet cat bites *can* be serious, for even though they are normally not as severe as dog bites, their potential for infection is probably greater.

It is a rare cat that will take off after and bite a person who is not directly interacting with him (except in play) as can happen with dogs, and because of the different contexts in which cats and dogs bite people, the liability issues involved with feline bites are often not taken as seriously. Don't be fooled into a false sense of security: Cat aggression cases can have serious ramifications. As an example, I have been involved as an expert witness in two lawsuits arising out of cat bite cases. Another pitfall to avoid is basing treatment recommendations on the idea of "dominating" the cat or showing him who's boss—an approach that simply will not work.

There is considerable disagreement among the experts surrounding the interpretation and understanding of feline social behavior. Furthermore, many of the interpretative statements in the literature[3] are unsupported by evidence and are contrary to generally accepted knowledge. I will do my best in this chapter to sort out the differences between interpretations that are based on scientific data and those that are my own (or someone else's) unsupported opinions.

The current state of the art in our understanding of cat behavior can be summarized as follows:

- Our knowledge of cat social behavior, particularly in a home setting, is shamefully inadequate, considering that cats have been domesticated for at least 4,000 years.
- There is enormous individual variation in cats' tolerance of other cats and in their sociability toward humans.
- The issue of dominance as it relates to cat social behavior is confusing and not at all well understood.

Given this lack of knowledge, it's surprising that cat aggression problems, at least those directed toward people, are as resolvable as they are! Cat-to-cat problems are much more variable.

As in the case of dog aggression and fearful behaviors, this chapter will be organized around the *types* of aggressive behavior rather than causes (genetics, lack of socialization, etc.) because the latter are poorly understood.

PROTOCOL

Determining the type of aggression can be a challenge when it comes to cats, partly because owners often cannot provide you with good descriptions of their animals' body postures.

1. Obtain a Description of the Problem Behavior

Owners don't usually have a hard time describing a cat bite. What they may have enormous difficulty with is describing the cat's body postures or what he looked like when he bit, as well as interpreting his communication signals, which are much more subtle than those of dogs and can be hard to interpret. They may also have difficulty recognizing threatening behaviors and body postures. Yet body postures are usually a critical component in determining the type of aggression the cat is showing. You may need to describe some of these postures to owners and have them provide you with more accurate descriptions during follow-up after the initial consultation. Body postures are described in the later section on types of aggression.

It is also important to obtain details about what was happening at least several minutes prior to the episode, for the context in which the behavior occurred is another important component in determining the type of aggression. Sometimes, this is not an easy matter. As you will see later, in cases of redirected aggression, the triggering stimulus can occur hours before the aggressive response, and it can be something as subtle as the odor of another cat[2]. Thus, in cases where there seems to be no triggering stimulus, a more thorough questioning of the circumstances leading up to the episode should be done.

2. Evaluate Potential Medical Causes for the Problem Behavior

As with dog aggression problems, a myriad of illnesses and medical conditions can potentially influence the manifestation of aggression. A starting point is anything that causes the cat physical discomfort and contributes to her irritability. One case stands out in this regard, as it concerned a cat who, for no apparent reason, had started to hiss, swat, and bite at anyone who approached her. A physical examination revealed a needle partially embedded in the cat's soft palate (the roof of her mouth). Of course, there are many other much more complex conditions that should be evaluated by a veterinarian prior to referral to a behavior specialist.

A thorough veterinary examination is important in any aggression case but perhaps even more so in situations in which there seem to be no eliciting stimuli (that is, when the behavior appears unprovoked). Some of these cases turn out to be either redirected or idiopathic aggression (see later section). However, pathophysiologic aggression caused by neurologic and other conditions[4, 5] is also possible. The manifestation of such aggression will not be consistent with normal, species-typical aggressive behavior patterns[2], and other abnormal neurologic and physiologic signs should accompany the aggressive behavior. In addition, infection, trauma, and infestations of parasites, as well as viral diseases such as rabies, could all be underlying causes. The criteria that support a diagnosis of aggression caused by seizure activity include the following[1]:

- The aggression does not fit a description of a normal, species-typical behavior.
- Concurrent neurologic or pathophysiologic signs, such as an abnormal electroencephalogram (EEG) or grand mal seizures, are seen.
- Epileptogenic drugs, such as phenothiazines, can elicit the aggressive behavior.
- Antiepileptic drugs can suppress the aggressive behavior.

Although the vast majority of cat aggression cases I see have been referred by veterinarians,

I have to admit to taking on a few that were not. During the initial telephone inquiry, if it seems as though the case is going to involve play-motivated aggression or problems stemming from the introduction of cats to one another, I sometimes will schedule a consult without the cats having been seen by their veterinarian. However, in my follow-up letter to the regular veterinarian, I make it a point to say that the cat has not been seen by the clinic since the onset of the problem and that medical causes have not, therefore, been evaluated. Thus, both the owner and the veterinarian are aware of this.

3. Educate Owners About the Problem Behavior

It is important for owners to understand the basics of agonistic behaviors. (Chapter 12 provides a more complete discussion of these behaviors, and definitions are included in Box 15.1.) Owners often get into difficulty either because they are unaware of their cats' body postures and communication signals associated with agonistic behaviors or because they don't know how to interpret them accurately.

> **Box 15.1 Glossary**
>
> **Aggression:** behavior whose goal is to harm another individual
>
> **Agonistic behaviors:** those behaviors that are associated with competitive interactions or social conflict between animals
>
> **Appeasement behaviors:** communication signals and behaviors whose goal is to "turn off" the threat or aggression being directed at the animal
>
> **Avoidance behavior:** a type of agonistic behavior in which the animal chooses to flee or leave the situation
>
> **Submissive behavior:** a behavior that may appear similar to appeasement behavior in form but that is displayed toward individuals within the animal's social group or with whom the animal has a social relationship. Submissive behaviors indicate an acknowledgment of the other animal's higher social status, and they also serve to inhibit aggression or threats. Submissive behavior has not been clearly identified in cats.
>
> **Threatening behaviors:** behaviors whose goal is to warn individuals to cease a social interaction or keep their distance. Threats may escalate to aggression.

Both threats and aggression in cats can be either offensive or defensive. For the cat, the goal of an offensive threat posture is to appear large and intimidating. Offensive threat postures consist of [1,2,6]:

- Stiff, straight-legged, upright stance
- Stiffening of rear limbs more than front so that hindquarters are elevated and back is sloped
- Direct stare

- Upright ears
- Backs of ears turned slightly forward
- Tail held still, continuing along the line of the body and then turning sharply downward; tip may twitch; alternatively, tail may be held upright and higher than the body
- Piloerection
- Constricted pupils
- Facing opponent, possibly moving toward him
- Possibly growling, howling, or yowling

Defensive threat postures are more protective of the cat's body and make the cat appear smaller. In general, they are the opposite (or antithesis) of the offensive postures. They include:

- Crouched body posture
- Head tucked in close to body
- Curved tail, tucked tight around the body
- Dilated pupils, but cat may stare
- Flattened ears, held close to the side or against the back of the head
- Piloerection
- Turning the side of the body toward the opponent
- Hissing or spitting with the mouth held open

In another type of defensive threat, exhibited in response to a "continued severe challenge[2]," the cat will roll over on his back or side, with his legs extended so that the claws are ready to use[3, 6]. This is the posture my cat Buffett assumes when Ashley, one of my Dalmatians, is harassing him. There is some disagreement in the interpretation of other agonistic body postures. Some authors describe yet another type of defensive posture (the "Halloween cat"), in which the cat arches his back, piloerects so that he appears larger, and turns slightly to the side rather than facing his opponent[3]. The tail in this posture is sometimes shown upright, sometimes shown down. Other authors describe this as a combination of offensive and defensive behavior[1, 7]. In fact, cats often are ambivalent, and their body postures can change rapidly from offensive to defensive or any combination in between. These differences in interpretation are a good example of one of the bottom-line statements I made earlier—that our knowledge of cat social behavior is pretty rudimentary. Regardless of how these postures are categorized, however, the take-home message is this: Don't touch these cats with fingers you want to keep!

Educate the owners about anthropomorphic and other misinterpretations.

Submission versus defensive threat. Owners frequently misinterpret the defensive rolling on the side or back with legs held stiff and extended as submission, analogous to what a dog does when he rolls over on his back. This is not the case. The cat is presenting a defensive threat, so attempting to touch the cat at this point is likely to trigger a bite.

Cats do not display submissive behavior analogous to that in dogs[1, 3], but they probably do show appeasement behavior. When two cats square off at one another, one will sometimes back down. This cat will avoid eye contact and very slowly walk away from the threatening individual[6]. His goal is to escape the situation without being attacked, so these body postures can be categorized as appeasement behavior. It has also been stated that a cat rolling on the ground (not to be confused with rolling on the back as described earlier) with his limbs splayed and relaxed is exhibiting submission[9]. The fact that young male cats who approach older males and would otherwise be targets for aggression unless they roll supports this interpretation.

"Vicious" cats versus cats displaying play-motivated behavior. The lack of meaning in the term *viciousness* as it is commonly used, as well as proposed behavioral criteria for the term, have been discussed in chapter 11. Yet as many professionals in our field can attest, we often receive calls in which the owner says something like, "My cat has turned vicious." The caller will likely elaborate by describing a wild-eyed cat racing around the house, darting out from underneath tables and around corners, and staging attacks on human body parts; in addition, the cat is usually young and the only cat in the house. Owners often conclude that something is wrong with the animal, and, in fact, such behaviors have been misdiagnosed as schizophrenic and even treated with psychotropic drugs[10]. The truth is, however, that these displays are almost always nothing more than play-motivated behavior.

Although the playful bites such animals deliver are usually inhibited, those inflicted by some rough-and-tumble cats can break the skin.

Jealousy. Owners often describe their cats as jealous of each other or of human family members, but jealousy is a human emotion of which there is no evidence in animals. The behaviors the motivation of which owners misinterpret as jealousy usually are urine marking, elimination, threats, aggression, or attention-getting behavior. A cat who is trying to control another cat's access to certain parts of the house, for example, is displaying territorial behavior, not jealousy.

Dominance between cats. The waters are extremely muddy on this issue. A "cut to the chase" sort of conclusion is that dominance hierarchies between cats may be seen in some relationships but not in others[11]. Not all cats living together show dominance relationships, as measured by which cat is the most frequent target of agonistic behaviors or by attaining priority access to resources[3]. Cats more often ward off aggressive approaches with defensive reactions; moreover, as mentioned, submissive behavior has not been clearly identified in domestic cats, and appeasement behaviors seem to be limited. When dominance hierarchies do exist, it is much more common to have one controlling individual within the group and no clear hierarchies among the rest of the group members[12]. Thus, when conflicts between cats arise, they are likely motivated by something other than dominance issues. Competition between male cats for territory and access to females does occur, but this is called intermale aggression rather than dominance because these males may not have an ongoing social relationship or live in the same social group.

Attributing aggression toward people as motivated by dominance. Cats will often turn and bite, or attempt to bite, after being petted. This will be discussed in more detail later, but suffice it to say for now that there is no evidence that this aggression should be attributed to dominance behavior[6, 9]. Attributing the behavior to dominance or labeling it "status aggression"[13] reflects only one of several hypotheses that attempt to explain the behavior. Given that the place of dominance in cat social relationships is not clear, other hypotheses are at least as viable.

Aggression as spiteful behavior. Any time owners don't understand why their cats bite (which is common in cases of play, redirected, and "don't pet me anymore" behavior), they are likely to conclude that their cats are mad at them or trying to get back at them. However, the fact is that cats threaten and aggress in response to the here and now (except possibly in the case of redirected aggression), and they are not aggressive because they hold a grudge. As was discussed in chapters 1 and 3, it is important to teach owners that their cats are not malicious little devils who have it in for them. After all, if owners believe this, they will have a negative attitude toward the cat and toward working with the problem, as well.

A related issue involves the owner who concludes that if her cat bites her, he doesn't love her. Such an owner should be told that biting is a normal behavior that can be part of any affiliative relationship for cats. Furthermore, there is no relationship between how attached a cat is to a person (how much he "loves" her) and the likelihood that he will bite her.

Declawing makes cats more likely to bite. This belief, discussed in chapter 5, has absolutely no supporting evidence. The argument has been that if a cat is declawed, he can't defend himself and will therefore resort to biting people for protective reasons. Yet when you look at this logically, it simply doesn't make sense. First of all, how many people do you know who would continue to handle a cat who is swatting, threatening, and struggling to be left alone, whether or not they were actually being scratched? Threats without claws can still be very effective, and many cats who are not declawed never use their claws when threatened but still accomplish their goal of getting people to leave them alone. Second, for declawing to make biting more likely, the cat would need to have experienced a sequence of events: (1) repeated episodes of hissing, swatting, and using claws that succeeded in getting people to leave him alone, (2) repeated episodes of hissing and swatting but without using claws that did *not* succeed in getting people to leave him alone (with the cat realizing it was the claws that made the difference), and (3) experiences that taught him that if he bit people, they would leave him alone. People just don't persist in handling unfriendly cats! I suggest a far more realistic explanation: The cat was simply not friendly even before he was declawed and would likely have escalated to biting regardless.

Educate the owners about myths regarding problem solving and techniques to avoid.

Letting fighting cats work it out. This approach will not work for the following reasons:
- Dominance hierarchies are not well defined in cats, and in some relationships, they don't seem to exist at all, so the cats may never be able to establish a stable dominant-subordinate position to each other.
- Related to this is the fact that submission and appeasement behaviors in cats are either absent or limited, which contributes to their inability to form a hierarchy.
- Cats more often ward off aggressive approaches with defensive reactions, which perpetuate fighting.
- Cats can stay aroused for several hours after being threatened, so they may continue to respond with threatening behavior toward the other cat for long periods.

Punishing a threatening or aggressive cat. In dealing with a threatening or aggressive cat, the criteria for effective punishment discussed in chapter 3 are just as difficult to meet as ever. Additionally, punishing an already aroused cat is likely to elicit further aggression and fear. Punishment should never be used when a cat is defensively aggressive (fear motivated). In addition to all of its other disadvantages, interactive punishment is potentially dangerous to the person delivering it.

Using remote punishment for a cat who has initiated an aggressive encounter with another cat usually creates even more negative associations with the presence of the other cat. Remote punishment can, however, sometimes be used judiciously to interrupt a behavior, provided that it is not the sole approach to treatment and that it meets the additional criteria for effectiveness. Although loud noises are often recommended as good remote punishers, they are not indicated in this situation because the noise will also frighten the cat who is being attacked. Use of a water pistol can be considered, but by the time an owner locates one, it is usually too late. Remote punishment for play-motivated aggression may be appropriate (see later section on treatment).

Scruff shaking. Scruff shaking is completely inappropriate. Remember that it has no ethological meaning to the cat: After all, cats don't control other cats in a social conflict by grabbing their scruffs and shaking them. The closest thing to this in cat behavior would be the killing neck bite, and giving a cat the impression that you, his owner, or some other person is trying to kill him is certainly neither warranted nor wise. I have had several cases in which owners had done this, with the result that their cats became defensive and could no longer be picked up or touched.

Forcing cats to get used to each other. This approach is similar to letting cats fight it out, but it is not quite the same thing. In the cases I've seen in this regard, the owners were, with the best of intentions, attempting to convince each cat that it was okay to be around the other one. Usually, one cat was afraid and therefore defensively aggressive, and the other wanted to play and be nice. The owners tried to overcome this by bringing both animals into a room and holding the fearful one or making her stay in the room in some other way (using a crate, a leash and collar, etc.)—a technique no defensive cat would find comfortable. Such an approach is a good example of an inappropriate attempt at desensitization, and it can result in owners being bitten.

Attempting to pick up, touch, or handle an aroused (frightened, defensive, aggressive, or even very playful) cat. Cats redirect aggression readily, so this is simply a dangerous thing to do. Owners may need to be educated about how to recognize body postures associated with these behavioral states.

Educate the owners about realistic expectations.

Some aggression, conflicts, and threats between cats are normal. According to data from questionnaires completed by cat owners visiting veterinary hospitals, 85 percent of cats swat at each other, 80 percent hiss at each other, and 70 percent fight with each other at least occasionally[2]. Although cats living in groups can develop affiliative relationships, in free-ranging conditions they are not inherently social animals who require group living for caring and raising of the young or obtaining food, as more social animals such as wolves do. Moreover, there are no reports of the wild ancestors of the domestic cat, *Felis silvestris lybicus*, living in groups[8]. In one of the few studies of the social relationships of indoor cats, it was calculated that a group of 14 cats living in a 125-square-meter house were at a density 50 times greater than any outdoor population of cats that has ever been studied[11]. No wonder some conflicts could be expected!

Some groups of cats will achieve more than mutual tolerance or avoidance. Studies of groups of outdoor cats[8, 15] and the indoor study[11] cited earlier reveal enormous variation in the relationships a specific cat will establish with others. A cat may form friendly relationships with some cats and be territorially aggressive to others. There is also no guarantee that cats who are related to one another (offspring, siblings) will get along well or that if two cats in a family are compatible, things will go well if a third cat is introduced. With some relationships, the best that can be hoped for is a lack of fighting, mutual avoidance, and the occasional spat, and in some severe cases of territorial problems, it may be necessary to find one of the cats another home. Thus, owners must sometimes realize that their cats are never going to be the best of friends. A great story in this regard, found in J. Wright's book[14], tells of two Ph.D. behaviorists (the author and a friend) who, with years of education and experience behind them, were unable to choose a companion cat who was friendly toward the author's resident cat. This is another indication of how limited our ability to make predictions about cat behavior really is.

Some cats will never be lap-sitters and cuddlers. Along the same lines, because of their past experiences, socialization history, and genetic influences, cats vary tremendously regarding their sociability with people. Some maintain the stereotyped behavior of the cat who is aloof, arrogant, and unsociable, allowing himself to be petted only on rare occasions. For people who expect and desire this from their cats, everything works out fine. If the expectation is for a cuddle-bug, however, owners of such a cat will be sadly disappointed. With hard work and patience, it is possible to effect some degree of change in these standoffish individuals, but usually things don't progress to the point of the cat craving attention. There are other cats, however, who are Mr. or Ms. Sociability. My cat Buffett is one of those. He follows us around the house just as much as the dogs do, meows plaintively at the window if we and the dogs are in the backyard without him, and is ready to jump in our laps the second one of us is comfortably planted in a chair. In fact, while writing this book, I had to move a second chair next to mine for Buffett to use as I sat at the computer, in order to keep him off my lap (which was often filled with reference books) and off the computer table. I also recall an owner who complained to me that her cat was too friendly because the pet's desire to lap-sit was interfering with her needlework.

The take-home message is that although aloof or frightened cats can be made somewhat more sociable and attention-loving cats can learn not to be constant nuisances, *a cat's personality is who he is.* Owners may need to learn to "love the one they're with!"

Many cats will not tolerate touching on certain areas of their bodies for long. In general, cats do not like to be petted in the same ways dogs do. Dogs usually like being patted on the head or side, rolling over for tummy-rubs, or being petted with long strokes from head to tail. Most cats like none of this. In fact, many refuse to have their abdomens touched and prefer to only be scratched around their heads. They seem to particularly enjoy having their facial scent glands rubbed (on the cheeks and chin, above the eyes, in front of the ears). It's much easier to adapt to how a cat likes to be petted rather than attempting to force him to tolerate the petting dogs so love.

4. Recognize the Common Types of Aggressive and Threatening Behaviors

Determining the type of aggression is critical so that predictions can be made about when the cat is likely to threaten or become aggressive. This is important not only in designing effective behavior modification programs but also in keeping people and other cats safe from the problem animal. Granted, categorization is somewhat arbitrary, and there is even more disagreement about conceptualizing cat aggression than there is regarding that of dogs. Ultimately, labeling a specific aggressive or threatening behavior is dependent on the context in which it occurs and on the cat's body postures and responses to the situation as it changes. Offensive and defensive body postures have been discussed in a previous section.

The classification scheme I have used has been derived from several sources[1, 2, 6, 10], and it is an attempt to reflect the most widely accepted views on cat aggression. Note that protective and possessive aggressions are typically not seen in cats, although they are common in dogs, and, as discussed, whether dominance aggression occurs in cats is a controversial issue.

I have chosen the following categories for this discussion:

- Intermale
- Fear/Defensive
- Territorial
- Play
- Redirected
- "Don't pet me anymore"
- Pain-Elicited
- Maternal
- Idiopathic
- Predatory

Components of a behavioral history. To categorize the type of aggression involved (and there may be more than one in any individual case), you will need to ask owners many detailed questions about the problem at hand. Whatever answers you receive to the sample questions that follow should not be viewed as a complete behavioral history. Behavioral histories are fluid.

Deciding what to ask depends partially on how the client answers other questions and what information you obtain as you go. Furthermore, taking good behavioral histories requires not only knowledge but practice. To help you organize the information, sample questions have been divided into different categories.

Description of the cat, description of the behavior.
- How old is the cat?
- What breed is the cat?
- Is she spayed/he neutered?
- Is the cat declawed? (This is irrelevant in diagnosing the type of aggression, but I always ask this question.)
- How old was the cat when obtained? Where was he obtained? What is known about his socialization history and previous relationships with other cats and people?
- What specifically is the cat doing? Describe his body postures and behavior, including tail carriage, ear position, etc. If the cat has bitten, describe the intensity of the bite: Did it break human skin, leave a puncture wound on another cat, pull out tufts of hair, etc.?
- If the aggression or threat is directed toward another cat, what is this cat's response? Describe it in the same detail as in preceding question.
- If there have been multiple episodes of aggression, how has each occurred? Describe each in detail (as in preceding question) and in chronological order, in order to reveal any changes in the pattern of behavior over time.

Description of the cat's daily routine, environment, and behavior patterns.
- Are any household cats allowed outside? If so, how often? Where do they go (e.g., do they wander far or stay in the backyard)? How long are they out per session and as percentage of a 24-hour day? What do the cats do when they are outside?
- If the cat is an indoors-only pet, has he recently escaped and spent time outside? If so, how long before the biting episode did this happen?
- Are there other free-roaming cats in the neighborhood? About how many? Does the family cat often encounter them? If so, what happens—does the family cat avoid, threaten, fight with, or have to defend himself against them? Is he friendly? Where do these encounters take place—in the cat's own yard, in other cats' yards, at additional locations?
- Do one or more family cats frequently view an outside cat through windows or open doors? What is the family cat's response? Is she alert, watchful, obviously agitated or aroused (growling, piloerecting, swishing tail, etc.), afraid, on "hyper-patrol," or racing from window to window? What does the outdoor cat do in response, if anything?
- How many cats are in the family? How big is the home?
- How long have the cats lived together? How were they introduced?
- What kind of interactions occur between each of these cats? Are they friendly and affiliative? Do they groom each other, play together, and sleep together? Are they afraid of one another? Do they avoid each other? Are they aggressive or threatening? Is there any stalking, chasing, ambushing, etc.? Describe as many body postures in each of these interactions as possible.
- Is any cat hiding and clearly avoiding another family cat, other pet, or a family member?

- Where does that cat hide? Does any family member attempt to force him to come out? Do other family pets harass him in this hiding place? Does the hiding place have several escape routes?
- Is the cat afraid of any human family member? If so, what triggers the fear specifically—the approach of the person, the sight of the person, particular interactions?
- How does the cat respond to visitors and houseguests? Is he friendly? Does he keep his distance, threaten, stalk, or stare? Include descriptions of the cat's body postures.
- Does the cat urine mark in response to visitors in the house?
- What is the cat's typical day like? Where and when is he fed? Where does he sleep? Which family members are home or away and when?
- What opportunities does the cat have for play? Does he play with another cat, with people? What kinds of toys does he have? How does he play and how often? Was the cat wrestled with or allowed to bite human hands and feet as kitten?
- Does the cat have kittens?
- Is there an intact female cat in the house?
- If the problem involves a cat who was recently introduced or reintroduced to the house, how did the introduction take place?

Specifics about the occurrence of the problem behavior.
- When did the problem start?
- Is the cat getting into posturing or stare-down contests with another cat?
- Is she chasing, ambushing, stalking, or lying in wait for the other cat? Does this occur only in specific locations or throughout the house? Describe the locations.
- Is one cat clearly afraid and displaying defensive behavior toward another? Is this cat attempting to avoid the other cat and only being defensive when caught?
- How often are aggression or threatening encounters happening between the cats or between the cat and a person?
- How does the cat respond to petting? Does she solicit petting, or does the owner initiate it most of the time?
- How often and for how long does the owner pet the cat? How long will the cat usually tolerate petting? How does the owner pet the cat? Describe the motions used and the part of body the owner touches.
- If aggression or threats are directed toward people, who is the target specifically—owners, visitors, or both? Is only one individual targeted?
- Does aggression toward people only occur if they attempt to directly interact with the cat? Describe these interactions.
- If the cat is aggressive toward people who are more or less ignoring him, what does she do? How have people responded?
- Does the aggression or threat to other cats or people appear to be unprovoked (i.e., is there no eliciting stimulus)? If so, describe the sequence of events (everything going on) for at least 30 minutes prior to the episode.
- Is any family member afraid of the cat?
- Has any cat been out of the house recently to go to the groomer's, the veterinary clinic, a boarding kennel, etc.? What happened when this cat returned?
- Does the cat intently watch birds, squirrels, etc.? If allowed outside, does she stalk these animals?

Owners' attempts at problem resolution and the cat's response.

- Has the owner attempted to punish the cat for this or any other behavior? How? How often in relation to the occurrence of the behavior? What has the cat's response been?
- Has the owner separated the cats if the problem is cat-to-cat aggression?
- If fights between cats have occurred, how has the owner intervened?
- Has medication been tried?
- If previously allowed outside, has the cat been kept inside instead to try to deal with problem? If so, how long has the cat been indoors only?
- How have people responded if aggression was directed toward them?

Differential results of the behavioral history. Answers to these questions will reveal the following patterns, depending on the type of aggression involved.

Intermale. This type of aggression is seen in intact males reaching sexual maturity who are competing with one another for mates and territory[2, 5, 6, 10]. These are the classic toms who roam the neighborhood yowling and howling, especially at night. Intermale aggression might occur in a cattery or in a home with two maturing male kittens who have not yet been neutered (although I can't imagine anyone in their right mind living with two intact male cats for long, unless they are professional cat breeders).

When two males confront one another, they will sit or stand stiffly and stare at each other[2], which are offensive postures, as described in a previous section. One cat may back down, or these encounters can lead to fighting. Only a few bites may occur, but because of the likelihood of abscesses, they can be serious. This behavior is directed only toward other cats, not people.

Fear/defensive. I think this is one of the most common types of aggression seen in pet cats, and it can be directed toward either people or other cats. Any time a cat becomes frightened, he can react with threats and aggression. When he does so, the cat will assume any of the defensive or even ambivalent postures described in a previous section. Defensive aggression is often misdiagnosed, frequently as territorial or "dominance" aggression, but *defensive cats are not going to chase or approach their opponents.* Common situations or stimuli that trigger defensive behavior are given in Box 15.2.

Box 15.2 Common triggers for defensive threats and aggression

- Being punished by a person
- Being cornered by an adult, a child, another cat, or a dog
- Being the target of redirected or territorial aggression from another cat
- Being startled by a stimulus that causes two cats to assume defensive postures in view of one another; each assumes the other is about to attack, and both react defensively[2]
- Being bathed or groomed
- Being in a veterinarian's office or any other unfamiliar environment
- Being reached for, petted, or picked up by a person (if the cat is not well socialized, is new to a home, or is afraid of the person for any reason)
- Being exposed to any stimulus that predicts a frightening event (e.g., if a person attempts to pick up the cat with nail clippers in hand)

Territorial. Territorial aggression is usually only directed toward other cats; it is rarely directed toward people. In fact, I can remember only two cases of cats who were territorially aggressive or threatening toward me as I entered their homes. In one, I could hear the cat yowling in response to the doorbell. When the owner opened the door, she held in her arms this hissing, spitting dervish (aptly named Rebel), who, I later learned, had recently chased a Denver policeman investigating a neighborhood robbery off the premises. This was truly an "attack cat." In the other case, the cat perched himself on an indoor ledge adjacent to the front door and stared at me threateningly as I entered. He jumped down and stalked his way to the living room, staying right next to my ankle all the way (but not rubbing against me). At this point, he assumed a sitting position about three feet in front of me, faced me squarely, and stared at me the entire time I was in the home until I got out the food treats!

Most territorial behavior, however, is directed toward other cats either in the family or in the neighborhood. Both males and females, intact or not, can display territorial aggression, and there is no evidence that territorial aggression is more common in males than females. The territorial cat often stalks, chases, and ambushes the cat he has targeted. These behaviors are usually not seen in intermale aggression, which involves much more posturing. Body postures in territorial aggression are primarily offensive and may include hissing, swatting, and growling. The animal's goal is to exclude or drive the targeted cat out of what the aggressive cat perceives to be his territory. This perceived territory may be all or part of the house, the yard, the block, or the neighborhood, depending on how frequently and how far the cat is allowed to roam. A cat may show territorial behavior toward some other family cats but not all. It is most often triggered when:

- A kitten who has previously been accepted reaches sexual maturity
- A new cat is introduced to the house
- A resident cat who has been away at the groomer's, veterinary clinic, etc., perhaps for only a few hours, is brought back to the house
- Free-roaming neighborhood cats appear in the other cat's territory

Cats often avoid territorial conflicts by "time-sharing" their territories[8, 11]. For example, favored spots in a room, such as window perches, may be occupied by different individuals at different times of the day. Furthermore, multiple cats in a family will sometimes divide the house into different territories, which is what happened between two of our cats. When my husband and I combined households, we each had two cats. One of his, an older neutered male named Vonnegut, and one of mine, a younger neutered male named Amos, immediately began to have territorial disputes. Over time, Amos took up residence primarily in the back part of the house, and Vonnegut assumed possession of the front rooms. Each of the several fights they had before we resolved the problem occurred in rooms that were the shared areas between the front and back of the house. Vonnegut always received the worst of it, but that never deterred him from mixing it up with Amos.

At other times, the targeted cat becomes a virtual recluse in the house, hiding and being afraid to venture out of a safe area. Secondary problems often result, including elimination, urine-marking, and stress-related problems (hair-pulling, licking) in the targeted cat.

Play. Play-motivated problems are most often seen in young cats who are the only cats in the family. It may be even more likely if these youngsters are left alone all day[10] or whose owners don't provide them with many opportunities for physical play. Playful aggression can be directed toward either cats or people and sometimes even toward family dogs. If I receive a call from an owner who describes her cat as turning "vicious," the first question I ask is how old the cat is. If the answer is under a year, I know I most likely have a play-motivated problem.

Kittens and young cats are among the most playful creatures on earth. Many owners, especially those who've never had a kitten before, have no idea how much playtime these critters require. They will play with anything that moves, including feet, hands, and elbows that hang off the arm of a couch as well as the slowly twitching tail of a resting older cat. Body postures include (usually) inhibited biting, scratching, swatting, pouncing, wrestling with other cats, leaping in the air, and chasing imaginary objects. Cats will also ambush other animals and people as they come around corners, walk by furniture under which the cat is hiding, come down stairs, step out of bed or the shower, or dangle their feet as they watch TV. When there is a kitten and an older, more sedate cat in the family, defensive aggression from the latter may become a secondary problem. It can sometimes be difficult to determine if conflicts and fights between family cats are play or more serious aggression. With play, either cat can initiate the attack or chase, neither cat seems afraid of the other, friendly behaviors are shown at other times, and generally no injuries result.

Redirected. Redirected aggression occurs when the cat is prevented from attacking the animal or person who triggered the aggressive behavior and instead directs it on the most available target. That target can be a person, another cat, or even a dog. Redirected aggression can occur hours after the cat has been exposed to the initial arousing event: In one case, the cat stayed agitated for more than 24 hours[6]. Especially when there is a long delay between the triggering stimulus and the attack, owners will often describe this aggression as unprovoked.

This type of aggression is extremely common in cats. In an analysis of 27 cases of cat aggressiveness toward people, the most common type (33 percent) was redirected aggression[2]. (Incidentally, a superb series of photographs that illustrate the setup for a redirected response can be found in the same source.) Redirected aggression can be either offensive or defensive, depending on the triggering stimulus, and my experience suggests that it is the most common type of aggression problem developing between cats who have a history of living together peacefully. The redirected attack usually only occurs when the target is close by or if he tries to interact with the aggressive cat. In other words, cats usually won't go stalking or chasing and then attack.

I remember a case of mine that involved a three-cat household. These cats had a history of living together peacefully for several years. However, a free-roaming cat had recently taken to sitting in front of the back screen door, which was located at the top of the stairs leading to the basement. One summer morning, the male cat in the family was looking out the back door when the cat outside pounced on the screen. This sent the male into a fit, and about that time, one of the female cats in the family came up the basement stairs. The male turned and launched himself at her, and a screaming fight ensued. It took over three months of work to overcome this event, which was triggered in a matter of seconds. Common situations that trigger redirected aggression are summarized in Box 15.3.

"Don't pet me anymore." This category describes a cat who, after being petted for a time, turns and bites or attempt to bite the person petting him. The bite is usually inhibited, or sometimes the cat barely touches the hand and then jumps up and runs off. I have seen a few cases, however, where cats delivered bites that broke the skin. For unknown reasons, the behavior is more common in males than females, but some females will also show the behavior. Although owners usually describe the bites as occurring without warning, the cat usually does give signals of an impending attack, which the owner either ignores or is unaware of. Warning signs include:

- Quickly turning the head toward the person's hand (intention movements)
- Flipping or twitching the tail
- Rotating the ears forward and back or flattening them
- Restlessness
- Eyes dilating

> **Box 15.3 Common triggers for redirected aggression**
>
> The cat can become aroused by any of the following stimuli and then initiate a redirected attack on a person or another animal within reach:
>
> - Watching another cat through a door or window
> - Watching or stalking birds, squirrels, or other prey-type animals
> - Sensing the odor of another cat on a person entering the house
> - Getting outside if the cat is exclusively an indoor pet
> - Being in a shelter, surrounded by sights, smells, and sounds from other cats
> - Hearing high-pitched noises
> - Being harassed by a dog
> - Having a person attempt to intervene in a cat fight

These signs are not seen if the cat is biting defensively.

This behavior is an enigma, and the reason for it is not known. All kinds of hypotheses have been presented to explain the behavior, but none have been proven (although some are more widely accepted than others).

Following is a list of possible explanations and my comments on them.

1. One theory suggests that the cat perceives the petting as social grooming, which cats will sometimes do to one another. Such bouts of grooming between cats tend to be rather brief, but owners may pet their animals for prolonged periods. The cat is merely signaling he wants the grooming to stop—enough is enough[3,6].

   —If this were the case, one would expect that other cats would occasionally exceed the time limit for grooming as well and that similar behavior would occur between cats. This probably does happen.

2. A variation on this theme is that for unknown reasons, perhaps just due to a low tolerance for petting, the cat begins to find the tactile contact unpleasant or irritating and bites to get the owner to stop it[2].

3. Another hypothesis is that the cat finds the petting so pleasurable that he falls into a light sleep, almost a trancelike state, and is not completely aware of his surroundings. As he awakens, he is disoriented, feels restrained by having someone's hands on him, and bites to free himself[5].

   — This theory seems somewhat far-fetched to me, and I have not seen it mentioned frequently in the literature.

4. A final idea is that this behavior is "assertion" or "status" aggression[13]. It is viewed as analogous to dominance aggression in dogs and as the manifestation of the cat's need to control the situation.

   — As previously discussed, the role of dominance in cat relationships is not well understood, and clear social hierarchies seem not to exist in some groups of cats. In addition, it is my experience that bites due to dominance aggression in dogs often break the skin and in general are more severe than most defensively motivated bites. The "don't pet me" bites of cats, however, are usually very inhibited, which does not support the analogy. In addition, the body postures cats show during a "don't pet me" bite are not offensive, which would be expected if the behavior was related to social status or dominance, and (as described later) the cats often run away after the bite. This is not a typical pattern of dominance behavior.

My own opinion is that this behavior may have different causes in different cats. Prolonged petting seems to arouse some cats into an agitated state, and for them, biting may be a release or a way to release tension and calm down. In other cats, I believe the petting does become annoying, just because the cat's tolerance for petting is lower than the owner's desire to pet; therefore, the cat bites just to say stop, and there is no underlying "status" problem. Perhaps, however, these explanations are one and the same—that is, agitation may be equivalent to being annoyed. In any case, I think the whole situation presents some degree of conflict for the cat, as he will often jump down from the owner's lap and begin grooming himself, and grooming, if you recall, is a displacement behavior.

Pain-elicited. This type of aggression is pretty straightforward: The cat is in pain, so he lashes out. (Veterinarians certainly know about this.) It can also happen in older cats who are uncomfortable due to chronic conditions such as arthritis or in response to something that the cat believes predicts a painful experience. If medicating the ears during an infection has produced discomfort, for example, attempting to touch the ears may elicit a bite. Body postures will usually be defensive.

Maternal. Maternal aggression—the aggression expressed by queens who are protecting their kittens from potential dangers—may more likely be directed toward other cats, but it can be targeted toward humans as well. Infanticide by nonpaternal males has been documented in free-ranging cats[15], so the queen's efforts to keep other cats at a distance is not surprising. Maternal aggression has not been correlated with the presence of other types of aggressive behavior.

Idiopathic. No behavioral or physiological cause can be determined for idiopathic aggression. Cats with this problem usually attack their owners violently; in one of my cases, the owner was hospitalized. The cats may also bite repeatedly and stay in an aroused state for a considerable time. Obviously, these cats are dangerous.

The one case I remember best began when the owner heard her cat making "funny noises" in the bedroom. When she went to investigate, the cat launched himself at her leg as she reached the door. He grabbed on, clawing and biting repeatedly despite her efforts to stop him. She finally got him off her by sticking her leg through a doorway and more or less prying him off as she closed the door and drew her leg back. There was a window on the enclosed porch where the cat landed, and he proceeded to throw himself at the window anytime she walked by it.

When taking a behavioral history for this case, I could find no evidence to categorize this as a redirected attack, which was the only other plausible behavioral cause. (The possibility of redirected behavior must be carefully evaluated in such a case before describing it as idiopathic.) It was several days before the cat was calm enough for anyone to approach him, and the cat had to be sedated for a physical examination and to have blood drawn. Nothing abnormal was discovered, and when a second attack occurred, the cat was euthanized. Nothing remarkable was found at necropsy.

Predatory. As discussed in chapter 11, some behaviorists do not feel predatory behavior should be classified as aggression. Their thinking is that if aggression is defined as an agonistic behavior, predation would not belong in that category because its goal is to obtain food (or at least kill the prey); it is not a reaction to social conflict. Predatory behavior involves searching or waiting for prey, stalking, pouncing, grabbing, and biting[2]. I am not familiar with any documented cases of predatory attacks by cats on people, as are described with dogs.

5. Discuss Ways to Manage or Control the Behavior over the Short or Long Term

General management procedures—no behavioral diagnosis. Successful management of aggression means not allowing the attacks to occur. Management of an aggression problem between cats often means separating the animals for awhile during treatment; aggressive behavior toward people can often be managed by simply leaving the cat alone. The two types of aggression in which this *may* not be successful are the play-motivated and redirected behaviors, and pain-elicited aggression may fall into this category if the cat must be subjected to ongoing medical treatment. Especially with aggression problems between cats, the more the cats fight, the more difficult the problem becomes to resolve. Over the short term, the fights should be stopped by separating the cats. If you are unable to determine the type of aggression and develop a treatment plan or if you are not interested in doing so, you should refer the case.

Medication should not be considered as a management tool without a behavioral diagnosis, i.e., without determining the type of aggression the cat is displaying.

Management procedures based on a diagnosis.

Intermale. Short-term management approaches include separating the cats, if the problem is occurring between cats in the same family, or medication (see chapter 18). If an estrous female in the house is contributing to the problem, she should be spayed. In a cattery situation in which intact animals live together routinely, separation is probably the only way to manage things. If the cat is fighting with other cats he encounters while roaming outside, not allowing the cat outside is an obvious management approach. Neutering is an essential part of treatment (see later section).

Fear/defensive. Some fear-related problems can be prevented with proper introduction techniques when the cat first arrives in a new household (see chapter 5). As with any fear-related problem, the first step in management is to control or modify the cat's environment so that the fearful response is not triggered. If there are specific behaviors from family members that trigger the aggression, these types of interactions should be avoided. If problems are being triggered by children attempting to interact with the cat, they should be instructed to leave the cat alone temporarily. Any punishment or aversive treatment of the cat should cease. If the problem occurs in reaction to another family cat or dog, the animals should be separated to avoid exacerbating the problem. Indeed, separation will likely be part of treatment anyway. If it is not possible to adequately control the cat's environment, antianxiety medication can be considered (chapter 18).

Territorial. As with fear problems, it *may* be possible to prevent territorial aggression from developing when a new cat is introduced by using proper introduction techniques (see chapter 5). Almost any cat-to-cat aggression problem is going to require temporary separation of the cats in order to prevent the fights: If there is any chance of permanent resolution, the fights must not be allowed to occur. In the rare situations in which cats are territorially aggressive to people, the problem should be managed by confining the cat in a bedroom or other area when guests are present.

Another management approach, which can also be part of the treatment, is to assist the cats' tendencies to divide up the indoor living space into separate territories. Each territorial area should be equipped with everything the cat needs—food, water, litterbox, resting places, toys, and scratching post—and ample opportunities for attention and social interaction with the owner. This is slightly different from confinement, as both cats have the opportunity to enter another territory but choose not to. Alternatively, they will learn to "time-share" the space as described previously. However, if these imaginary boundaries are not respected and fights are still occurring, confinement is necessary. Medication may have limited value (chapter 18).

Play. For play-motivated problems, treatment may be easier than management. Managing the problem would require avoiding those situations in which the cat would be likely to initiate the behavior. Because the behavior occurs so rapidly, this might require confinement of the cat, and for a young and playful animal who is already having problems because of inadequate opportunities for play, this is only going to make things worse. Medication is not appropriate for a play-motivated aggression problem (chapter 18) unless there are extenuating circumstances (e.g., a cat living in the home of an immune-compromised individual).

Redirected. Depending on the sequence of events, management for redirected aggression may be a moot point. In other words, if a redirected attack has occurred and resulted in another problem (most likely a fear-related or defensive problem), management must be directed at the secondary problem. However, it may be appropriate to implement management procedures to prevent another redirected attack from occurring. How this is done will vary tremendously, depending on the circumstances. See Table 15.1 for examples. If it is clear the cat has become aroused, do not go near her until she has calmed down. It is usually safe to do so after she has engaged in another behavior, such as playing, eating, grooming, etc.,[2] and the cat can be enticed into playing with a dangle toy to assist in this.

"Don't pet me anymore." Management in this case requires not exceeding the cat's threshold for being petted. If the threshold is very low, then don't pet the cat at all temporarily. Some cats will tolerate being petted only on the head, so the petting could also be restricted to that part of the body. Management can also involve educating owners about the warning signs the cat displays

Table 15.1 Possible ways to prevent repeated redirected aggression

Trigger for Redirected Aggression	Prevention/Management
Watching another cat through a door or window	Blocking cat's view by closing drapes, blinds, or door or putting foil or cardboard over the door or window temporarily. Discouraging presence of outdoor cats (using humane traps, talking to neighbors about keeping their cats indoors, using environmental booby traps described in chapter 13 and product appendix).
Odor of another cat on person entering the house	Have visitor remove coat, hat, or shoes if these are the source of the odor. Have person wash hands before handling cat. Use a pungent masking odor such as a room deodorizer spray. Confine cat away from visitors, have them ignore cat, or do both. Feliway could be tried (see chapter 13).

(Table continues)

Exclusively indoor cat who gets outside	Do not interact with cat. If he must be enticed inside, do so with food or toys rather than picking him up. If he must be touched, use a heavy towel or gloves. Take precautions to prevent recurrence.
Being in an animal shelter, surrounded by sights, smells, sounds from other cats	No magic answers! Try to block the sight of other cats as much as possible by putting towels over cages, etc. Try a masking noise (quiet, classical music). Feliway could be tried (see chapter 13).
High-pitched noises	Control environment to prevent recurrence, desensitize the cat to the noise, or do both.
Being harassed by a dog	Control environment to prevent recurrence, work on relationship between cat and dog, or do both. Ignore cat after any such episodes.
Person attempting to intervene in a cat fight	Don't! Improve relationship between cats. If must intervene, do so remotely using water, towels, noise, etc.

that indicate he is approaching his limit for petting. When any of these signs are observed, the owner should stop petting the cat at once. The signs include:

- Twitching of the tail just at the tip or swishing of the entire tail very deliberately
- Eyes dilating
- Restlessness
- Intention movements, or quick turns of the head toward the owner's hand
- Rapid changes in ear carriage, from the neutral, forward position to either flattening to the side or rotating the backs of the ears forward

Many times, the cat becomes more affectionate in other ways if the owner does not pet him too much[2]. The cat may feel more comfortable just sitting next to the person.

Pain-elicited. Management is easy in cases of pain-elicited aggression—don't cause the cat pain. If this is not possible because of a medical condition, the veterinarian should be consulted for treatment or pain medication. A humane cat hood (analogous to a muzzle in dogs), a cat bag, or even a towel may be needed to prevent injury to people who must handle the cat (say, a person trying to rescue a cat hit by a car) or provide medical treatment (see product appendix).

Maternal. Managing maternal aggression problems means that individuals whom the cat is reacting to should not be allowed near the queen and the kittens. If the queen is not allowing anyone near and she or the kittens require care, then a problem-resolution approach may be necessary. Do not overlook the kittens' need for socialization.

Idiopathic. It is impossible to either manage or treat true idiopathic aggression cases because the attacks are completely unpredictable, that is, no triggering stimulus can be identified. True, the cat can be confined to prevent contact with people or he can become an outdoor cat. However, in my opinion, these options bring up serious quality-of-life issues for the cat, and I don't think either of them is appropriate. As mentioned previously, the possibility of redirected behavior must be thoroughly evaluated before assuming the problem is idiopathic.

An example of a mishandled case involved a cat who was euthanized after repeated attacks that did not improve when the cat was treated with megestrol acetate and diazepam[6]. Further investigation into the case after the cat's death revealed that the attacks only occurred after the person had intervened to break up aggressive encounters between the cat and the family dog and that this was therefore likely a redirected problem.

Whether medication is appropriate should be left to the judgment of the veterinarian (see chapter 18), and because the type of aggression is undefined, some medications could potentially exacerbate the problem. If the attacks are severe and people are in danger, euthanasia may need to be discussed (see chapter 17).

Predatory. Cats are natural predators, although experience and genetic factors influence how likely a particular cat will be to engage in the behavior[16]. Management could involve not allowing the cat outdoors, constructing an outdoor pen for the cat, using a leash and harness, or letting the cat out only under supervision. A bell can also be put on the cat's collar to make his hunting attempts less successful.

6. Explain the Goals of an Appropriate Behavior Modification Plan

At this point, you need to decide if you will limit your role to helping the owner understand the goals of treatment or if you will serve in a problem-solving capacity and actually devise the treatment protocol. Make sure that you don't take cat aggression cases lightly and that you have familiarized yourself with as much literature as possible on feline ethology and behavior modification techniques. Cats are not small dogs, and their behavior should not be viewed in this light. If you decide you don't have the time or expertise to continue, refer the case to someone who is well versed in cat behavior.

Intermale. Castration has about a 90 percent probability of stopping or reducing intermale aggression, regardless of the age at which the cat is neutered[17]. Essentially, then, neutering is a necessity for problem resolution. If the problem persists and if it is occurring primarily between a family cat and those he encounters outside, then suggest changing his lifestyle, making him an indoor cat. A lot of environmental enrichment—toys, playtime, bark or wood to scratch, etc.—should be provided to keep the indoor environment stimulating. The other option is to construct a cat enclosure that allows him outside access without the ability to roam.

The use of counterconditioning and systematic desensitization (CCSD) is another option, as it often is for territorial and fear-related problems as well (see Box 15.4 for a partial sample program). The goal of this approach would be to have the cats no longer treat each other as competitors but tolerate each other because each associates the other with something pleasant. These techniques are not mentioned much in the literature as treatments for intermale aggression, but in neutered cats in the same family, they are an option. However, CCSD requires consistent work on the owner's part, so many people elect a management approach instead, which is less time intensive. Progestin therapy may be helpful in contributing to the success of these behavior modification techniques. However, significant side effects can result from this medication (see chapter 18).

Box 15.4 Example of a hypothetical, partial counterconditioning and systematic desensitization plan for a defensive aggression problem between cats

This is not a "cookbook" recipe for the problem because the characteristics of the situation and how they are manipulated are completely dependent on the specifics of each case. See chapters 11 and 16 for a review of the CCSD protocol.

By manipulating different characteristics of the situation, similar procedures can be used for territorial, intermale problems and defensive aggression directed toward people.

In this hypothetical case, one cat is growling, swatting, and then running away when the other cat approaches or attempts to interact with him. Factors that could influence the behavior of the cat are used in the examples that follow.

1. **Evaluate all the characteristics of the stimulus or situation that influence the animal's response.**
   A list of possibilities might be:
   - How close the cats are to each other—the farther away, the less defensive
   - Whether the defensive cat can see the other cat approaching—if he is startled, he is more defensive
   - The size of the room where the encounter occurs—if the defensive cat is caught or trapped in a small area (perhaps he's in a bathroom and the other cat comes to the door), he's worse
   - The other cat's behavior—the cat is less defensive when the other cat ignores him, more defensive if the other cat approaches him or attempts to interact with him

2. **Determine the importance of these characteristics relative to each other, from most to least important.**
   1. Distance
   2. Cat's behavior
   3. If startled
   4. Size of room

3. **Determine the behavioral starting point (a situation involving these characteristics in which the aggression is not elicited).**
   The easiest situation might feature the cats across a large room from each other (perhaps a living room), where the defensive cat can clearly see the other cat. The other cat is quiet and calm.

(Box continues)

4. Use the prioritized list to create "practice" situations.

This means exposing the cat to the modified and controlled versions of the problem situation while pairing these experiences with enjoyable stimuli for the cat, such as food, toys, petting, etc.

1. Both cats in the living room, at opposite ends, both quiet and calm, problem cat is given tuna as soon as the other cat is brought into the room (to make the situation workable, the person managing the second cat will need to provide tidbits for her as well)
2. The previous step is repeated but in a slightly smaller room
3. The first step is repeated (back to the large room), but rather than the problem cat watching the other cat coming into the room, he can't see her until she's in the room (startle factor)
4. Repeat step 1 while the second cat is slightly more active, perhaps batting at a ball
5. Repeat step 1 but bring the second cat a foot or so closer to the problem cat (how close will depend completely on what the problem cat will tolerate without becoming defensive)

Continue progressing by increasing the intensity of each characteristic one at a time. **Many repetitions of each step may be required before a behavior change is seen.** Variations of each characteristic will also be necessary, such as having the other cat engage in various activities (including directing his attention to the problem cat, etc.). Obviously, implementation will have some logistic problems because the behavior of the second cat cannot be precisely controlled. In addition, if the defensive reactions cannot be prevented during treatment, the cats may need to be separated or at least supervised. Medication would be another option. This example assumes the second cat is not exhibiting any problem behavior (fear, aggression). If both cats were showing defensive behavior, the plan would become much more complicated.

5. Each characteristic should be intensified individually, not simultaneously.

The characteristics that are manipulated first are those that are less relevant to the cat. When one characteristic is made more difficult (e.g., the second cat becoming more active), another characteristic may initially need to be made less difficult (e.g., increasing the distance between the cats). Refer to the examples in the previous step.

6. Stimulus intensities should be increased gradually.

For example, decreasing the distance between the cats might mean doing so literally one step at a time. Other cats might be able to tolerate increments of several feet. Each version of the practice situation should be repeated until the cat is anticipating a pleasant outcome (e.g., looking for a tidbit) and his body postures and behavior are relaxed, without any sign of threats or aggression.

Fear/defensive. The treatment for this type of aggression involves CCSD. A partial sample plan can be found in Box 15.4. The goal of the treatment is to use classical conditioning to make the fear-producing stimulus (the other cat, dog, person, etc.) predict the occurrence of good things rather than elicit fear. This must be done at the behavioral starting point, that is, the context in which the cat can have limited exposure to the individual she is afraid of without becoming fearful. In the case of two cats or a cat and a dog, this is usually accomplished by having the animals on either side of a solid door, where olfactory and auditory contact is possible but visual and tactile contact is not. In the case of a cat and person, it may be done by having the cat see the person at a distance or having the person sit down and make no attempt to interact with the cat. Whatever characteristics of the person trigger the fear need to be modulated to a tolerable level for the cat. Gradual introduction procedures that are similar to treatment are discussed in chapter 5.

For CCSD to be successful, the feared individual cannot, in fact, do things that frighten the cat. For example, the dog must not lunge at the cat, the children must not antagonize the cat, or the adult must not try to pet the cat if this elicits defensive behavior.

Fear-related aggression between cats has a good prognosis[10]. Antianxiety medication may be indicated if it is difficult to find a behavioral starting point, if the treatment time needs to be shortened, and if the CCSD plan gets "stuck" at a certain point (chapter 18). Medication, however, should not be the sole intervention.

Territorial. The goal of using CCSD with territorial problems is to change the cat's "attitude" from viewing the other cat or person as a territorial intruder who needs to be driven off to seeing that individual as a welcome guest because she causes good things to happen for the cat. The good things are usually either food or opportunities to play, as described in Box 15.4. In the case of problems between cats, it is very likely that the target of the territorial aggression has now become defensively aggressive herself, a problem that will also need to be treated.

If separate territories are created in the house as part of the treatment or management, care should be taken to equalize the attractiveness of the territories. Creating multiple territories should *not* entail one cat having access to a large part of the living area while the other continues to hide in fear in one small room. When we helped Vonnegut and Amos divide up the house as part of the treatment for their territorial problems, the back part of the house and the front part were of roughly equal size. In addition, we used a large, completely screened-in patio as a third area that Vonnegut and Amos could time-share under our control.

If the territorial behavior is directed toward people, it is likely that the doorbell or a knock at the door is the initial trigger, just as it commonly is in dogs. The owner can begin to counter-condition the cat to the sound of the doorbell by having family members ring the bell as the owner simultaneously drops treats on the floor or dangles a toy. The treatment can progress to working with visitors in the same way. Practice sessions could begin with a cooperative person playing the part of a guest (even a family member will suffice at first for the behavioral starting point) who enters the house, drops a treat or a toy for the cat to chase, and leaves.

Relevant characteristics of situations eliciting territorial behavior that can be ranked and manipulated incrementally in a CCSD plan (as in the examples in chapter 11 and Box 15.4) might include:

- Cat's degree of acceptance of the person (e.g., family member, familiar guest, unfamiliar guest, delivery person)
- How long the visitor remains in the home
- What the visitor does while in the home (ignores the cat, appears nonthreatening, approaches the cat)

Unfortunately, the literature on territorial problems between cats reports that the prognosis is poor[2, 6, 10]. Medication may be a helpful adjunct to a behavior modification plan, but it is unlikely to be beneficial by itself[10] (see chapter 18). In my consulting practice, I have had some success in treating and managing territorial aggression (in addition to our personal experience with it). However, owners must be willing to invest time in working with the cats or managing their environment, and as with Vonnegut and Amos, occasional spats may continue to occur. The other possibility is to place one of the cats in another home. For us, as for many of my clients, this was not an option.

Play. This is one of the easier cat aggression problems to resolve. The goal is not to stop the playful behavior but to redirect it onto appropriate objects. The approach includes the following options:

- Provide plenty of opportunities for play, with toys that allow for different types of play (chasing, batting, swatting, carrying objects in the mouth, etc.). Any version of the toys on flexible rods that can be dangled work well for interactive play with the owner. Also provide opportunities for the cat to hide (such as in a box or paper bag) and dart out to chase moving toys.
- Interrupt playful attacks on people with a loud noise (a blast from an air horn or an ultrasonic device usually works well) or a squirt from a water pistol. This requires that the owner or the target of the attack have a device on their person, immediately available. For this reason, I prefer the ultrasonic devices that have a belt clip on the back or the miniature water pistols that can be held in the palm of the hand. Another option is a small, soft plastic bath toy that squirts water.
- Immediately redirect the behavior by tossing a toy, such as a fur mouse (see product appendix), for the cat to chase.
- Even better, take a proactive approach and identify those situations in which the cat is likely to initiate a playful attack (most owners can do this). Rather than waiting to interrupt the behavior after it happens, the owner will almost reflexively throw a toy for the cat as soon as she steps out of bed, sits down on the couch and crosses her legs, or sets up any other situation in which the probability of the cat biting is high.
- Another possibility is to obtain a young cat as a playmate. Play-motivated aggression is one of the few problems in which this approach can be beneficial. However, the family should be comfortable with the idea of having a second cat.

Redirected. The focus for this type of problem is on treating the type of aggression that results, which is usually fear-related or defensive aggression. Do not allow the cat to continue to get triggered into a redirected response by using the management procedures previously discussed (see Table 15.1). Refer to other sections on other types of aggression.

"Don't pet me anymore." Management is part of the treatment for this kind of aggression. While attempting to raise the cat's threshold for what he will tolerate, the petting sessions should be kept brief enough so that the aggression is not elicited. Many owners choose management as a permanent solution to the problem, which is quite appropriate. If the owner wishes to raise the cat's threshold, petting should be paired with something very appealing to the cat, such as little pieces of tuna or boiled chicken or commercial cat treats. The goal is actually counterconditioning—changing the cat's attitude so that he views petting as something pleasurable, not unpleasant. There may, however, be limits to how far this can be taken.

The treats should be presented either right before or as soon as any of the warning signs begin. The duration of petting paired with treats past the cat's existing tolerance should be slowly increased, by 5 to 10 seconds at a time. The tidbits should be provided frequently at first but come more intermittently as the cat's behavior improves. If the cat does bite, the owner can quickly stand up, dumping the cat to the floor. However, in many cases, the cat bites and takes off, so he is already running by the time the owner tries to stand up!

Pain-elicited. Theoretically, the goal of the treatment procedures for this problem would be to help the cat tolerate pain without showing aggression. This is obviously not appropriate if the pain is the result of punishment or inappropriate handling. However, in contexts in which medical treatment must be administered (treating infected ears, changing bandages, etc.), trying to treat the aggressive response is a reasonable goal. This could be attempted through CCSD. An example would be to barely touch a leg that is later going to need a bandage change while offering a tasty treat. As the cat comes to anticipate the treat when he sees a hand reach for his leg, the touching can become a little more intense (e.g., a gentle squeeze). Unfortunately, the drawback to this technique is that the bandages are probably going to need to be changed before the incremental approach is complete. Thus, CCSD may lessen the cat's aggression because at least some of the time reaching for the leg results in a positive outcome, but it may not completely prevent aggression because bad things continue to happen at other times.

Maternal. Treating maternal aggression is probably best attempted using CCSD. The goal is to change the queen's attitude from thinking that people coming near her and her kittens are bad and a source of potential danger to welcoming their approach. Food treats are likely the most enjoyable stimulus. These would be gently tossed to the cat from a distance sufficient enough so that the aggression is not elicited. An alternative would be to call the queen away from the kittens and then go back to them with her, using a Hansel and Gretel trail of treats to keep her from dashing ahead.

Idiopathic. Refer to the section on management.

Predatory. Treatment techniques for predation cases could theoretically involve punishment, but it is almost impossible to meet the criteria for effective punishment in such instances. Can you imagine an owner chasing her cat around the neighborhood in an attempt to consistently punish him when he leaps at birds? It's not realistic to think that counterconditioning is going to work—I can't believe that a mature cat who is accustomed to hunting will ever be convinced to view birds as pals rather than prey. That typically only happens during early socialization. The bottom line is that treatment and management for this problem are about the same, and they focus on not allowing the cat the opportunity to hunt or, secondarily, making his hunting less successful by using a belled harness or collar. It is *not* appropriate to punish the cat when he brings his prey home, for, as you know by now, the behavior that would be punished would be standing at the back door with the prey, not hunting.

SUMMARY

Although cat aggression problems may not present quite the same type of liability concerns as similar problems in dogs do, they still can be challenging to resolve, depending on the type of aggression involved. At times, our lack of knowledge about the cat's social behavior limits our ability to accurately diagnosis and treat these problems. For this reason, we desperately need additional research devoted to observing and understanding cat social behavior in the home environment.

REFERENCES

1. Borchelt, P.L., and V.L. Voith. 1996. Aggressive behavior in dogs and cats. In *Readings in companion animal behavior*, ed. V.L. Voith and P.L. Borchelt, 217–29. Trenton, N.J.: Veterinary Learning Systems.

2. Borchelt, P.L., and V.L. Voith. 1996. Aggressive behavior in cats. In *Readings in companion animal behavior*, ed. V.L. Voith and P.L. Borchelt, 208–16. Trenton, N.J.: Veterinary Learning Systems.

3. Overall, K.L. 1998. Tracing the roots of feline elimination disorders to aggression. *Vet. Med.* 93 (4):363–66.

4. Reisner, I. 1991. The pathophysiologic basis of behavior problems. *Vet. Clinics of North Amer. [Small Anim. Pract.]* 21 (2):207–24.

5. Beaver, B.V. 1992. *Feline behavior: A guide for veterinarians.* Philadelphia: W.B. Saunders.

6. Chapman, B.L. 1991. Feline aggression: Classification, diagnosis and treatment. *Vet. Clinics of North Amer. [Small Anim. Pract.]* 21 (2):315–27.

7. Leyhausen, P. 1979. *Cat behavior: The predatory and social behavior of domestic and wild cats.* New York: Garland STPM Press.

8. Bradshaw, J.W.S. 1992. *The behaviour of the domestic cat.* Wallingford, Oxon, United Kingdom: CAB International.

9. Crowell-Davis, S.L., K. Barry, and R. Wolfe. 1997. Social behavior and aggressive problems of cats. *Vet. Clinics of North Amer. [Small Anim. Pract.]* 27 (3):549–68.

10. Marder, A.R. 1993. Diagnosing and treating aggression problems in cats. *Vet. Med.* 88 (8):736–42.

11. Bernstein, P.L., and M. Strack. 1996. A game of cat and house: Spatial patterns and behavior of 14 domestic cats (Felis catus) in the home. *Anthrozoos* 9 (1):25–9.

12. Hart, B.L. 1979. Feline life-styles: Solitary versus communal living. *Feline Pract.* 9 (6):10–15.

13. Overall, K.L. 1994. Feline aggression, Part 3. *Feline Pract.* 22 (6):16–17.

14. Wright, J. 1994. *Is your cat crazy?* New York: Macmillan.

15. Kerby, G., and D.W. Macdonald. 1988. Cat society and the consequences of colony size. In *The domestic cat: The biology of its behaviour,* ed. D.C. Turner and P. Bateson, 67–81. New York: Cambridge University Press.

16. Martin, P., and P. Bateson. 1988. Behavioral development in the cat. In *The domestic cat: The biology of its behaviour*, ed. D.C. Turner and P. Bateson, 9–22. New York: Cambridge University Press.

17. Hart, B.L., and R.E. Barrett. 1973. Effects of castration on fighting, roaming, and urine spraying in adult male cats. *JAVMA* 163:290–2.

CHAPTER 16

Fear and Anxiety Behaviors in Cats

When I was working at an animal shelter, my data collection showed that housesoiling was the most common behavioral reason why cats were surrendered. However, fearful behavior was the most common reason cats were *returned* to the shelter within the first 30 days after adoption. This difference illustrates two points. First, cats (at least those coming through an animal shelter) often have difficulty adapting to unfamiliar environments. Second, many new cat owners either have unrealistic expectations about how long this process takes or they lack the knowledge to help their cats in this situation.

Interestingly, although fear- and anxiety-related problems are fairly common in cats, phobias seem to be rare (see Box 11.1 for definitions of these terms). For instance, cats do not seem to have the tendency for the noise phobias that we see in dogs. When cats are startled by a loud sound, they may run and hide, but they don't exhibit the extreme destructive or escape reactions that dogs are prone to. I've seen literally hundreds of thunderphobic dogs, but only one thunderphobic cat. And this cat had a good reason—he'd experienced a tornado!

There are an infinite number of types of fears, and cats can become afraid of anything ranging from a crying baby to clothespins. Basically, we don't always know why cats become afraid of things. Traumatic experiences, a lack of socialization, genetic tendencies toward fearful behavior, and fears that are classically conditioned are all potentially contributing causes. However, as discussed in chapter 11 on fears and phobias in dogs, the cause of the problem doesn't really affect the treatment plan. The behavior modification plan will be based more on what the cat is afraid of and how she is behaving rather than on whatever cause is at the root of the problem. Of course, if the cat is being exposed to ongoing traumatic experiences (e.g., receiving noncontingent, interactive punishment or being forced to experience what she is afraid of), such procedures must be stopped.

However, the cause *may* have a bearing on the prognosis because there is usually a limit to the amount of improvement that can be made with fearful behaviors caused primarily by genetic tendencies or a lack of socialization.

PROTOCOL

The protocol for fears and anxiety problems in cats is organized in the same way as the protocol in chapter 11, which covered similar problems in dogs. The chapters on both fear-related problems and aggression problems are organized differently from those addressing the remaining problems discussed in this book.

1. Obtain a Description of the Problem Behavior

For fear and anxiety problems in a cat, as with any other type of problem, it is important to obtain a very specific description of what the cat is doing. This should include body postures, actual behaviors, and whether the behaviors can be associated with a defined event or trigger (see following sections). You need to know whether you are dealing with fearful behavior, which occurs in reaction to a specific event, or anxiety behavior, which may or may not have an identifiable trigger.

Fearful behaviors. Hiding and avoidance are among the most common manifestations of fear in cats. For many owners, some degree of hiding doesn't seem to present much of a problem, so they often don't seek treatment until the hiding and avoidance become excessive and interfere with the owners' expectations of the cat socially (e.g., if they rarely see the cat or if the cat isn't really behaving as a companion animal) or if they are concerned about the cat's well-being.

Hiding is often accompanied by some or all of the manifestations of fear listed in Box 16.1. If a cat becomes extremely fearful, she can evacuate her bladder and bowels, as any veterinarian can attest. Buffett was once chased up the window blinds by a visiting dog, and he was urinating all the way. A recent case of mine involved a cat who had become fearful of the other family cat as a result of a redirected aggression problem. The fearful cat was urinating when approached by the other cat.

Box 16.1 Behavioral manifestations of fear

Body postures
- Ears flattened to the side or back against the head
- Tail held low or tucked against the body
- Head held low
- Body crouched or curled up, body often held low to ground when fleeing

Vocalizations: Cats are usually quiet when they are just afraid. Vocalizations typically occur when there is a defensive or threatening component as well.

Other manifestations
- Dilated eyes
- Hiding
- Shaking
- Drooling
- Panting
- Avoidance (fleeing, escaping)
- Freezing
- Threats or aggression
- Urination or defecation
- Expression of anal sacs
- Footpad sweating
- Shedding hair

Anxiety, displacement, and stereotypic behaviors. Anxiety is related to fear, but it is different from it. Fear is triggered by a specific environmental stimulus (Buffett being chased by the dog, for instance), but anxiety is the anticipation of or reaction to the *possibility* of such an event[1]. For example, a cat may run and hide in fear in reaction to being chased by the family dog, but if the same cat is frequently harassed by the dog, she may become anxious because she is concerned about the *possibility* of being chased.

Cats, even more than dogs and human infants, like routines, and those whose environments are unpredictable and chaotic are prone to anxiety-related problems. In fact, one study of caged cats found that unpredictable husbandry routines (different caretakers, irregular feeding schedules, etc.) produced elevated cortisol levels and increased hiding behavior in the cats[2]. Moving, conflicts among family members (the two-legged variety), a new baby, or the addition of another pet, which all create changes in the cat's routine, may trigger an anxiety problem.

Some cats are very easygoing and handle changes and stressors in their environment with aplomb (Buffett is one of these), but many others become stressed and anxious about the littlest thing. One cat expert describes some cats as inflexible[3], and it may be that cats who are timid and shy or, at the other extreme, active and aggressive, as described in chapter 5, may be most bothered by changes in their environment.

Anxious behaviors in cats have not been well studied, but they can include a wide range of behaviors. Common manifestations of anxiety are vocalizing, restless pacing, spraying, and possibly destructive scratching. Some inappropriate elimination problems are motivated by anxiety or fear (see chapter 13).

Displacement behaviors. As described in chapter 11, displacement behaviors can be associated with anxiety. Displacement behaviors occur out of context and are irrelevant to the situation[1], and they can be triggered by conflict when an animal can't decide how to react in a particular situation. Given that conflict can produce anxiety, displacement behaviors are therefore related to anxiety. Grooming is an extremely common displacement behavior in cats that can also be a manifestation of anxiety. For example, a cat may sit down and begin grooming after being chased by the family dog (displacement behavior) because he can't decide whether to attack the dog or go and hide; but if this same cat is frequently harassed by the dog, he may begin grooming excessively as a pattern because he is concerned about the *possibility* of being chased (anxious behavior). This type of grooming can become excessive, to the point of hair loss and injury.

Stereotypic behaviors. Stereotypies (also referred to as compulsive disorders)[4] are ritualized, repetitive behaviors that are not goal oriented or do not serve any purpose[5, 6]. They are another example of conflict behavior (although they also often occur when animals are in impoverished environments), which is why they are associated with anxiety problems as well[7, 8]. Examples of common stereotypies in cats include tail chasing and hair pulling.

To learn more about these interrelated concepts, refer to some of the basic literature on fear and anxiety [9, 10, 11], as well as fear-related problems in cats[3, 10].

Determining the eliciting stimuli. Another aspect in describing the behavior is to determine what specific stimulus triggers the very first, least intense manifestation of fear. For example, a cat who is afraid of another cat in the family might become very tense and watchful, scanning her environment constantly before she runs and hides or lashes out at the other cat. It is crucial to determine what triggers the earliest sign of fear or anxiety, as this will be relevant in determining the behavioral starting point for the proper implementation of behavior modification procedures. The specific event should be described in detail, as well as similar events that may *not* trigger the behavior. This will help identify what elements of the event are actually eliciting the behavior.

Because there may not be a specific stimulus preceding anxious behaviors, you should look for stressors in the environment that can produce conflict or examples of chronically occurring fear-eliciting stimuli that may trigger an anxiety problem. Common examples of these are given in Box 16.2.

> **Box 16.2 Examples of common conflict- or anxiety-producing situations**
>
> - Excessive confinement
> - Addition or loss of other family pets
> - Barren, impoverished, or restricted environments
> - Social isolation or crowding (too many animals for the available space)
> - Unpredictable, changeable daily routines (unfamiliar people in and out of the house frequently, owner's changing routines, repeated moves to new environment)
> - Noncontingent punishment
> - Inconsistent social interactions involving punishment (sitting in the owner's lap is acceptable one time but the next time results in severe punishment)
> - Social conflicts or continued harassment between family pets
> - Food restriction (diet)

2. Evaluate Potential Medical Causes for the Problem Behavior

As mentioned in chapter 11, some of the manifestations of fear and anxiety, both physiological and behavioral, can also be signs of illness or disease. Cats can freeze or hide when they are in pain or ill; excessive licking and hair pulling can be due to infections, allergies, parasites, or a myriad of other medical conditions; stereotypies can have neurological causes; and inappropriate elimination can have a host of medical causes. So a good physical examination is imperative. Cats can also become fearful or anxious when they can't see or hear well, common conditions in geriatric animals, so sensory function should also be evaluated.

3. Educate Owners About the Problem Behavior

Educate the owners about anthropomorphic and other misinterpretations. Cat owners may not relate an elimination, scratching, or hair-pulling problem to fear or anxiety. They may instead believe that the cat is mad at them or trying to get back at them (for moving or having a baby, for instance) or that he is simply "neurotic."

Many people, including some animal professionals, also have a difficult time recognizing defensive or fear-motivated aggression in cats. It is my experience that many cases of fear-motivated aggression are misdiagnosed as some other type of aggressive behavior or considered the result of the cat trying to be dominant or "the boss" (see chapter 15 for a discussion of feline aggression). Body postures, as well as the context in which the behavior occurs, are important in diagnosis.

Cat owners also often attribute fearful behavior in their cats to a previous history of abuse or traumatic experience[12]. Any time an animal exhibits an unexplained fearful reaction to a harmless stimulus, such owners jump to the conclusion that the cat was abused. There are, however, several alternative explanations. First, there may be a lack of socialization. Poorly socialized cats have not had the pleasant experiences with people, places, and things that well-socialized cats experience, and therefore they react with fear to anything unfamiliar. Second, the fear may have been classically conditioned (see chapter 3). Many cats are afraid of unfamiliar people; thus, for instance, because the doorbell predicts the arrival of visitors, cats frequently learn to be afraid of the doorbell and run and hide when they hear it. Third, cats inherently seem to be predisposed to be afraid of novel, unfamiliar things, including some odors. Fourth and finally, there are some elements of the human environment that naturally appear threatening to an animal. One classic example is the vacuum cleaner—it's big, it advances toward the animal, it makes the ground shake, and it makes growling or roaring noises. Who wouldn't be afraid?

Educate the owners about myths regarding problem solving and techniques to avoid. One misconception expressed by many owners is the belief that their cats will grow out of fear-related problems. In fact, cats sometimes do *habituate* to a fear-producing stimulus—that is, they stop responding because of repeated exposures without any positive or negative consequences. However, there are two important points here: (1) This usually only happens with mild fears, and (2) habituation has nothing to do with maturation (or outgrowing the fear) but instead results from repeated exposures to the stimulus that have neutral outcomes.

Another common misconception about the treatment of fears involves the belief that one way to make a cat less fearful is to show her that the thing she is afraid of won't hurt her. Most people attempt this by forcing the cat to experience whatever she fears. If she is afraid of children, for example, they may hold her while a child tries to pet her. This approach is likely to backfire. In this instance, by being forced to tolerate the child's approach, the cat now has even more reason to be afraid of children. She will probably try to escape, possibly hurting the person holding her in the process, and she will then learn that escaping reduces her fear. So, in the future, rather than watching the child from a distance, as she may have done previously, she will bolt for another room as soon as she sees the child.

The "showing you it won't hurt you" approach can be viewed as an attempt at flooding (see Box 11.1 and chapter 11), a method that is not generally recommended as a treatment technique except in cases of very mild fears. Flooding entails constant exposure to the feared stimulus until the fearful reaction goes away, and it presents a number of logistical problems and potential dangers. It is difficult to implement because it is usually impractical to present the stimulus for the long periods often required for a response to dissipate. Moreover, animals can become dangerous to themselves or others if they attempt to escape from the fearful situation, and if the animal does escape or if the stimulus terminates while he is still afraid, the behavior will actually be made significantly worse. Obviously, too, flooding is stressful for the animal. (One example of the successful use of flooding comes from a colleague of mine who worked with a cat who was mildly afraid of clothespins. [Don't ask why because I haven't a clue!] Her approach was to have the owner scatter clothespins on the floor all over the house so the cat couldn't avoid them. Within a few days, the cat couldn't have cared less about clothespins and was walking about the house with ease.)

Another technique to avoid is punishing a cat for being afraid, even if the fear is manifest in threatening or aggressive behaviors. Punishment is not going to make the cat less afraid, which is a requirement of any successful treatment, and punishing fear-motivated aggression, especially in a cat, is likely to exacerbate the problem.

It is best not to try to pet or touch a fearful cat. Fearful cats frequently become defensively aggressive and bite anyone trying to touch them. Although dogs will often seek out the company of their owners when they are afraid, cats are more likely to hide. Thus, the use of reassurance in coping with fearful behavior in cats usually isn't an issue.

Educate the owners about realistic expectations.

Fear as normal behavior. Many owners don't even think about treating fear-related problems in a cat unless the cat's behavior becomes a problem for them (spraying, elimination, vocalizing, scratching, etc.). They may believe that most fearful behavior in cats is normal[13]. In the midst of an in-home visit for a dog problem, I frequently observe that the family cat is afraid of visitors or the dog. Yet the owners are very nonchalant about the cat's reaction; they typically just remark that he hides under the bed when the doorbell rings or that he has taken to spending more time in the basement since the dog came. They usually aren't interested in seeking help for the problem. If the dog behaves in this way, however, most owners want to help the dog overcome his fears.

I'm not sure why there's a difference in owner attitudes and expectations in this regard. One possibility is that, historically at least, owners spend more money on veterinary care for dogs than for cats[14], and perhaps the same difference holds true for behavioral care. Another possible reason is that people expect their dogs to be friendly, sociable, and an active part of the family. Cats, by contrast, are more in the background in many (but not all) families. That doesn't mean people are less attached to their cats or that they care less about them, but their expectations for how cats and dogs fit into the family may be different.

Fearful behaviors are common in cats because, in my opinion, many cats are undersocialized, and though there is a large body of literature about the importance of socializing puppies, very little material encourages kitten socialization (one exception is K. Seksel[15]). Perhaps people just assume that fearful behavior is normal for a cat because so many are timid around visitors, new places, other animals, etc. It doesn't have to be this way. I once knew a couple who, over the years, had three or four different cats, each of whom they taught to enjoy not only riding in the car but also going on camping and fishing trips! They would put the cats on harnesses and leashes while they fished the stream and relaxed at their campsite, and the cats would sleep in the tent or the car, depending on the weather. All the cats loved these outings. Yet there was nothing unique about these cats, other than the fact that the couple started exposing them to short day trips from the time they were kittens.

Consider talking to the owners about improving the quality of life for a cat who is constantly hiding or only appearing when the dog is outside or the kids are in school. Encourage them to work with the cat's fear. Owners also may not realize the effect environmental changes are having on their cats; J.C. Wright gives some excellent examples of this in his case history book[3]. Although the cat may never become a sociable, outgoing kind of animal, it is possible to reduce his fear. Provide realistic expectations for the owner, given the limits imposed by the animal's lack of socialization, genetic tendencies, or both.

Feral cats. In discussing this issue, we must first define some terms. When I was working at the animal shelter, it surprised me to learn that many of the staff used the terms *wild* and *feral* interchangeably. Technically, they are distinct. Although different opinions still exist among ethologists about the exact definitions of *wild, tame, domesticated,* and *feral,* most would agree with the basic definitions given in Box 16.3. If a population of cats has been in a feral state for several generations, these cats are likely to be genetically different from the domestic house cat, and genetic differences, among other things, influence how tolerant animals are of human presence. Remember, too, that the sensitive period for socialization in kittens is between 2 and 7 weeks[16]. Feral cats are extremely fearful of people, and, given what we know about behavioral development, the more generations its ancestors have been feral and the less human contact a feral kitten receives prior to 7 weeks of age, the less likely it is that such a kitten can ever overcome its fear of people and live comfortably as a companion animal. Socializing feral kittens older than 7 weeks takes a tremendous amount of effort, often with poor results. Of course, there are always the exceptional success stories, but as a rule, it is not realistic to expect socialization or behavior modification techniques to successfully rehabilitate an extremely fearful feral cat.

> **Box 16.3 Useful definitions**
>
> **Domesticated animal:** an animal who has been both behaviorally and genetically changed from the wild state and whose breeding and survival have been under the control of humans for at least several generations
>
> **Feral animal:** a domesticated animal who has reverted to a wild state; genetic changes may or may not have taken place
>
> **Tamed animal:** a wild animal whose flight distance in response to humans has been reduced to zero (a fancy way of saying the animal allows itself to be handled by people)
>
> **Wild animal:** an animal who has never been domesticated and whose breeding and survival is governed by natural selection

4. Causes Versus Types of Fear-Related Problems

As explained in the beginning of this chapter and in chapter 11, the cause of a fearful behavior (e.g., genetic influences, inadequate socialization, classical conditioning) is not going to determine how it is treated. What is important in treatment is identifying the specific behavior and what stimuli elicit it.

Components of a behavioral history. If the cat hides in fear in response to the sound of the doorbell, for example, the behavioral history can focus on obtaining additional information about this situation. Problems related to anxiety may be more complex and require a more extensive behavioral history. The source of the anxiety may be difficult to identify, so detailed questions about the cat's environment, behavior patterns, daily routines, and the problem behavior itself will need to be asked. Asking these questions is the next step in the protocol. If you do not have the time, interest or experience to do so, you should refer the case. You may or may not wish to discuss management procedures with the owner prior to referral.

Description of the cat, description of the behavior.
- How old is the cat?
- What breed is the cat?
- Is she spayed/he neutered?
- Is the cat declawed?

Usually, these questions are not relevant to identifying the triggers for the fear or its manifestations, but it is always a good idea to obtain the signalment (i.e., gender, age, and breed).
- Can the owner describe, in detail, exactly what the cat does?

For illustrative purposes to describe the problem here and in later passages, I'll focus on four common types of fears for cats: (1) fear of the husband in the family, (2) fear of the new baby, (3) fear of the family dog, and (4) fear of another cat in family.

In response to the question "What does the cat do?" the owner might offer the following information:

1. The cat watches the husband closely as he's walking around. She seems tense but doesn't actively avoid him. If he talks to her, she'll just sit there and watch him. When he approaches her and puts his hand out, she'll run away.
2. When the baby is cooing or whimpering, the cat is anxious. She looks around and is tense and very watchful. When the baby cries, she runs and hides, usually under the bed. She stays there sometimes for up to half an hour after the baby is quiet.
3. When the dog gets within several inches of the cat, she puts her ears back and swats him. If he backs off, that's all she does, but if he persists, she runs away a few feet and then stares at him.
4. As soon as the kitten comes into the same room, the cat tries to sneak out of the room by going behind the couch or underneath a table. She hides in a closet if she can get there before the kitten notices her.

Description of the cat's daily routine, environment, and behavior patterns.
- Where was the cat obtained?
- How long has the cat lived in the home?
- What is known about the cat's socialization history?
- Do any of the cat's known relatives have fear-related problems?
- Has the cat always been fearful, even as a kitten?
- When did the fearful or anxious behavior start?
- Have any changes occurred recently in the cat's environment? If yes, describe them.
- Does the beginning of the problem behavior correlate with the occurrence of any of these changes or other specific events?
- Has the problem gotten worse, stayed the same, or gotten better since it began?
- How would the owner describe the cat's personality—calm and easygoing, timid, shy, etc.? (Although the answers to the preceding two questions won't change the treatment plan, they may provide information regarding the prognosis.)
- What is a typical day in the life of the cat like? Look for consistent routines or erratic patterns. Would a description of a typical day be different before as compared to after the onset of the problem?
- What other animals are in the family? How does the cat get along with these pets? Are there any conflicts?
- Is anyone in the family treating the cat harshly or using punishment inappropriately or excessively?
- Is the cat actively avoiding any member of the household (human or animal)?
- Where does the cat spend most of her time?
- When and how often is the cat exposed to the fear-producing event?
- Can the cat's environment be modified to prevent or minimize this exposure?

Specifics about the occurrence of the problem behavior.
- Describe variations of the fearful situations in which the cat is least afraid, when he is most afraid, and when he isn't afraid. The most recent (say, the last three incidents) may be most helpful. This is another way of determining exactly what

the cat is responding to and arriving at the behavioral starting point for a treatment program. Within the sample scenarios, you may learn, for example, that:

1. She's the least afraid when the husband ignores her or if she can approach him on her own when he's sitting down. She's worse if he tries to initiate contact through petting or picking her up. Recently, after he tried to make her sit in his lap, she ran away whenever she saw him for a few days.

2. She does best when the baby is quiet. If the baby is in the bedroom with the door closed so the crying or other sounds are muffled, she's better. The cat will sit next to the owner on the couch when she's holding the baby. When the baby begins to coo and gurgle, she moves away slightly, and if the baby cries, she jumps down and runs to another room. Rather than getting used to the baby crying, the cat seems to be getting worse. Recently, when the baby was crying and the owner was going to check on the child, the cat dashed in front of her while running for her hiding place, and the owner, out of frustration, yelled at the cat.

3. She's better if the dog isn't moving around too much. When the dog is walking around the room or playing with a toy, she's very tense, but she usually doesn't swat at him or run until he's right near her. She doesn't avoid the dog when he's in the same room, but when he gets within a few inches or touches her, she leaves. The dog is really gentle—he doesn't chase her, and he just wants to sniff her and play with her. She's gotten better compared to when the dog first came. At first, the cat would hardly come up from the basement.

4. She's best when the kitten isn't even in the room. The closer the kitten comes to her, the worse she is. She also becomes more frightened if the kitten becomes more playful or active.

Owners' attempts at problem resolution and the cat's response.
- Has the cat been scolded or punished (interactively) not only for the fearful behavior but also for any other misbehavior?
- Has the cat been forced to experience what she is afraid of (e.g., has someone tried to force her to sit on his lap, or has she been held and forced to tolerate a dog nearby or approaching her)?
- What else has been done?
- Has any medication been tried?
- How has the problem been affected by these and any other attempts at resolution?

Differential results of the behavioral history. When you finish a behavioral history for a fear-related problem, you should be able to identify the specifics regarding the type of fear the cat is exhibiting. You should know exactly what the cat is afraid of and what she is doing in many varying contexts that involve the feared event. You should know what characteristics of the different situations make the cat more or less fearful. You should know when she is the most fearful and what version of the feared event will elicit very little, if any, fear. This information provides you what you need to know to complete the first three steps in the implementation of a counterconditioning and desensitization treatment plan (Box 16.4). The goals of this plan and how they can be accomplished will be discussed in a later section, but let's see how our four examples differ from each other in these first three preliminary steps from Box 16.4.

Box 16.4 Guidelines for implementing counterconditioning and systematic desensitization procedures

1. **Evaluate all the characteristics of the stimulus or situation that influence the animal's response.** Examples are distance; loudness; speed; characteristics of people, such as age, gender, and size; behavior of animals or people, such as approaching or attempting to interact with the cat; environmental factors, such as which room of the house, time of day, etc.

2. **Determine the importance of these characteristics relative to each other.** Make a prioritized list, from most to least relevant.

3. **Determine the behavioral starting point.** Determine what contexts or interactions the animal can tolerate without exhibiting the fearful behavior. These contexts will contain some or all of the relevant characteristics presented to the animal at subthreshold levels. In other words, the behavioral starting point is the easiest version of the situation the cat can tolerate.

4. **Use the prioritized list to create "practice" situations.** This means exposing the cat to the modified and controlled versions of the feared situation or stimulus, while pairing them with an enjoyable event for the animal, such as receiving food, toys, or petting. The feared stimulus should predict the occurrence of the pleasant one. Each stimulus intensity should be repeated until a clear behavior change has been observed (the cat anticipates the toy, tidbit, or attention).

5. **Intensify each characteristic individually, not simultaneously.** The characteristics that are manipulated first are those that are less relevant to the animal. When one characteristic is made more difficult (from chapter example, kitten closer to cat), another characteristic may initially need to be made less difficult (kitten is less active).

6. **Increase stimulus intensities gradually.** Begin at the behavioral starting point, and from there, devise intermediate situations composed of increasingly difficult intensities of each characteristic. Finish with the most difficult situations that approximate "real" ones. Progression to the next level of intensity should be accomplished without eliciting undesirable behavior. If such behavior does occur, decrease the size of the incremental increases and repeat additional practice sessions at less intense levels.

7. **Remember that implementing these procedures inconsistently, haphazardly, too rapidly, or otherwise incorrectly can exacerbate the problem or at least be ineffective.** Correct implementation of these procedures requires planning and a knowledge of theory.

Step 1. Evaluate all the characteristics of the stimulus or situation that influence the animal's response.
- Scenario 1:
    - How close the husband is to the cat
    - Whether the husband is stationary or moving
    - If the husband attempts to interact with the cat
- Scenario 2:
    - What type of sounds the baby makes
    - Whether the baby is crying
    - Whether the sound is muffled
- Scenario 3:
    - The behavior of the dog
    - How close the dog is to the cat
- Scenario 4:
    - How close the kitten is to the cat
    - What the kitten does
    - Whether the kitten is in the room

Step 2. Determine the importance of these characteristics relative to each other. Rank them from most to least important. A ranking of these characteristics for each scenario would be:
- Scenario 1:
    - If the husband attempts to interact with the cat
    - If the husband is stationary or moving
    - How close the husband is to the cat
- Scenario 2:
    - Whether the baby is crying
    - What type of sounds the baby makes
    - Whether the sound is muffled
- Scenario 3:
    - How close the dog is to the cat
    - The behavior of the dog
- Scenario 4:
    - Whether the kitten is in the room
    - How close the kitten is to the cat
    - What the kitten does

Step 3. Determine the behavioral starting point. This is the easiest version of all the relevant characteristics; no fear should be elicted.
- Scenario 1: the husband sitting down at a distance from the cat, ignoring her
- Scenario 2: cat near the owner and the baby, who is quiet
- Scenario 3: dog lying quietly, a distance from the cat
- Scenario 4: kitten at the other end of a long hallway, lying or sitting quietly

Creating these behavioral starting points to which the cat should be exposed, as you can see, may be very easy or very difficult.

5. Discuss Ways to Manage or Control the Behavior over the Short or Long Term

Managing fear-related problems almost always means controlling the environment so that the cat doesn't become afraid. This may mean keeping animals separated from each other temporarily, putting the cat in a quiet part of the house when guests are visiting, etc. Related to this, any ongoing interactions with people that continue to frighten the cat must be stopped. Cat owners sometimes don't realize how environmental changes or stressors can affect a behavior problem, so you may need to help them make the connection, based on the behavioral history. Medication can also be used to decrease the cat's fear or anxiety (see chapter 18).

6. Explain the Goals of an Appropriate Behavior Modification Plan

Most fear-related problems in cats are resolved using CCSD (see chapters 3, 11, 12, and 15). The goal of these procedures is to condition the cat to expect a pleasant outcome (something good) from the stimulus that he now fears. When this happens, the cat will no longer be afraid. The steps by which this goal is accomplished are outlined in Box 16.4. We have already worked through the first three steps in our four scenarios. The next three steps follow for each scenario.

Counterconditioning and desensitization.

Steps 4, 5, and 6. Use the prioritized list to create "practice" situations. Intensify each characteristic individually, not simultaneously. Increase stimulus intensities gradually. Pair each situation with an enjoyable event.

- Scenario 1:
  — The husband sits down at a distance from the cat and ignores her while dangling a cat dancer (her favorite toy). This continues until the cat shows some anticipatory playful behavior when the husband appears (perhaps she approaches him or shows play-solicitation behaviors [see chapter 5]) or at least doesn't avoid him.
  — The first step is repeated with the husband closer to the cat (the least important characteristic, distance, is made more difficult).
  — The first step is repeated with the husband walking around (the next characteristic is made more difficult, but the distance is increased).
  — The first step is repeated, but the husband looks at the cat (the most important characteristic—the husband's behavior—is made more difficult, other characteristics are made easier).
  — The husband walks around (instead of sitting) and is closer to the cat while dangling the toy.

These steps will need to be repeated as the husband moves closer to the cat and with a variety of behaviors from the husband—approaching the cat, talking to the cat, reaching toward her, etc.

- Scenario 2:
  — While the cat is near the baby, who is quiet and sleeping, the owner begins to scratch the cat under the chin (something he really enjoys).
  — The first step is repeated when the baby is making cooing or gurgling sounds behind a closed door or at a distance from the cat (muffled, "safer" sounds).
  — The first step is repeated when the baby is making cooing or gurgling noises closer to the cat or with the door partially or all the way open.
  — The first step is repeated when the baby is perhaps whimpering or whining (sounds more like crying) but at a distance from the cat or behind a closed door.

Obviously, it is very difficult to control what the baby does and when he does it. An alternative approach would be to make an audiotape of the baby's sounds and use it in the desensitization process.

- Scenario 3:
    - The dog is on a down-stay, and the cat is allowed to see her at a distance (perhaps across the room) while receiving a small piece of tuna (his favorite treat).
    - The first step is repeated with the dog several inches or several feet closer to the cat (depending on the cat's tolerance).
    - The dog is again at a distance from the cat but moving around a bit while the cat receives his tuna.
    - The previous step is repeated several inches or several feet closer to the cat.

  As in the first scenario, behaviors from the dog that are gradually more active will need to be elicited. This process is much easier with a dog who is moderately to well trained. Some training of the dog may be needed before certain of these incremental steps can be achieved.
- Scenario 4:
    - The kitten is at the other end of a long hallway, lying or sitting quietly while the cat is fed some canned food.
    - The previous step is repeated while the kitten bats at a ball.
    - The first step is repeated with the kitten quiet but closer to the cat.
    - The first step is repeated while the kitten jumps for a cat dancer (increased distance but the kitten is more active).
    - The previous step is repeated with the kitten batting the ball closer to the cat (less active than in the previous step but closer to the cat).

  This is another example in which the incremental steps may not be very realistic, as it is difficult to control the behavior of the kitten. Implementing each step will require a second person working with the kitten and perhaps also feeding her to keep her relatively quiet. This process may take many repetitions at each step.

In all these scenarios, rather than changing the environment to create the incremental steps, medication in graduating doses can be used to do so (see chapter 18).

There is a long way to go in each scenario from these initial sample steps to more realistic, everyday situations. Consequently, cat owners need significant support and assistance to implement a CCSD program successfully, especially if the animal's fear is severe. They often have a difficult time devising the increments, they use increments that are too large (taking giant steps instead of baby steps), and they do not do a sufficient number of repetitions at each step. In other words, they generally attempt to do too much too fast. If you are going to direct a problem-resolution plan, you must be able to deal with these potential difficulties successfully. One way to do this is with frequent telephone follow-ups. It's probably not realistic to attempt to explain all the incremental steps in the first consulting session. It may be less overwhelming to the owner to give her a manageable number of situations to practice (depending on the specifics of the problem) and ask her to contact you for a follow-up consultation so you can discuss the cat's progress and devise additional steps.

Counterconditioning without desensitization. Sometimes, it may be difficult to sufficiently control the cat's environment so that experiences with fear- or anxiety-producing stimuli are limited only to the incremental exposures during desensitization. For example, there is a limit to how much desensitization can be used with a new baby in the house: We can't have the baby there only for brief times at first and then gradually lengthened sessions! In these situations, counterconditioning by itself may be necessary. This may affect the treatment's length or success.

Keeping the cat's environment predictable. This is especially important in anxiety-related problems. If a new routine must be put in place because of household changes, it should be expected that the cat will take some time to adapt to it. Continuing fluctuations in routines should be avoided. If the specific change in routine that triggered the behavior can be identified, the owner should try to go back to the original routine.

Flooding. Another possible treatment technique is flooding, which was discussed earlier in this chapter and in chapter 11. In general, this technique should be avoided, but some behaviorists use a modified flooding technique in which they create easier versions of the feared situation (e.g., a tape of a baby crying played at a very low volume), flood the cat beginning with the easiest version possible, and incrementally make the situations more difficult (e.g., increase the volume). I would not recommend attempting this if you are a novice in the field, as you can easily exacerbate the problem if you implement such a plan incorrectly or if something goes wrong.

Difficulties in treating anxiety-related problems. Anxious behaviors such as stereotypies (tail chasing) and self-injurious behaviors such as hair pulling or excessive licking can be very difficult to treat. Obviously, it is always important to thoroughly evaluate medical causes for these problems.

If the stimuli that trigger the problem can be clearly identified, a CCSD plan or other appropriate treatment measures can be implemented. For example, if a cat is anxious because of harassment from another family cat, the cats' relationship must be improved using the information from chapter 15. Unfortunately, in many cases, the triggering stimuli can't be identified.

In such cases, it may be helpful to suggest the owner begin keeping a behavioral log to attempt to identify what the anxious behavior might be correlated with. Another option is to treat the problem symptomatically, using appropriate medication (see chapter 18). These types of problems are often best referred to behavior specialists who may have more experience working with them.

Medication. Detailed information regarding medication can be found in chapter 18. There are several ways in which medication could be considered appropriate:

- As a management tool to prevent the cat from displaying fear-motivated behaviors that are problems for the owner; this may be more likely for anxious behaviors (spraying, etc.)
- As a way of preventing the cat from being triggered into a fearful response, which would impede the progress of the counterconditioning and desensitization program
- As a way to move the plan along if the desensitization plan gets "stuck" or if incremental exposures are not possible
- As a means to work with the problem if there is no behavioral starting point because the cat's fear is too intense or generalized (most likely seen in a poorly socialized cat or a cat having an extreme reaction to a move or being adopted into a new home)

SUMMARY

Fear-related problems can often be treated successfully. However, attention to detail is critical. It is possible to exacerbate problems by implementing behavior modification techniques incorrectly. If you are not familiar or comfortable with the techniques explained in this chapter, you may want to work with someone who is experienced before attempting them on your own.

REFERENCES

1. McFarland, D., ed. 1987. *The Oxford companion to animal behaviour.* New York: Oxford University Press.

2. Carlstead, K. 1991, as cited in J.W.S. Bradshaw, 1992, *The behaviour of the domestic cat,* Wallingford, Oxon, United Kingdom: CAB International.

3. Wright, J.C. 1994. *Is your cat crazy?* New York: Macmillan.

4. Heweson, C.F., and U.A. Luescher. 1996. Compulsive disorders in dogs. In *Readings in companion animal behavior,* ed. V.L. Voith and P.L. Borchelt, 153–8. Trenton, N.J.: Veterinary Learning Systems.

5. Immelman, K., and C. Beer. 1989. *A dictionary of ethology.* Cambridge, Mass.: Harvard University Press.

6. Mason, G.J. 1991. Stereotypies: A critical review. *Anim. Beh.* 41:1015–37.

7. Luescher, U.A., D.B. McKeown, and J. Halip. 1991. Stereotypic or obsessive-compulsive disorders in dogs and cats. *Vet. Clinics of North Amer. [Small Anim. Pract.]* 21 (2):401–14.

8. Overall, K.L. 1997. *Clinical behavioral medicine for small animals.* St. Louis: Mosby.

9. Gray, J.A. 1987. *The psychology of fear and stress.* 2nd edition. New York: Cambridge University Press.

10. Voith, V.L., and P.L. Borchelt. 1996. Fears and phobias in companion animals. In *Readings in companion animal behavior,* ed. V.L. Voith and P.L. Borchelt, 140–52. Trenton, N.J.: Veterinary Learning Systems.

11. Denny, M.R., ed. 1991. *Fear, avoidance and phobias.* Hillsdale, N.J.: Lawrence Erlbaum Associates.

12. Heidenberger, E. 1997. Housing conditions and behavioural problems of indoor cats as assessed by their owners. *Appl. Anim. Beh. Sci.* 52:345–64.

13. Askew, H.R. 1996. *Treatment of behavior problems in dogs and cats.* Cambridge: Blackwell Science.

14. Center for Information Management, American Veterinary Medical Association. 1992. *The veterinary service market for companion animals, 1992.* Schaumberg, Ill.: American Veterinary Medical Association.

15. Seskel, K. 1997. Kitty kindy. In *Proceeding of the first international conference on veterinary behavioural medicine*, ed. E.S. Mills, S.E. Heath, and L.J. Harrington, 28–30. Potters Bar, Great Britain: Universities Federation for Animal Welfare.

16. Karsh, E.B., and D.C. Turner. 1988. The human-cat relationship. In *The domestic cat: The biology of its behaviour*, ed. D.C. Turner and P. Bateson. New York: Cambridge University Press.

CHAPTER 17

The Dilemma of Euthanasia
for Behavior Problems

Whether euthanasia is an appropriate option in severe behavior problems is an emotionally laden issue. It presents dilemmas for everyone involved—the veterinarian, the pet owner, the animal behavior specialist, the dog trainer, the shelter staffer, or anyone attempting to assist an owner in decision making. I don't have to tell you how difficult these decisions can be. The vast majority of veterinarians and other animal care professionals take these situations very seriously and do not make snap decisions or spur-of-the-moment judgments. Unfortunately, however, there are exceptions.

A client who had a cat with an inappropriate elimination problem called her veterinarian for help. Astoundingly, the veterinarian told her that if it was his cat, he'd just take it out and shoot it. The owner was, to put it mildly, displeased with this recommendation, so she sought help on her own and called me; together, we resolved the problem. Another veterinarian, without ever seeing a certain dog, told the owner unequivocally that she should have the animal euthanized because it had snapped at a child (he had grabbed hold of the child's parka without tearing it). I have talked to many clients who had been to trainers who recommended euthanasia for their dogs because they were "too aggressive"—assessments made after the trainers had either strung the dogs up, grabbed them by the scruff and thrown them to the floor, hit them, or subjected them to other types of abusive "training" techniques and the dogs, in self-defense, had bitten them. Many of these animals turned out to be very workable dogs.

In my 15 years or so of behavior consulting work, I have only directly recommended to two owners that it would be best if they euthanized their dogs because of the danger they presented. In general, I feel strongly that it is not my role—or yours—to tell owners whether they should choose euthanasia for their pets. My opinion is based on my own experience as a cofounder of the pet-loss counseling program at the Veterinary Teaching Hospital at Colorado State University and on what I learned from my colleagues in that program who were trained in the human service field.

As an animal care professional, you are viewed by owners as the authority on their pet. You are the expert; you know more than they do. Consequently, if you tell an owner that you think her pet should be euthanized, she will most likely follow your recommendation. Given the power you hold, you must not take this responsibility lightly.

Owners really do not want you to make a decision for them or to be told what they should do, even if they ask you, "What would *you* do if it was your pet?"[1] What they are asking for is your guidance, accurate information to assist them in decision making, and support for whatever decision they do make. They don't want you to judge them for making a decision that might be different from yours. In my opinion, you are sometimes led into responding to that difficult question—"What would *you* do?"—with a definitive answer—"I'd put him to sleep" or "I'd keep working with it"—because you may not know what other answer to offer. This chapter will give you some options.

A CONCEPTUAL FRAMEWORK

To explore the different dilemmas involved in the issue of euthanasia for behavior problems, to help you sort out your options, and to provide resources and skills that can help you, I've developed a conceptual framework, illustrated in Figure 17.1.

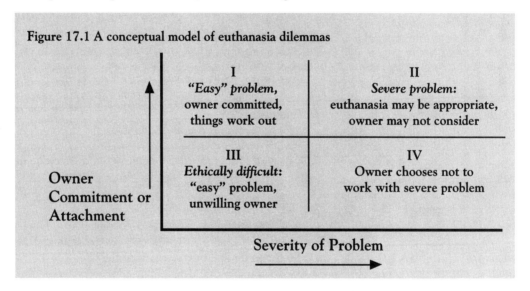

Figure 17.1 A conceptual model of euthanasia dilemmas

	I	II
	"Easy" problem, owner committed, things work out	*Severe problem:* euthanasia may be appropriate, owner may not consider
Owner Commitment or Attachment	III *Ethically difficult:* "easy" problem, unwilling owner	IV Owner chooses not to work with severe problem

Severity of Problem

As the graph in Figure 17.1 reveals, a choice about euthanasia for a behavior problem is dependent on two factors—the severity of the problem and the commitment of the owner. I recognize that this is an oversimplification of a complex issue, but it is useful to concentrate on these two factors when a decision about euthanasia is being considered. In later sections, I'll define and discuss the terms *severity* and *owner commitment*, but for now, take a look at the four quadrants. Keep in mind that both "severity" and "commitment" exist on continuums, so that the dividing lines I've drawn between quadrants are arbitrary. They could have been drawn anywhere along the x or y axes.

Quadrant I

In a Quadrant I case, the owner or family is clearly committed to the pet. They'll do anything they're told to do to resolve the behavior problem. Getting rid of the pet (surrendering him to a shelter, finding him a new home, or euthanizing him) is not an option. Luckily, the behavior problem their pet is manifesting is an easy one by anyone's assessment (housetraining a puppy, for instance, or dealing with a playful kitten, a dog who is jumping on people, or a cat who is scratching the furniture because she doesn't have an adequate scratching post). The problem, with appropriate intervention, is easily resolved, and everyone will be happy. In essence, then, there are no dilemmas surrounding euthanasia in regard to Quadrant 1 problems. (As an aside, the real tragedy is when, through inappropriate intervention, these cases are shifted to Quadrant II or Quadrant IV.)

Quadrant II

This quadrant incorporates those cases in which owners are still willing to do or try everything but, unfortunately, the behavior problems are severe by anyone's definition. A typical Quadrant II case might be a dog who has bitten more than one person, inflicting injuries requiring medical treatment each time; a dog who is severely thunder- or noisephobic and repeatedly hurts himself in his panic; or a cat who incessantly attacks her tail even after medication has been tried. For a variety of reasons (having an ethical objection to euthanasia, dealing with unresolved grief issues, being unable to say good-bye, denying the danger their pet presents, or just not wanting to give up on an animal they love dearly), the owners cannot bring themselves to choose euthanasia, even though it is reasonable and perhaps even the best option they have. In the interim, the pet's quality of life may be compromised, the family may be making enormous sacrifices in their attempt to manage the problem, and people, other animals, and the pet himself are being put at risk because of the nature of the problem. In cases in which owners do choose euthanasia, although sad, there are no dilemmas involved because everyone has agreed it is an appropriate choice. Owners who do not consider euthanasia present the dilemma.

Quadrant III

Quadrant III encompasses the ethically difficult situations, such as dealing with an owner who requests euthanasia or surrenders a pets for a problem of the type mentioned in Quadrant I. You know the problem can be easily resolved, but the owner isn't interested in doing anything about it. If you are a veterinarian, do you perform the euthanasia? What if you are a shelter staffer who *must* take the animal in, having no choice but to euthanize him if there is no kennel space available or he is not adopted?

Quadrant IV

In Quadrant IV cases, the behavior problem is severe or difficult by anyone's assessment. There is no disagreement, for example, that a certain dog is dangerous. Although the owner isn't very interested in working with the behavior, it's sort of a moot point because the problem is severe enough that euthanasia would be a reasonable option even for the most committed owner (Quadrant II). Although these are sad and emotionally difficult cases, there is no dilemma surrounding the choice that must be made. The euthanasia seems justified.

The real dilemmas, then, lie in Quadrants II and III. This is where decisions become difficult. And there are other dilemmas as well—being able to assess where along the severity continuum a particular behavior case lies and how committed the owner is to the pet. That leads us to a discussion of those terms.

Severity of the Problem

There are at least three different perspectives from which *severity* can be defined:

- The potential danger the pet presents to itself, people, or other animals
- The likelihood that the problem can be successfully resolved

- What will be required from the owner to work with the problem, in terms of time, financial cost, changes in lifestyle or routine, changes in expectations, etc.

The owner's tolerance for the problem and the pet is going to affect her assessment of the severity, and this tolerance level may change throughout the course of the problem. This is another example of the way that inappropriate intervention can backfire, as discussed in chapter 1: The problem may be perceived as more severe when the owner's tolerance drops out of frustration because the behavior isn't improving if ineffective solutions have been tried.

Because there are different ways to view severity, knowing where along the continuum a particular problem falls becomes part of the dilemma in making a euthanasia decision. You may have a hard time judging the severity (if you don't know the prognosis, for example), or your assessment of the severity may differ from that of the pet owner, whether from the same or a different definitional perspective. Ultimately, however, it is the *owner's* assessment of severity that is important. If that assessment is based on misinformation, your job is to provide her with accurate information, not attempt to talk her into viewing the problem differently.

Owner Commitment

This could also be called owner attachment. One study found that owners who surrendered their dogs and cats to shelters were less attached to them than a comparison population of owners who had not surrendered their pets[2, 3]. The measures of attachment used were (1) whether the owners carried a picture of the pet, and (2) how strongly the owners agreed with the statement that the pets were members of the family. Another study found that people who relinquished their animals to shelters often struggled with the decision to do so for months or even years and finally did it when they believed they had no other options[4]. In many cases, the study showed behavioral problems were tolerated until it no longer became possible to do so; in addition, many owners had used ineffective problem-resolution approaches, did not know how to resolve the problem, or stated that they didn't have the time or money to work with the pet. Based on these results, it is probably true that the more attached people are to their pets, the less likely they are to surrender them or choose not to work with a behavior problem. However, this is not the same thing as concluding that owners who don't want to work with the problem are *not* attached to their pets. Attachment issues can create problems in euthanasia decision making if you:

- Ignore the owner's strong attachment to the pet in the decision-making process. Two examples of this were given earlier—the recommendations to shoot the cat for housesoiling and euthanize the dog for snapping. Ignoring the owner's attachment causes veterinarians, trainers, and other animal care professionals to lose clients. Devoted pet owners do not want to hear euthanasia mentioned as the first or only option for a behavior problem.
- Assume the owner has a low degree of attachment because he is choosing not to work (or continue to work) with the problem, without having additional evidence that this is, indeed, the case. Shelter staffers too often get into trouble here. I remember a dog with severe separation anxiety that I worked with for almost a year. The dog continued to have episodes of severely destructive behavior despite receiving various medications and going through behavior modification programs that the owners implemented religiously. The owners were devastated when they finally decided to surrender the dog to a shelter for euthanasia. They requested euthanasia because they were concerned that a new adoptive family might not be as tolerant as they had been and would abuse the

dog because of her misbehavior. They were also worried that the dog would eventually injure herself severely during one of her panicked, destructive episodes (certainly a possible scenario). These were not low-attachment owners, but because they came to the shelter with a euthanasia request for a young, healthy golden retriever, they were not treated kindly.

- Judge people as "bad" pet owners if they fall anywhere below the very highest point on your own mental attachment scale. Those of us who work as animal professionals are almost by definition animal lovers. We tend to be more tolerant of the chaos and problems that pets sometimes bring into our lives, and we are probably willing to do more for our pets than many other owners. Yet we should never forget that people can still be responsible, loving owners who provide their pets a good quality of life even if they aren't willing to put up with the same amount of trouble that we do or invest the same amount of time or money that we are willing to invest. If we judge everyone else by the standard of care we use for our own pets, we will label many people as "bad" owners and treat them as such. In sum, if you are dealing with people from this perspective, you are not likely to be a helpful, compassionate resource when discussing euthanasia.

DEFINING THE DILEMMAS ABOUT EUTHANASIA

Based on the conceptual framework, the dilemmas surrounding euthanasia for behavior problems involve:

- Accurately assessing and taking into account the owner's commitment or attachment to the pet
- Assessing the severity of the problem by one or more definitions
- Dealing with cases in Quadrant II
- Dealing with cases in Quadrant III

The goal of this book, as set forth in the first chapter, is to provide you with a plan or guidelines that will allow you to respond to behavior problems and questions in a systematic way, one step at time. With euthanasia issues, I can accomplish this goal by first helping you define the dilemmas, as I just did, and then discussing (1) the options for working through each dilemma, (2) the resources you may need, and (3) the other professionals who may be able to assist you.

Assessing and Taking into Account the Owner's Commitment and Attachment

To recount, veterinarians and others can have difficulty talking to an owner about euthanasia for behavior problems if they ignore the owner's attachment to the pet or if the owner is more attached to the pet than they realize. The dilemmas presented by those who are not very attached will be discussed in the section on Quadrant III cases.

Talk to owners about what they are willing to do to resolve the problem. Sometimes, we jump to the conclusion that a particular owner will not want to do much to solve the problem at hand. To avoid this pitfall, I often ask people how far they are willing to go to work with a problem. This is a very direct question, and most people respond very directly. They'll say things ranging from "whatever it takes" to "well, I've got a lot of commitments at work right now, and I want to spend more time with my kids—I don't think I should have to come home from work and devote all my time to this dog." The response gives you a clear picture of where things stand. I have also found that owners don't always respond in the way I think they are going to, which means that had I not asked the direct question, I probably would have wrongly assessed their commitment.

In a shelter setting, if you are talking to someone who has come in to relinquish their pet because of a behavior problem, you can ask a similar question: "Would you be interested in talking to someone who may be able to help you resolve the problem?" It's been my experience, however, that by the time someone has arrived at the shelter, the decision has been made, and most (but not all) owners are no longer willing to try other options. Still, it never hurts to ask.

Acknowledge the importance of the pet to the family. If you are having a conversation about the possibility of euthanasia, it is helpful to preface any other remarks you offer with some sort of acknowledgment about how important the pet is to the family. Try saying something like: "I know how much Jake means to you and that even considering the possibility that he may be too dangerous to keep is extremely painful." This acknowledges that the pet's life is significant and that his well-being will be an important consideration in decision making. Owners who love their animals don't want to feel as though the pet's life has become a secondary consideration.

Offer a variety of options, with the risks of each presented. People who are attached to their pets do not want to hear that their only option is euthanasia. In aggression cases, although it may be appropriate to mention that the only way to guarantee that the dog or cat will not hurt anybody is euthanasia, this idea should not be presented out of context. When I receive an inquiry call about a consultation for an aggression problem, I go through a list of possible options—take the pet to the veterinarian to rule out medical causes (this should have been done by the time I'm contacted), manage the problem by keeping the pet out of situations in which he might bite, muzzle the dog, work with behavior modification to try to change the behavior— and the last thing I'll say is, "Unfortunately, the only option that comes with a guarantee of safety is euthanasia." Later on, during a consultation, I'll talk in more detail about the specifics of these choices and what the risks of each may be in this particular case.

Assessing Severity

When euthanasia is under consideration, assessing severity may become a dilemma in itself. If there is a difference of opinion between you and the owner about the severity of a problem or if you are having difficulty assessing the severity yourself, based on any of the possible definitions, keep the following points in mind.

Consider consulting a behavior specialist if you are contemplating a life-and-death situation. If you are a veterinarian, you would no doubt refer a case to a medical specialist (or at least consult with one) if you were unsure of a medical diagnosis, prognosis, or the treatment options available. Behavior cases are worth the same effort. Although the field of applied animal behavior (or behavioral medicine) has not yet reached the level of sophistication of predicting prognoses based on presenting signs, the perspective and clinical experience of a board-certified veterinary behaviorist or certified applied animal behaviorist can be invaluable. Specialists see many more cases of each particular type of problem than a general practitioner, so their perspective on the issue of severity, regardless of how it's defined, is based on a much larger sample of cases. Their assessment of severity may therefore be more representative than your own.

Problems with a prognosis. In my experience, if a behavior problem is so serious that euthanasia is under consideration (excluding cases in Quadrant III), one of the following problems is usually involved:

- Dog aggression
- Feline elimination or marking
- Separation anxiety in dogs
- Severe thunder/storm/noise phobias in dogs
- Stereotypies that are resulting in self-injury in both cats and dogs

The information in Table17.1 synthesizes my experience with these cases and the factors that seem to be associated with a poor prognosis. When I'm finished taking a behavioral history and I find that I just don't have a good feeling about the case, these factors are, I think, at the root of that feeling. There is nothing scientific about this information, and because it is based only on my personal experience, other behavior specialists may not agree with my conclusions. I've had cases I was convinced would resolve easily but didn't and others I thought had very little chance and things improved nicely. This is one area where the field of applied animal behavior or behavioral medicine desperately needs some objective research and data gathering. The take-home message is that prognoses should not be given with a cavalier attitude, as it sets the owner up for what may become unrealistic expectations. The generalizations I've incorporated in Table 17.1 do not substitute for a thorough evaluation of the case by you or a behavior specialist.

Assess the risk in dog aggression cases. To the discussion of risk assessment in canine aggression cases that was offered in chapter 12, I would add here that no studies correlate presenting signs with successful resolution or management of the problem. The data in I.R. Reisner's study involve correlations between characteristics of the case and whether the owners ultimately chose to euthanize their dogs[5]. However, the factors listed in Box 12.5 seem to make intuitive sense, and similar ones have been offered by others in the field[6].

Understand the owner's perceptions. Sometimes, we assume a problem is not too severe without considering what it's like to deal with the particular pet and problem within the framework of the owner's family life. I've learned a lot about this issue from having Ashley, whom you've heard about in other sections of this book. Ashley is a "high-maintenance" dog and requires additional training and supervision to prevent her from digging, chewing, barking, and engaging in other behavior problems that I see professionally every day. Until we live with a problem animal, we may not really understand the toll such animals take on owners or families. Ask owners detailed questions to get a better feel for what kinds of problems their pet's behavior is creating for them. Also, remember that some people's tolerance levels for pet-related problems may be very low.

There are, as well, some people who shouldn't have a pet. I encountered such a couple recently. They adopted a baby about the same time they acquired a Labrador puppy. Both spouses had challenging jobs that required more than a 40 hours a week. The 8-month-old dog's problems were nothing more than normal puppy behaviors that had gotten out of control because the owners did not have the time to work with her. Watching the owners at home with the dog and the baby, I could definitely see why they considered the dog's behaviors to be severe problems. In another household, this might not have been the case.

On the other side of the coin, some owners do not recognize the severity of their pet's problem. Here, I am referring to dog aggression cases and owners who do not understand the potential danger their dog presents. Your job in these cases is to explain to them, in a sensitive,

Table 17.1 Factors to consider in assessing the severity of a problem based on prognosis

Type of Problem	Factors that Possibly Indicate a Poor Prognosis*
Dog aggression	See box 12.5 in chapter 12, Simpson 1997[6], Reisner et al. 1994[5]
Feline elimination or marking	Those for which no obvious triggers or reasons can be found from a complete behavioral history (this assessment is best done by a behavior specialist) or chronic problems (maybe); appropiate medication and behavior modifications have not been helpful
Separation anxiety in dogs	No behavioral starting point, i.e., a very low threshold for extreme behavioral manifestations (dog reacts with full-blown panic as soon as owner walks out the door) and/or medication has not been successful in managing the problem
Thunderstorm/noise phobias in dogs	No behavioral starting point, i.e., a very low threshold for extreme behavioral manifestations (dog's fear is triggered by wind, clouds, precursors to the storm that precede the thunder by considerable time periods) and/or medication has not been successful in managing the problem
Stereotypes resulting in self-injury, mutilation	No medical or behavioral triggers can be identified and/or behavior has not responded to medication

*This information is based on practical/clinical experience, not scientific data. No studies have demonstrated an association between presenting characteristics and likelihood of problem resolution.

nonjudgmental manner, some of the negative outcomes that can occur if they don't take the problem seriously. Many owners, for example, don't realize they can lose their homeowners' insurance if they are found guilty of having a "vicious" dog, and in some communities, people can be cited for owning a "vicious" dog if their animal attempts to bite someone, even if no injuries occur. Unfortunately, some people, even after lengthy explanations, maintain their nonchalant attitudes. I know behaviorists who refuse to take on a case under such conditions.

Don't force your assessment on the owner. The preceding statements should not be understood to mean that you should try to convince owners to see a problem in the same light that you do. Once people have accurate information about the problem, the conclusions they draw will be their own. They will only resent you if you try to force them to see things your way. You will then need to decide what role you want to have in the case in order to feel comfortable.

Provide accurate information. If clients are making a decision about euthanasia, they deserve the best possible assessment of their pet's prognosis, what treatment will entail, and the potential dangers that lie ahead.

It is grossly unfair to them and to their pets if their decisions are based on misinformation. Yet I recall a number of clients, for example, who've been told that once a cat stops using a litterbox, they are facing a lifelong problem—an assessment I know from experience to be unfounded. Blanket statements and unfounded generalizations have no place in assessing the severity of an individual case.

Set an initial time frame for treatment and then reassess. Another strategy to employ if you or your clients are having difficulty assessing the severity of the case is to initiate treatment and see what happens. You and the owners together can set a reasonable time at which to reassess the situation, perhaps in two weeks or a month. If there is sufficient improvement, the owners can decide to continue working with the problem for another period of time and reassess the situation again. If, at that point, there is no further improvement, then other options can be discussed.

Cases in Quadrant II: Difficulty in Facing the Choice of Euthanasia

It is never easy for an owner to make a decision to euthanize a pet. Having been through it too many times as my animals reached the end of their normal life spans, I know just how gut-wrenching this is. Even with all my experience working in the pet-loss program, when it came down to my own animals, I was just as panicked, grief-stricken, confused, and guilty about saying, "It's time, let's do it tomorrow," as any other owner. All these feelings are experienced with a euthanasia done for medical reasons, when the goal is to prevent, minimize, or end suffering, but when the decision is made because of a behavior problem in an otherwise healthy pet, I think they are magnified many times over.

There are some questions you can gently pose to owners and issues you can discuss to help them in the decision-making process. It is crucial that this not be done in a judgmental way but rather in a compassionate tone of voice and a genuine spirit of helping. An example of a way to open the conversation is given in Box 17.1.

Help the client who feels guilty or believes she hasn't done enough. It can be helpful to tell the client that feeling guilty about choosing euthanasia for a pet is a normal reaction. Keep in mind that guilt sometimes serves to let people avoid the real pain of loss; by focusing on the guilt, they avoid thinking about how painful the situation is. Gently point out all the things they *did* do and how their pet has been so lucky to have an owner who was willing to do so much. If you can say so truthfully, tell them there really isn't anything else that can be done: Not all behavior problems can be solved, anymore than all diseases or illnesses can be cured. Sometimes,

> **Box 17.1 Opening the conversation about euthanasia**
>
> "Judy, I'm concerned about you and your family. I see you struggling to manage Jake, and I know it's been difficult for all of you. I know how hard you've worked, but things just don't seem to be getting better. I'm also concerned about Jake—this must be hard for him, too, not being able to go with you as much, being afraid so much, having his activities limited [whatever makes sense for the case]. I know how much you love Jake, and I know we've talked about euthanasia before. You seem to be unsure about what to do from here, so I thought we might talk about your concerns some more and discuss what your options are."

it helps to make the analogy that even though a behavioral condition is involved rather than a medical one, the pet has an incurable illness that everyone has done their best to "cure" but it just wasn't possible.

Help the client who isn't able to say good-bye. If a person is considering euthanasia, she may not be able to imagine how or what it will be like when it comes time to spend the last day, hour, or minute with the pet. How will it be possible to end this relationship and never see the pet again? You can help by encouraging people to find meaningful ways to say good-bye and to spend some special time with their pets. Ideas include taking a dog for a walk in his favorite place in the mountains, letting a cat have some supervised time outside to explore the flowers, or just taking a few moments to pour out their hearts to the pets—telling them how much they are loved and how much they've meant to them. The last week or days with the pet should be a special time for the family and the animal.

Help the client who is panicked about choosing an arbitrary date and time. For an owner who has made the decision to euthanize a pet, it often feels so hard-hearted to pick a date and time, and it is painful to hear the veterinarian say, "Bring Brandy in at noon tomorrow." Well, the owner thinks, if it can wait until tomorrow, why can't it wait until the next day or next week or next month? Choosing a time creates normal feelings of panic and loss. If you are a veterinarian, you can help by giving clients more control over the situation[1]: "Let's go ahead and schedule the euthanasia for tomorrow, and if you change your mind, call me and we can talk more then."

Help the client weigh the consequences of *not* doing the euthanasia. About 8 years ago, when I was trying to decide if it was time to choose euthanasia for my 16-year-old German shorthaired pointer, considering the consequences of not doing the euthanasia was what finally made the difference for me. Not choosing euthanasia for Brandy meant I was running the risk that she would suffer alone and die by herself when we were at work, rather than dying peacefully in the arms of people who loved her.

When euthanasia is indicated for a behavior problem, not choosing it can have other consequences, as well. For example, it leaves open the very real possibility that the dog will bite someone else or that the cat will injure herself with her compulsive tail chasing.

Help the client understand the process and know what options are available in planning it. When I began working in the pet-loss program at CSU, it came as a surprise to me that clients often did not know what euthanasia entailed. In fact, I recall one person saying to me, "So the veterinarian will give her the shot, and I'll take her home, and she'll die a few days later, is that right?" Only in the past 10 years or so has veterinary medicine begun to encourage people to be present when their pets are euthanized. Historically, the pet was taken to the back room, and owners were told they couldn't or shouldn't watch the process. Consequently, pet owners may not understand how painless and peaceful a properly performed euthanasia is.

Perhaps a client has had a bad experience in the past with another pet. The most horrific one I ever heard was from an owner whose cat's leg was broken as the veterinarian and technician tried to restrain the unsedated, struggling cat in an attempt to find a vein. There is no excuse for a situation like that. Can you blame a person for not wanting to repeat such an awful experience?

If you are a veterinarian, you can help by asking owners what questions they have about the process of euthanasia. Many people will want you to describe exactly what happens. You should also make sure that you let the clients know what their choices are in the process. They can choose to be present or not, choose an in-home euthanasia, and choose the time and day that's best for them, and they also have options about body care after the pet's death (cremation with ashes returned, for example). If the client chooses an option you don't offer (such as in-home euthanasia), refer them to someone who does.

It's my opinion that veterinarians may spend more time talking to clients about the process of euthanasia when a medical problem is involved as compared to a behavioral one. With the latter, it may be that they feel the less said the better. I don't think that's true. Not talking about it is not going to make the experience less painful. Often, in fact, just the opposite is true. Just because you can avoid witnessing some of the visible signs of grief (clients crying, for example) by not talking about these issues, does not mean that you are helping the pet owners avoid the pain of grief. The more clients can talk about it, be prepared for it, and know what their choices are and what to expect, the better for them.

Help the client with unresolved grief issues. A person's reluctance to choose euthanasia may stem from issues that have absolutely nothing to do with the current situation. The impending death of a pet often brings up all kinds of unresolved grief issues from the person's past, sometimes even from childhood[1]. A client of mine a few years ago had decided it was probably best to euthanize her dog because of aggressive behavior that wasn't improving. She was having a difficult time reaching a final decision, however, and soon after told me that her brother had recently died of AIDS; he had been abandoned by the rest of the family, and she was the only one with him when he died. It turned out that she felt her family had given up on her brother, and she believed that if she chose euthanasia for her dog, she would be giving up on him the way her family did with her brother.

These kinds of situations are complicated and involve more complex issues than any of us are capable of handling without special training. The best thing you can do for your client is to refer her to either a pet-loss program conducted by a human service professional or paraprofessional (not an untrained animal lover) or to a private therapist. This should be done in a way that is kind and compassionate, without sounding as though you think the client is mentally ill. There are a number of excellent resources available (several through AAHA) to assist you in knowing exactly what to say[1, 7, 8].

Help the client who is concerned that you or others will judge him harshly. If your client has a history of making commitments for the life of his pets and having the pets be a part of the family until they reach old age, concerns about your reaction to his decision on euthanasia may be particularly acute. The client may feel he can never face you again, never bring his other pets in for medical care, or his other dogs to obedience classes because you'll be judging him as a failure. You need to make a point of reassuring your client that you think he's made a good decision and that you know what a wonderful, caring pet owner he is. You may not completely agree with the client's decision, but at least you should be able to understand it.

Discuss the client's fears and what can be done to alleviate them. If you are a veterinarian, you have performed hundreds of euthanasias. Most of your clients, however, have only been through the experience with a few pets at most or maybe none at all. Similarly, you may have helped many people work through a decision about euthanasia, but your clients haven't had much practice in this regard. For them, the whole process is scary and uncomfortable, regardless of the reason for euthanasia. Recognizing this, you can ask general, open-ended questions about what their most serious concerns are and what would help them be less worried.

Provide referrals to grief counselors, grief educators, pet-loss support programs, and human services. Anytime a person gets "stuck" somewhere, whether it's in decision making or grieving after the death, making a referral is a compassionate kindness, not a judgmental act. Some excellent examples of ways to open a conversation on this subject appear in Laurel Lagoni's *Practical Guide to Client Grief*, also published by AAHA Press[7]. These are reproduced in Box 17.2.

Box 17.2 Making a referral to a grief professional

"Paul, if you had a broken arm, you wouldn't walk around for three weeks without having it looked at. The same is true with a broken heart. I know someone who can help you with the process of healing from Molly's death. I talk with her sometimes about cases that are tough for me, too. I'd like to give you her name and number."

"I know how hard its been for you to make a decision about Molly. It's understandable how your feelings about your brother are complicating things for you. I know your feelings can be sorted out, but I'm simply not trained in this area. I'd be doing you a disservice if I tried to be the one to help you work through them. I do know someone who can help you though. I know him well and recommend him highly. Let me get his phone number for you."

Source: Modified from L. Lagoni, 1997, *The Practical Guide to Client Grief: Support Techniques for Fifteen Common Situations*, Denver, Colo.: AAHA Press. Used by permission.

Remember that it is ultimately the client's decision, not yours (let go of it). Clients don't always make the same decision you would under similar circumstances. That's okay. You wouldn't want someone to force you into something you believed wasn't right for you and your pet anymore than your clients do. The best way you can be helpful is to provide accurate information, answer questions truthfully and without bias, and support your clients through the decision-making process but not attempt to push them into a choice of your making, not theirs.

I remember a case involving three cocker spaniels and a couple who clearly were having marital difficulties. In fact, they admitted during my in-home consultation with them that they were seeing a marriage counselor. The pet problem I was being consulted about involved the third cocker, who had been recently obtained from a shelter. This dog was starting fights with one of the other dogs, had snapped at two neighbors, and had bitten the wife several times, so she was now afraid of her. I expressed my concern about the dangers and difficulties in working with this dog because of everything else they were currently coping with. Both the referring veterinarian and I felt that the best thing would be to either take the dog back to the shelter or euthanize her. Yet the couple was determined to work with the dog. It's been over a year since I last heard from them, but I talked with the veterinarian recently, and he informed me that the dog was much improved and things were going well. Needless to say, this was one instance where I was happy to be wrong!

Cases in Quadrant III: Ethically Difficult Euthanasias for What Seem to Be Trivial Reasons

If you are a veterinarian or a euthanasia technician in a shelter and you have been asked to perform a euthanasia in a case of this type, the bottom line is this: Can you personally justify the necessity for doing so? What is considered justifiable is obviously a very individual judgment, affected by many different factors, and the issues involved for shelter staff members and veterinarians are somewhat different (see the next section for more on shelters).

Issues for the veterinarian. If you are a veterinarian, you must identify the criteria you will use to decide that the particular euthanasia you've been asked to perform is justifiable. A number of resources offer discussions on the subject that may be helpful[1, 8, 9, 10]. In addition, some pertinent points to consider follow.

Getting enough information to categorize the case. You should not be shy about asking to have a conversation with the client to discuss how she decided on euthanasia before agreeing to perform the procedure, particularly if you don't know the client and pet well. Sometimes, what on the surface may not seem a justifiable euthanasia becomes so once all the details are known.

We all make snap judgments from time to time that later turn out to be inaccurate. If you decide, after talking to the client, that this is not a euthanasia you can perform, you can refuse in a way that does not alienate the client.

Communicating your right to refuse. When telling an owner you cannot perform the euthanasia, there is a big difference between sharing your own feelings about doing so and telling the client what he or she should do. Consider the difference between the following:

> "I can't euthanize Jake for you because I don't believe you've tried hard enough to work with his problems. He deserves better, and you should try harder to resolve his problems."

> "I understand why you want me to put Jake to sleep. However, I have to tell you that I can't do this. I just wouldn't feel right about it. I feel there are other options for you and Jake. I think that in another family, his problems might be workable, and I believe he should have the opportunity for a second chance. Would you consider letting me find a home for him [or taking him to a shelter or contacting a breed rescue group or whatever is appropriate for the case]?"

The difference should be obvious.

As you decide whether to perform the euthanasia, you must consider the possible outcomes of your decision and be prepared for any of them[1].

- The client may abandon the pet
- The client may take the pet to a shelter, where he is later adopted or euthanized by shelter staff members
- The client may go to another veterinary clinic where the pet is euthanized
- The client may reconsider the situation and either keep the pet or find him a new home
- The client may be so upset about your refusal that he never returns to your clinic
- The client may be so appreciative of your decision and the explanation you offered that she becomes or remains a loyal client

Issues for shelter personnel. The problem for most shelter workers is that they often cannot personally justify the necessity for a euthanasia and yet, as part of their jobs, they must still perform it. Let me explain that so I'm not misunderstood. For many people who work in shelters, a given euthanasia may be justifiable at a proximate (immediate) level (not enough kennel space, animal has an upper respiratory infection, it's better than having the animal roaming the streets, etc.), but it is not acceptable in an ultimate sense (animals should not have to die, euthanasia cannot continue to be the solution to unwanted pets, etc.). Moreover, there may come a time when the proximate justifications may not work anymore if they have been performing euthanasias for many years.

Shelter staffers also become overwhelmed because they become surrogate grievers for huge numbers of animals[12]. In other words, they do the grieving and experience the pain that should be felt by the pet owners who surrendered the animals. There are no easy answers to take away the pain that shelter workers must deal with, but more supportive literature is now available[13, 14].

If you work in a shelter, consider the following options:

- *Participate in a stress management group.* Some shelters now have in-house support groups or debriefing sessions for staffers on a regular basis. Sometimes these are led by experienced employees and sometimes by outside facilitators. If your shelter doesn't have one, take it on yourself to initiate one.
- *Find ways to memorialize the pets who die.* Some shelters bring interested staff together for a commemorative service weekly, monthly, or quarterly. In these meetings, people can talk about pets whose deaths were particularly painful, can light candles, and can offer prayers for the animals who have died.
- *Design better intervention programs to offer assistance to owners whose animals have behavior problems before the shelter becomes the last resort.* Today, shelters are offering better and more innovative programs. For example, I am working with a shelter in Colorado to test the success of crate training animals while they are at the shelter and to attempt a problem-prevention program for separation anxiety, which is so common in dogs from shelters. Other possibilities include:
  — Problem prevention programs
  — Improved adoption counseling and matching
  — Mandatory adoption follow-up contacts, especially for those pets at risk for developing problems (e.g., those surrendered for behavior problems)
  — Behavior help lines
  — Timely referrals to behavior specialists

If your shelter does not provide these types of programs, start working with your administrative staff to design them.

- *Reinterpret the situation.* While not denying the pain of having to euthanize so many animals, also view the issue in as positive a light as possible. Remind yourself that these pets were cared for by loving people (you and your colleagues) before they died, that the owners were responsible enough to bring them to the shelter rather than turning them loose to fend for themselves, and that the animals will not be mistreated by any future owners because of their behavior problems. Although these may seem to be small consolations, they should not be overlooked.

- *Get another job.* I am not saying this lightly. Shelter workers are extremely dedicated people, and some would never want to work anywhere else. However, for others, the stress ultimately becomes overwhelming, until it is affecting their own quality of life. It is important to recognize your own limits. Furthermore, there are other ways you can be of service to animals. I left the shelter I worked at for 4 years for reasons unrelated to euthanasia stress, and though I learned an incredible amount working there, I am, to be very honest, a happier, less stressed person since I left. And I know I am still making a positive difference for animals in the work I am doing now.

ANSWERING THE QUESTION "WHAT WOULD YOU DO?"

I said at the beginning of this chapter that I would offer options for responding to this question. These are drawn from articles I and others have written on the subject[1, 15, 16].

> "To be honest, I don't know what I'd do. Let's sit down and talk about the situation and see if we can help you decide what *you* will do."
>
> "If I were you, I'd be just as confused and scared as you are right now. Let's talk about your options again."
>
> "If it were me, I wouldn't want someone else telling me what I should do. I'd want to be able to make a decision that I thought was best for me and my pet. I'd want support and guidance from people I trust. And that's what I'm offering you now."
>
> "I know how you are struggling with this decision, but honestly, I'm not you. The choice I might make for myself could be totally wrong for you. You know your pet and the situation better than anyone else. I trust that you will make the best decision for all of you. I'll do whatever I can to help."

SUMMARY

Talking about euthanasia is not easy, yet the way in which you do it has a huge impact on the client's ability to make an informed decision that she can live with for months and years to come. Your handling of this difficult matter also affects the client's opportunity to express her grief in healthy ways and influences her opinion of you and your business. In turn, it impacts how you yourself feel about the case and about euthanasia, grief, and loss. Today, there are many excellent resources available to help you talk to clients about these issues and manage your own stress surrounding them[1, 17, 18, 19]. I encourage you to read them.

As the field of applied animal behavior and behavioral medicine advances and better treatments and preventative procedures for behavior problems are devised, as we learn more about why people surrender their pets to shelters, and as we devise better intervention programs to prevent it, there will be less need for discussions about nonmedical euthanasias. I look forward to that future.

REFERENCES

1. Lagoni, L., C. Butler, and S. Hetts. 1994. *The human-animal bond and grief.* Philadelphia: W.B. Saunders.

2. Patronek, G.J., L.T. Glickman, A.M. Beck, G.P. McCabe, and C. Ecker. 1996. Risk factors for relinquishment of dogs to an animal shelter. *JAVMA* 209:572–81.

3. Patronek, G.J., L.T. Glickman, A.M. Beck, G.P. McCabe, and C. Ecker. 1996. Risk factors for relinquishment of cats to an animal shelter. *JAVMA* 209:582–8.

4. DiGiacomo, N., A. Arluke, and G. Patronek. 1998. Surrendering pets to shelters: The relinquisher's perspective. *Anthrozoos* 11:41–51.

5. Reisner, I.R., N.E. Hollis, and K.A. Houpt. 1994. Risk-factors for behavior related euthanasia among dominant aggressive dogs: 110 cases (1989–1992). *JAVMA* 205:855–63.

6. Simpson, B.S. 1997. Aggression—Dogs. In *The 5 minute veterinary consult: Canine and feline,* ed. L.P. Tilley, F.W.K. Smith, and A.C. MacMurray, 10–1. Baltimore: Williams and Wilkins.

7. Lagoni, L. 1997. *The practical guide to client grief: Support techniques for fifteen common situations.* Lakewood, Colo.: AAHA Press.

8. American Animal Hospital Association. 1989. Pet Loss and Bereavement Series (workbooks included): Understanding client pet loss; Counseling clients; The loss of your pet. Videotapes.

9. Antelyes, J. 1988. Convenience euthanasia revisited. *JAVMA* 193:906–8.

10. Hart, L.A., B.L. Hart, and B. Mader. 1990. Humane euthanasia and companion animal death: Caring for the animal, the client, and the veterinarian. *JAVMA* 197:1292–9.

11. Gage, L., and N. Gage. 1992. *If wishes were horses: The education of a veterinarian.* New York: St. Martin's Press.

12. Lagoni, L., and C. Butler. 1993. Stress management for animal care and control professionals. Presented at Animal Control Seminar, Laramie, Wyo., April 4.

13. Arluke, A. 1991. Coping with euthanasia: A case study of shelter culture. *JAVMA* 198:1176–80.

14. Ellis, B.J. 1993. *Paws for thought: A look at the conflicts, questions and challenges of animal euthanasia.* Columbia, S.C.: Paw Print Press.

15. Hetts, S. 1996. Facilitating euthanasia decisions regarding animals with behavior problems. In *Readings in companion animal behavior,* ed. V.L. Voith and P.L. Borchelt, 271–9. Trenton, N.J.: Veterinary Learning Systems.

16. Butler, C., and L. Lagoni. 1994. Facilitating euthanasia decisions. *Compend. Contin. Educ. Pract. Vet.* 16 (11):1469–75.

17. Sife, W. 1993. *The loss of a pet.* New York: Howell Book House.

18. Steinback, D. 1997. *Without guilt: Loving, caring and letting go: A compassionate but straight-forward look at pet euthanasia.* Highland City, Fla.: Willow Bend Pub.

19. Peterson. L. 1997. *Surviving the heartbreak of choosing death for your pet: Your personal guide for dealing with pet euthanasia.* Las Vegas, Nev.: Greentree Pub.

CHAPTER 18

Guidelines for the Use of Psychotropic Drugs for Behavior Problems

Amy R. Marder, VMD, and Laurie Bergman, VMD

New developments in the field of veterinary psychopharmacology have made drug therapy a valid option for the treatment of many canine and feline behavioral problems. In most cases, drugs are most effective when used as adjuvants to behavioral therapy, and as with any behavioral treatment modality, they should only be used in accordance with the protocol outlined in previous chapters. *Medication can only be prescribed by and should only be managed by licensed veterinarians.*

Before any therapy is prescribed, a diagnosis must be made. A thorough and accurate behavioral and medical history is first obtained. A physical exam and laboratory tests are often necessary to rule out contributing medical problems. After the behavioral diagnosis is made, the owner must be counseled about treatment options. Stories in the popular press of "pets on Prozac," cured of just about every "behavioral ill," have led to misconceptions about drugs and their effectiveness. Although drug therapy may be the easiest type of therapy to implement, owners must be aware of its limitations and drawbacks. Sometimes drug therapy is prescribed on an as needed basis (e.g., for thunderphobia), sometimes for the duration of the behavior modification program (e.g., for separation anxiety), and sometimes for the life of the animal (e.g., for canine cognitive dysfunction).

EDUCATE THE CLIENT

The following points should be discussed with the client before initiating drug treatment.

1. Most drugs are not approved for use in dogs and cats. In most cases, there are no well-controlled studies to prove their effectiveness, proper dose, or toxic side effects. Diazepam had been used for years for the treatment of many problems in cats, yet only recently was it reported that diazepam can cause fatal liver changes in some cats[1]. In other words, even commonly used drugs must be considered experimental. They may have health risks (some unknown), and their effectiveness is uncertain. It's best to have clients sign a written consent form explaining "extralabel" use and known side effects.

2. As any underlying organic disease may increase the risk of medical complications, a complete blood count (CBC) and biochemistry profile should be obtained prior to beginning drug therapy, particularly for unapproved drugs. A urinalysis may be indicated to rule out disease of the urinary tract, and an electrocardiogram may be warranted for animals with a history of cardiac disease. Most clients do not object to pretreatment tests that will enable the veterinarian to choose the safest course of therapy.

3. Many psychotropic drugs are expensive. It is not unusual for a drug to cost up to $100 per month. This additional cost must be discussed with clients, as in most cases it will influence their choice of therapy.

4. Drugs alone should not be expected to cure a problem. A drug may temporarily mask or attenuate the symptoms of a problem behavior, but it may not address the underlying cause. Dangerous animals need to be managed appropriately even if medicated. Except in rare cases (e.g., spraying in cats, noise phobias in dogs), drugs are relatively ineffective in the absence of behavior modification. When medication is relied on alone, hopeful clients become disappointed and frustrated, bringing them a step closer to giving up on their pets. Drugs are best used to facilitate a behavior modification program: One client described the Prozac that was prescribed as "an enabler" for her dog's behavior modification program.

5. Many drugs take weeks to become fully effective, and in many cases, change is gradual. Again, behavior modification, although time-consuming, is necessary.

6. Known side effects in both animals and humans should be fully discussed. As there may be idiosyncratic reactions in individual animals, owners should stay home to observe their pet's response the first time the drug is given. Clients should contact the prescribing veterinarian if they notice any side effects.

THE VETERINARIAN'S RESPONSIBILITIES BEFORE PRESCRIBING DRUG THERAPY

1. Obtain a behavioral diagnosis and complete medical profile of the patient (see preceding section).

2. Know the commonly used psychotropic drugs: their mechanism of action, routes of metabolism, side effects, contraindications, and previously reported effective dosages and therapeutic effects. Especially important is how the drug will affect the animal's behavior. If the veterinarian doesn't know what to expect, he or she will be unable to properly counsel a client.

3. Know simple, commonly used behavior modification methods that may be suggested along with medication.

4. Plan for frequent client communication and patient follow-up. A CBC and biochemistry profile may be advised at 3 months and then every 6 to 12 months thereafter. Follow-up should be especially vigilant with aggressive animals.

5. Know the household: ability to administer medication, potential for substance abuse. If the drug is not given or is taken by an owner, the animal's behavior is unlikely to change.

6. If the veterinarian is uncomfortable about treating a serious behavior problem, rather than just reaching for a drug, he or she should refer the client to a competent animal behavior specialist.

CATEGORIES OF PSYCHOTROPIC MEDICATION

Antipsychotics and Tranquilizers

The phenothiazines acetylpromazine (Acepromazine) and chlorpromazine (Thorazine) are the most commonly used antipsychotics in veterinary medicine. These dopamine antagonists produce behavioral quieting with a decrease in response to external stimuli, thereby depressing normal *and* abnormal behaviors. The phenothiazines are metabolized in the liver, conjugated with glucuronic acid, and excreted in the urine or, to a lesser extent, in the bile. Side effects of phenothiazines are many, e.g., sedation, ataxia, incoordination, lowered seizure threshold (acetylpromazine), hypotension, paradoxical excitement, and increased sensitivity to noises. They are useful, although unpredictably, for restraint of fractious animals. Although their antianxiety effects are debatable, the sedative effects of this drug class make them helpful in the treatment of anxious animals (e.g., dogs with separation anxiety or noise phobias). The phenothiazines are also antiemetic, making them useful to treat anxiety associated with motion sickness.

Antihistamines

Antihistamines used in behavioral medicine include diphenhydramine HCl (Benadryl) and chlorpheniramine maleate (Chlor-Trimeton). These drugs act by competitive inhibition of the H1 receptor site. Antihistamines have mild hypnotic and sedative effects. These compounds are almost completely metabolized in the liver, with little, if any, of the drug excreted unchanged in the urine. Antihistamines can have anticholinergic and atropine-like side effects and so should be used with caution in animals with urinary retention, glaucoma, or hyperthyroidism. The mild central nervous system (CNS) depression they cause makes them useful to treat animals with mild anxieties (e.g., for car travel, spraying in cats).

Tricyclic Antidepressants

The tricyclic antidepressants (TCAs) include the drugs amitriptyline HCl (Elavil), clomipramine HCl (Anafranil, Clomicalm), doxepin (Sinequan), and imipramine HCl (Tofranil). These drugs block deamination of amines, effectively blocking the reuptake of serotonin, norepinepherine, and, to a lesser extent, dopamine. The liver metabolizes TCAs into active intermediate metabolites via demethylation, aromatic hydroxylation, and glucuronide conjugation. In humans, it can take 2 to 3 weeks of treatment before achieving theraputic blood levels. Owners should be made aware that it may take a few weeks on TCA treatment before they see changes in their pets' behavior. It also takes several days for TCAs to be inactivated and excreted. Thus, there may also be a lag between discontinuing treatment and the cessation of drug effects, including side effects. The side effects of TCAs reflect their anticholenergic activity. They include mydriasis, dry mouth, tachycardia, sedation, constipation, and urine retention. TCAs may also cause changes in appetite, cardiac conduction disturbances, and sedation. The bitter taste of many drugs in this class makes administration difficult in cats. TCAs range in cost from the fairly inexpensive amitriptyline (Elavil) to the moderately expensive clomipramine (licensed for treatment of seperation anxiety in dogs). TCAs have been used in behavioral medicine to treat separation anxiety, aggressive behaviors, feline urine marking, generalized anxiety, compulsive grooming, and submissive urination.

Benzodiazepines

The anxiolytic effects of the benzodiazepines (e.g., diazepam [Valium], alprazolam [Xanax], clorazepate [Tranxene], oxazepam [Serax], and clonazepam [Klonopin]) are believed to result from their binding to receptors of the inhibitory neurotransmitter gamma aminobutyric acid (GABA). This binding increases the inhibitory effects of GABA on the limbic system and reticular formation. Benzodiazepazines are metabolized in the liver through a variety of enzyme systems, including conjugation with glucuronic acid. Side effects of the benzodiazepines include sedation, depression of learning, muscle relaxation, and increase in appetite. Recently, there have been reports of fatal idiopathic hepatic necrosis in cats on short-term diazepam therapy[1]. Although there are no published reports, there are anecdotal reports of other benzodiazepines having the same effects. The benzodiazepines have been used to treat feline urine marking, intercat aggression, generalized and specific anxieties, and thunderstorm phobias. Care must be taken when using these drugs in aggressive animals, as some forms of aggression may be disinhibited and worsen. These drugs can cause physiological dependence, so gradual withdrawal after long-term therapy is recommended.

Stimulants

The sympathomimetic drugs dextroamphetamine (Dexedrine) and methylphenidate HCl (Ritalin) are CNS stimulants. In addition, these drugs have a variety of effects on peripheral alpha and beta adrenergic receptors. Metabolism of these drugs takes place in the liver with urinary excretion. Side effects include tachycardia, tachypnea, CNS arousal, convulsions, hypertension, anorexia, and hyperthermia. These stimulants should not be used in animals with cardiovascular disease or glaucoma. They are used to treat hyperkinesis/hyperactivity in dogs, a rare diagnosis. The serious potential side effects and high abuse potential of these drugs make their use limited.

Monoamine Oxidase Inhibitors

The only monoamine oxidase (MAO) inhibitor currently used in veterinary behavioral medicine is selegiline, also called L-deprenyl (Anipryl). Selegiline is an MAO-B inibitor that increases CNS levels of dopamine. It is metabolized in the liver and excreted in the urine. Selegiline is a relatively safe drug, causing few serious side effects. It may, however, cause vomiting, diarrhea, restlessness, disorientation, and anorexia. Because of the risk of serious drug interactions, it should not be administered concurrently with antidepressants (TCAs and SSRIs), narcotics, or other MAO inhibitors, including amitraz. Owners should also be made aware of a nonmedical "side effect" of selegiline: its high cost. Although generic forms are available, they are not approved for use in animals. Anipryl is licensed for the treatment of canine cognitive dysfunction.

Progestins

Synthetic progestins used to treat behavioral disorders in companion animals include medroxyprogesterone acetate (Depo-Provera) and megesterol acetate (Ovaban, Megace). Progestins have nonspecific calming effects and suppress male-related or sexually dimorphic behaviors. They are metabolized in the liver, and conjugates are excreted in the urine. Their serious side effects have made them last-resort treatments. These include increased appetite, lethargy, hyperglycemia, diabetes mellitus, mammary gland hyperplasia and adenocarcinoma, pyometra/stump pyometra, and adrenocortical suppression. These drugs have been used to treat aggression, urine marking, and excessive grooming.

Azapirones

Currently, the only drug in this unique class of anxiolytics used in small animal behavioral medicine is buspirone (BuSpar). A serotonin agonist, buspirone acts by blocking both pre- and postsynaptic serotonin type 1 receptors. Buspirone is not sedating and, unlike the benzodiazepines, does not cause muscle relaxation or ataxia. Buspirone is metabolized in the liver and excreted in the urine and feces. The side effects of buspirone can include mild disorientation, gastrointestinal upset, and alterations in social behavior. Buspirone may also disinhibit aggression, especially between cats. This is one of the more expensive drugs used in behavioral medicine. Buspirone has been used to treat thunderstorm and other noise phobias, feline urine marking, generalized anxiety, and fearfulness.

Selective Serotonin-Reuptake Inhibitors

The selective serotonin-reuptake inhibitors (SSRIs), most notably fluoxetine HCl (Prozac) and paroxetine HCl (Paxil), have recently garnered much attention in the popular press for the treatment of pets with behavioral problems. As the name suggests, this class of drugs acts to enhance the action of serotonin in the brain by preventing its reuptake by presynaptic neurons. SSRIs produce less sedation than do TCAs, which are also serotonergic. SSRIs are metabolized in the liver with inactive metabolites excreted in the urine. SSRIs can have a long latency period before achieving theraputic effects (3 to 4 weeks in humans) and have a long half-life of their active metabolites (especially fluoxetine). This results in a lag time between the end of therapy and the end of effects. Most of the drugs in this category are expensive. Side effects of SSRIs include anorexia, nausea, diarrhea, anxiety, restlessness/insomnia, and agitation. SSRIs have been used to treat stereotypies, separation anxiety, panic disorders, aggression, and both canine and feline urine marking.

Beta-Blockers

Beta-blockers, as the name suggests, block the effects of norephinepherine on beta-adrenergic receptors. Included in this class of drugs are nonselective beta-1 and beta-2 antagonists, such as propranolol HCl (Inderal), and selective beta antagonists, such as atenolol (Tenormin), a beta-1 antagonist. These drugs decrease the physiologic responses of anxiety: increased heart and respiratory rate and trembling. The beta-blockers are metabolized by the liver or are excreted unchanged by the kidneys. Beta-blockers are contraindicated in patients with asthma, COPD, diabetes, hyperthyroidism, or peripheral vascular disease. Because of the risk of drug interactions, they should not be used with barbiturates or MAO inhibitors. These drugs have been used to treat mild situational anxieties (e.g., specific noise phobias, fear of groomers, fear at dog shows).

Narcotic Agonists/Antagonists

This class of drugs includes the pure opioid antagonists naloxone and naltrexone HCl (ReVia), the mixed agonists/antagonists nalorphine and pentazocine, and the narcotic analgesic hydrocodone bitartrate. The pure antagonists appear to block delta-, mu-, and kappa-receptors equally. Metabolism is in the liver, with renal excretion of metabolites. The most commonly seen side effect of these drugs in humans, constipation, may also be seen in small animals. Other side effects of the mixed agonists/antagonists include sedation, dizziness, or nausea. These drugs have been used to treat stereotypies, including canine lick granulomas, feline self-mutilation, tail chasing, and circling. Hydrocodone has been used to treat lick granulomas.

Anticonvulsants

The barbiturate phenobarbital is the most widely used anticonvulsant in veterinary medicine. Barbiturates are relatively nonspecific depressants that enhance the actions of GABA-mediated inhibitory synapses. Phenobarbital is partially metabolized by inducible hepatic enzymes and excreted both changed and unchanged in the urine. Side effects of barbiturates include sedation, paradoxical excitement, and hepatotoxicity. Anticonvulsants have few uses in treating conditions that are strictly behavioral and do not have a seizure component. They may be useful, however, when sedation alone is needed (car travel).

Alpha Adrenergic Agonists

The alpha agonist phenylpropanolamine HCl (Dexatrim) increases smooth muscle tone through stimulation of alpha adrenergic receptors. This action may result in side effects of restlessness, hypertension, and irritability. Phenylpropanolamine has been used to control excitable or submissive urination.

CANINE BEHAVIOR PROBLEMS

Aggression

Before advising the use of drug therapy for any type of canine aggression, safety and liability issues must be thoroughly discussed with owners (see chapter 12). Owners should be reminded that no "antiaggression" drug exists: If there were such a drug, there would be more people on medication and fewer in prison!

Dominance aggression. Once the diagnosis of dominance-related aggression has been made, drug therapy may be prescribed as an adjunct to a behavior modification program. Progestins, megesterol acetate (Ovaban, Megace), or medroxyprogesterone (DepoProvera) have been used to treat dominance aggression directed toward both people and other dogs[2,3]. B.L. Hart[4] recommended using the phenothiazine chlorpromazine to reduce aggression unrelated to fear. In an incomplete crossover study, N.H. Dodman et al.[5] found that the SSRI fluoxetine (Prozac) was effective in reducing owner-related dominance aggression in eight of nine dogs. The other SSRIs (paroxetine [Paxil] and the serotonergic TCA clomipramine [Anafranil]) may have similar effects. These drugs may also be useful to treat dominance aggression between dogs.

Possessive aggression. Possessive aggression is best treated through behavior modification. The medications recommended for the treatment of dominance-related aggression may also be helpful.

Fear-induced aggression. Drug therapy may be used to help supplement a behavior modification program for fear-induced aggression. However, keep in mind that some dogs may become more aggressive as reducing fear or anxiety also reduces inhibitions. This may be especially true if treating with anxiolytic drugs such as benzodiazepines or buspirone. Tricyclic antidepressants and beta-blockers have also been used.

Territorial or protective aggression. Fear-induced and territorial aggression often occur simultaneously, so the use of drug therapy in the treatment of territorial aggression may be risky. Reducing the inhibitory fear component may cause a more complete expression of the offensive territorial component. For this reason, anxiolytics (benzodiazepines and buspirone) should be used cautiously. Tricyclic antidepressants have also been used in the treatment of territorial aggression.

Pain-induced aggression. Dogs that are aggressive because of pain may require treatment with analgesics, as prescribed by a veterinarian. In cases of arthritic pain, chondroprotective agents may also be useful.

Maternal aggression. Drug therapy is not indicated.

Play-related aggression. As most cases of play-related aggression respond to behavioral therapy alone, drug therapy is usually not indicated. However, if owners are unable to implement training (usually due to owner-related factors—age, infirmity, etc.), TCAs or mildly sedating drugs, acepromazine or antihistamines, can be tried.

Idiopathic aggression. Given the severe and unpredictable nature of idiopathic aggression and the variable response to therapy, drug therapy should not be relied on. The same medications recommended for use in treating dominance aggression may be used but with utmost caution. In cases with an identified seizure component, anticonvulsants are indicated.

Predatory aggression. The only types of drug therapy that may be beneficial to control predatory aggression are those that cause sedation (e.g., phenothiazines, barbiturates). If effective, the dog may be medicated at times when prey *are* likely to be encountered.

Fears and Phobias

Defensive aggression, destruction, excessive vocalization, housesoiling, escape, and stereotypic behaviors may all be associated with fears. As described in chapter 11, medication is used to decrease the dog's reaction to the fear-eliciting stimulus. It may be considered in the following situations:

- As a management tool to prevent specific fear-motivated behaviors (housesoiling or destructiveness) that are not tolerated by owners
- To aid the implementation of a counterconditioning and desensitization program by preventing a fearful response to a stimulus that cannot be avoided (e.g., thunderstorm)
- When the desensitization plan gets "stuck" or if incremental exposures are not possible
- When the behavioral starting point cannot be found because the dog's fear is so intense, generalized, or both

Noise phobias. Dogs with noise phobias (thunderstorms, fireworks, traffic, hot-air balloons) may tremble, pant, exhibit destructive behaviors, vocalize excessively, housesoil, and attempt escape. The anxiolytics benzodiazepines and buspirone, phenothiazines, and beta-blockers have all been used to reduce these behaviors. In a study comparing the behavioral effects of diazepam and chlorpromazine, Hart[4] concluded that diazepam was the better choice to add to behavioral therapy for fears. E.A. Shull-Selcer[6] compared the effectiveness of alprazolam, chlorazepate, acepromazine, diazepam, and propranolol for the treatment of thunderstorm phobia. Although she treated only a small number of dogs with each drug, she found the benzodiazepines and acepromazine to be most helpful. Propranolol was not effective. Drugs that have a short latency period (alprazolam) may be administered on an as needed basis, even after a noise has started (e.g., a storm) Those that have longer effects (acepromazine, chlorazepate) are more useful when the owners cannot be with an animal at the initiation of the stimulus. These drugs can given in advance and may be effective while owners are not present.

Other fears. Behavioral therapy for specific fears, such as fear of people or new places, and generalized anxiety may be most effective when combined with the administration of an anxiolytic. Buspirone may be the first choice because it is does not cause physiological dependence. Its cost, however, may make it prohibitive for larger dogs. The benzodiazepines are effective antianxiety agents, but they may impede the learning necessary for behavior modification. The antianxiety effects of the TCAs also make them possibilities for use in a treatment plan. The treatment of fearful behavior that involves aggression is discussed in the section on defensive aggression.

Stereotypies. Stereotypies (obsessive-compulsive disorders, or OCDs), as discussed in chapter 11, are repetitive nonfunctional behaviors that often arise out of anxiety. Common examples are self-mutilation (excessive licking or chewing), tail chasing, spinning, and shadow or light chasing. Narcotic agonists and antagonists, tricyclic antidepressants, and SSRI s have been used to treat these conditions. Dodman et al.[7] reported that the narcotic antagonists naltrexone and nalmefene significantly reduced or eliminated time spent self-licking, self-chewing, or scratching in 7 out of 11 dogs treated. S.D. White[8] found that daily administration of oral naltrexone stopped licking and resulted in reepithelialization in 7 out of 11 dogs treated for acral lick granulomas. E. Goldberger and J. L. Rapoport[9] reported reduced licking after treatment with clomipramine, but not with desipramine, in 6 of 9 dogs. Rapoport[10] also found that clomipramine but not desipramine reduced licking behavior by 50 percent in 6 of 13 patients with lick granulomas. When comparing the effect of clomipramine to fluoxetine and other serotonergic agents, they found fluoxetine to be more effective than placebo (and desipramine, fenfluramine, or sertraline) at reducing licking behavior in 14 dogs. Two dogs on fluoxetine showed complete remission of signs. N. Shouldberg[11] reported reduction or cessation of self-damaging behaviors in 3 out of 5 dogs treated with fluoxetine. The narcotic, antitussive hydrocodone is thought to be especially useful for long-term treatment of lick granulomas[12]. In a study of 18 tail-chasing terriers (16 were bull terriers), A. Moon-Fanelli and N.H. Dodman[13] reported that clomipramine along with behavioral therapy and diet change reduced the behavior by 75 percent in 9 dogs after 1 to 12 weeks of treatment. K.L. Overall[14] also reported clomipramine to be helpful to treat ritualistic motor behaviors (e.g., tail chasing) in 3 dogs. C.J. Hewson and A. Luescher[15] reported that clomipramine was more effective than a placebo in reducing licking and spinning in 45 dogs. Treatment for 4 weeks, however, was not curative.

Destruction

Separation anxiety. As mentioned in chapters 7, 8, 9, and 10, medication may be an aid in behavior modification programs for separation anxiety. The drug chosen should lower the dog's anxiety without causing excessive sedation or interfering with learning.

For cases of mild or occasional separation anxiety (e.g., when owners take a trip), antihistamines may be helpful. Their side effect of urine retention may be especially helpful for dogs who urinate as a result of anxiety. For more severe cases of occasional separation anxiety, the benzodiazepines or the phenothiazines are more effective.

When the signs of separation anxiety are frequent or daily, drugs that maintain therapeutic blood levels are indicated. These include TCAs (amitriptyline[3], clomipramine[16]), SSRIs (fluoxetine, paroxetine), and buspirone. Urine retention and constipation may be useful side effects of the TCAs in dogs that eliminate due to anxiety. The benzodiazepines have also been used either alone or in combination, but they may impede learning. The more sedating phenothiazine tranquilizers may be indicated in cases in which the dog is endangering itself through escape attempts or severe destruction.

Hyperkinesis. Truly hyperkinetic animals are rare. In positively diagnosed cases (see chapter 8), treatment with stimulants (dextroamphetamine [Dexedrine], methylphenidate [Ritalin]) can cause paradoxical calming. S.A. Corson et al. reported that in a group of hyperkinetic/hyperactive dogs treated with amphetamines or methylphenidate, 50 percent of the dogs responded to treatment[17]. As mentioned in chapter 8, clomipramine (Anafranil) and buspirone (Buspar) may also be useful, although in our opinion, they may be of more benefit in cases of excessive activity related to anxiety.

Other causes of destructive behavior. Drug therapy is not indicated to treat destructive behavior caused by play, investigation, teething, social isolation, or comfort seeking. The use of drugs for destructive behavior due to fears and phobias and territorial aggression is discussed in the appropriate sections.

Inappropriate Elimination and Urine Marking

Housetraining. No drug therapy is indicated for puppies or adult dogs that are not yet housetrained. Geriatric, previously housetrained dogs that begin to urinate, defecate, or both in the house should be evaluated for canine cognitive dysfunction. This syndrome, characterized by Confusion/disorientation, Responsiveness/recognition decreases, Activity pattern changes, Sleep-wake cycle disturbances, and Housebreaking lapses (**CRASH**)[18], is treated with the MAO-B inhibitor selegiline (Anipryl)[19].

Urine marking. Canine urine marking, a male-related behavior, may respond to synthetic progestins[20]. SSRIs have also been used. → Selective Serotonin-Reuptake Inhibitors.

Submissive urination. Another commonly seen cause of inappropriate elimination in dogs is excitement or submissiveness. The alpha-agonist phenylpropanolamine has been used to control this behavior. The TCA imipramine has also been found to be useful[21]. Other TCAs that cause urine retention may also be tried.

Other causes of elimination behavior. Elimination problems due to separation anxiety, fears, and phobias are discussed in the appropriate sections.

Barking

Separation anxiety. In addition to the previous treatment recommendations (see section on destruction), treatment with amitriptyline alone[22] has been effective for dogs whose only sign of separation anxiety is barking.

Other causes of barking behavior. Barking and other vocalizations caused by excitement, greeting, play, attention seeking, frustration, or group-motivated behaviors are best treated by behavioral therapy alone. Barking due to aggression, fear, anxiety, or pain is discussed in the appropriate sections.

FELINE BEHAVIOR PROBLEMS

Inappropriate Elimination

Drug therapy is not necessary to treat routine cases of feline elimination! (See chapter 13.) One study[23] reported that 70 percent of 60 cats with inappropriate elimination problems were either cured or much improved on long-term follow up 12 to 54 months after treatment. None of the cats required drug therapy, and most responded between 1 and 3 weeks after the initiation of a behavior modification program. (The addition of a litterbox and keeping it clean are far less risky and costly than drug therapy.)

In some rare cases, however, drug therapy may be helpful. A diagnosis and determination of causative factors are essential in order to determine which drug should be used. Antianxiety medication (alprazolam or buspirone) may be indicated in cases caused by fears or separation anxiety. If intercat aggression is a contributing cause, drug therapy may be helpful to resolve the aggression problem. (See section on intercat aggression.)

Urine Marking and Spraying

As opposed to feline inappropriate elimination problems, drug therapy is often necessary to control feline marking and spraying. As described in chapter 13, a program of environmental manipulation and behavior modification should always be tried first. If it is ineffective or only partially effective, drug therapy is used to decrease the cat's response to the initiating stimuli. The drugs that have been used to control marking and spraying include (not in order of preference):

- Synthetic progestins: medroxyprogesterone acetate (DepoProvera) and megestrol acetate (Ovaban)
- Anxiolytics: benzodiazepines (diazepam, alprazolam), buspirone (BusPar)
- Antidepressants:
    —Tricyclics: amitriptyline (Elavil), clomipramine (Anafranil)
    —Selective serotonin reuptake inhibitors: fluoxetine HCl (Prozac) and Peroxetine HCl (Paxcil)
- Antihistamines: chlorpheniramine (Chlor-Trimeton)

Unfortunately, data exist only for a few of the preceding drugs. For others, recommendations are based on anecdotal reports. Hart[24] reported an overall effectiveness of 30 percent in 43 cats treated with either medroxyprogesterone acetate or megestrol acetate for either urine spraying or urine marking. A.R. Marder[21] reported that 74 percent of 23 spraying cats treated with diazepam exhibited a 75 percent or more reduction in spraying. L. Cooper and Hart[25] found that only 55 percent of 20 cats experienced a 75 percent or greater reduction in spraying after treatment with diazepam. Between 75 percent and 95 percent of the cats resumed spraying after the drug was discontinued. Hart and others[26], evaluating the effectiveness of buspirone, reported a 75 percent or greater reduction in spraying in 55 percent of 62 cats; 53 percent of cats resumed spraying after the drug was discontinued. Marder[27] reported that urine marking or spraying was reduced by 80 percent or more in 68 percent of cats treated with clomipramine.

We prefer to begin drug therapy with clomipramine or buspirone. In multicat households, because of the possibility of intercat aggression with buspirone, we prefer clomipramine. It also has the advantages of once-a-day administration and low cost. If the effect is insufficient, fluoxetine or peroxetine is tried. In cases where obvious but infrequent specific stimuli are causing spraying, alprazolam may be used.

Fears and Anxieties

As covered in chapter 16, fears and anxieties often lead to behaviors that become problems for owners. Defensive aggression, urine marking, inappropriate elimination, and stereotypic behaviors are often associated with fear and anxiety.

The anxiolytics (benzodiazepines, buspirone) are often used to reduce fears. Short-term anxiolytics may be helpful after a move or on introduction of a new person or animal into a household. Precautions should be taken in aggressive or potentially aggressive animals, as reduction of the fear may increase the probability of aggression. Severe, generalized fears may respond to treatment either with an anxiolytic or tricyclic antidepressant. The benzodiazepines (diazepam, alprazolam), buspirone, antihistamines (chlorpheniramine), tricyclic antidepressants (amitriptyline, clomipramine), and SSRIs (fluoxetine, peroxetine) have also been used to treat urine-marking and inappropriate elimination problems elicited by anxiety. (e.g., separation anxiety). The TCAs and SSRIs have also been effectively used to treat excessive vocalization.

Stereotypic (compulsive) behaviors may arise out of anxiety or arousal. Tail chasing, excessive grooming, and wool chewing are common examples. Pharmacologic therapy is often required to reduce the frequency of these behaviors. The tricyclic antidepressants, SSRIs, and narcotic antagonists (naloxone, naltrexone) may be helpful in treatment. L.S. Sawyer and others[28] reported that clomipramine and amitriptyline were effective in reducing excessive grooming in a retrospective study of 11 cats with psychogenic alopecia.

Feline Aggression

Drug therapy is often helpful in the treatment of feline aggression. However, because different classes of drugs are more effective for some types of aggression than for others, a behavioral diagnosis is essential before drug therapy is initiated. Some commonly used drugs may disinhibit aggressive tendencies and consequently should be used with caution.

Intermale aggression. This may be reduced by treatment with synthetic progestins. Some of the psychotropic drugs that cause generalized sedation (tricyclic antidepressants, phenothiazines) may also be considered.

Fear-induced or defensive aggression. This type of aggression is often treated with a combination of counterconditioning and desensitization and drug therapy. As mentioned in chapter 15, pharmacologic intervention is indicated if it is difficult to find a starting point for the CCSD program or if the program gets "stuck." The anxiolytics, the benzodiazepines, and buspirone may be very effective in reducing fears. They may be especially effective for fear of people, as both drugs may cause cats to become "friendlier." They may, however, disinhibit aggression. The tricyclic antidepressants amitriptyline and clomipramine may also be useful. Mild cases may be helped with antihistamines (chlorpheniramine).

Territorial aggression. As discussed in chapter 15, territorial aggression, whether the target is another cat or a person, rarely responds to either behavior modification or drug therapy. Other family cats who are targets often exhibit fearful behavior that elicits further attacks by the aggressor, so drug therapy to reduce the victim's fear may be warranted. Any of the drugs mentioned in the section on fear-induced aggression may be helpful.

Redirected aggression. In cases of redirected aggression between cats, one cat usually exhibits offensive redirected aggression resulting in fear-induced or defensive aggression in the cat that was attacked. Although the initial aggressor may only be aggressive for a short period of time, a persisting fear response in the attacked cat often causes repeated incidents of aggression. One of the antianxiety drugs used for the treatment of fear-induced aggression may shorten the length of treatment by separation and CCSD. The incidence of redirected attacks in cats who repeatedly redirect onto feline housemates or people may be reduced by treatment with tricyclic antidepressants or SSRIs.

Play-motivated aggression. Drug therapy is not indicated in most cases involving aggressive play, as behavior modification or the addition of a playmate is usually effective alone. In rare cases in which an owner is unusually susceptible to infection if bitten, drug therapy that mildly sedates the cat may be tried (antihistamines or tricyclic antidepressants).

"Don't pet me anymore" syndrome. It is uncertain whether drug therapy may be helpful in cats who don't tolerate petting. In most cases, educating the owners to reduce petting time is effective. When owners are at high medical risk or if they resist behavior modification, psychotropic drugs, including the anxiolytics or TCAs, may be indicated.

Pain and maternal aggression. Cases of pain-elicited and maternal aggression are best handled through avoidance. Of course, analgesics or other pain killers should be administered for pain. Psychotropic drugs are not indicated.

Idiopathic aggression. Because of the severe and dangerous nature of most cases of idiopathic aggression, drug therapy should not be depended on. If attempted, major precautions should be taken to avoid injury (protective clothing and restraint devices).

SUMMARY

Recommended drug dosages can be found in Table 18.1. (The dosages in Table 18.1 are drawn from personal experience and other sources.) As this and other chapters have pointed out, before psychotropic medication is even considered in behavior cases, a thorough medical workup should be done and a behavioral diagnosis should be obtained. Based on these findings, a treatment program should be developed. Although medication is a useful adjunct to behavior modification programs, drugs should not be viewed as a shortcut or quick fix. Medication alone is rarely effective as the sole intervention for behavior problems. Yet in spite of its limitations, behavioral pharmacotherapy expands our treatment arsenal and may increase the effectiveness of some behavioral treatment programs.

Table 18.1 Sample drug dosages

Drug	Dogs	Cats
Acepromazine	0.55–2.2 mg/kg PO 0.055–0.11 mg/kg IM,SQ,IV IM,SQ, IV	1.1–2.2 mg/kg PO 0.11–0.22 mg/kg IM,SQ, IV
Alprazolam	0.125–1.0 mg/kg PO q 12h Do not exceed 4 mg/day	0.125–0.25mg/cat PO q 12 h
Amitriptyline HCl	1–4 mg/kg PO div bid or q 24h	2.5–10 mg/cat PO q 24h
Atenolol	0.25–1.0 mg/kg PO q 12–24h to 20–100 mg/dog PO q 8h	6.25–12.5 mg/cat PO q 24h
Buspirone	2.5–15 mg/dog PO q 8–12h	2.5–7.5 mg/cat PO q 12h
Chlorpheniramine maleate	2.0–8.0 mg/kg PO q 8–12h	1–2 mg/cat PO q 8–12h
Clomipramine HC	0.5–4 mg/kg PO div q 12h or q x24h	2.5–5.0 mg/cat PO q 24h
Clonazepam	0.55–2.2 mg/kg PO q 4h	1.5 mg/kg PO q 8h
Clorazepate dipotassium	5.6–22.5 mg/dog PO q 12–24h	1.875–3.75 mg/cat PO q 12–24h
Dextroamphetamine	0.2–1.3 mg/kg PO prn	No published dose
Diazepam	0.55–2.2 mg/kg PO q 6–24h	0.2–0.4 mg/kg PO q 12–24h
Diphenhydramine HCl	2–4 mg/kg PO q 8h	2–4 mg/kg PO q 8h
Doxepin	3–5 mg/kg PO q 8–12h	0.5–1.0 mg/kg PO q 12–24h
Fluoxetine HCl	Up to 1.0 mg/kg PO q 24h	0.5–1.0 mg/kg q 24h
Hydrocodone bitartrate	0.25–1.0 mg/kg PO q 8–12h	1.25–5.0 mg/cat PO q 12–24h
Imipramine HCl	1–4 mg/kg PO div bid or q 24h	0.5–1.0 mg/kg PO q 12–24h
Medroxyprogesterone acetate	5–10 mg/kg SQ, IM	10–20 mg/kg SQ, IM
Megestrol acetate	2.2–5 mg/kg PO q 24h x 14d then taper	2.5–5 mg/cat PO q 24h x 7d, then taper
Methylphenidate HCl	2–4 mg/kg PO q 12–24h	No published dose
Naltrexone HCl	1.0–2.2 mg/kg PO q 8–12h	25–50 mg/cat PO q 24h
Oxazepam	0.2–1.0 mg/kg PO q 12–24h	0.2–0.5 mg/kg PO q 12–24h
Paroxetine HCl	Up to 1.0 mg/kg PO q 24h	0.5–1.0 mg/kg PO q 24h
Phenobarbital	2–6 mg/kg PO q 8–12h	1–2 mg/kg PO prn
Phenylpropanolamine HCl	12.5–50 mg/dog PO q 8–12h	No published dose
Propranolol HCl	1 mg/kg or 5–20 mg/dog PO q 8h	0.25 mg/kg PO prn
Selegiline HCl	0.5–1.0 mg/kg PO q 24h	No published dose

Note: Dosages are drawn from personal experience and other references[29, 30, 31, 32, 33, 34]

bid	twice a day	IM	intramuscular	prn	by mouth	
d	day	IV	intravenous	PO	as needed	
div	divided	kg	kilogram	q	every	
h	hour	mg	milligram	SQ	subcutaneous	

REFERENCES

1. Center, S.A., T.H. Elston, P.H. Rowland, D. Roscn, B.L. Reitz, I.E. Brunt, I. Rodan, J. House, S. Banks, L. Lynch, L. Dring, and J. Levy. 1996. Fulminant hepatic failure associated with oral administration of diazepam in 12 cats. *JAVMA* 209:618–25.

2. Hart, B.L. 1981. Progestin therapy for aggressive behavior in male dogs. *JAVMA* 179:1070–1.

3. Voith, V.L. 1984. Pharmacological approaches to treating behavioral problems. In *Nutrition and behavior in dogs and cats*, ed. R.S. Anderson, 227–34. Oxford, England: Pergamon.

4. Hart, B.L. 1985. Behavioral indications for phenothiazine and benzodiazepine tranquilizers in dogs. *JAVMA* 186:1192–4.

5. Dodman, N.H., R. Donnelly, L. Shuster, P. Mertens, W. Rand, and K. Miczek. 1996. Use of fluoxetine for the treatment of dominance-related aggression in dogs. *JAVMA* 209:1585–8.

6. Shull-Selcer, E.A. 1994. Analysis and treatment of noise phobias. Paper presented at annual American Veterinary Medical Association (AVMA) meeting, San Francisco, July.

7. Dodman, N.H., L. Shuster, S.D. White, M.H. Court, D. Parker, and R. Dixon. 1988. Use of narcotic antagonists to modify stereotypic self-licking, self-chewing, and scratching behavior in dogs. *JAVMA* 193:815–9.

8. White, S.D. 1990. Naltrexone for treatment of acral lick dermatitis in dogs. *JAVMA* 196:1073–6.

9. Goldberger, E., and J.L. Rapoport. 1991. Canine acral lick dermatitis: Response to the antiobsessional drug clomipramine. *J. Amer. Anim. Hosp. Assoc.* 27:179–2.

10. Rapoport, J.L. 1992. Animal models of obsessive compulsive disorder. *Clin. Neuropharm.* 15 (Suppl. 1):261A–71A.

11. Shouldberg, N. 1990. The efficacy of fluoxetine (Prozac) in the treatment of lick and inhalant allergic dermatitis in canines. *Proc. Amer. Acad. Vet. Derm. Amer. Coll. Vet. Derm.* pp. 31–2.

12. Luescher, A. 1998. Compulsive behavior in dogs. *Proc. Friskies Petcare Symposium*, May.

13. Moon-Fanelli, A., and N.H. Dodman. 1998. Description and development of compulsive tail chasing in terriers and response to clomipramine treatment. *JAVMA* 212:1252–6.

14. Overall, K.L. 1994. Use of clomipramine to treat ritualistic stereotyped motor behavior in three dogs. *JAVMA* 205:1733–41.

15. Hewson, C.J., and A. Luescher. 1998. Efficacy of clomipramine in the treatment of canine compulsive disorder. *JAVMA* 213:1760–6.

16. Simpson, B.S. 1997. Treatment of separation-related anxiety in dogs with clomipramine: Results from a multicentre, blinded, placebo controlled clinical study. In *Proceedings First International Conference on Veterinary Behavior Medicine*, pp. 143–54.

17. Corson, S.A., E.O. Corson, V. Kirilcuk, J. Kirilcuk, W. Knopp, and R.E. Arnold. 1972. Differential effects of amphetamines on clinically relevant dog models of hyperkineses and stereotypy: Relevance to Huntington's chorea. In *Advances in neurology*, vol. 1, ed. A. Barbear, 681–97. New York: Raven Press.

18. Patrick Melese, DVM. 1998. Personal communication.

19. Reuhl, W.W., and B.L. Hart. 1998. Canine cognitive dysfunction. In *Psychopharmacology of animal behavior disorders*, ed. J.H. Dodman and N. Shuster, 283–304. Boston: Blackwell Scientific.

20. Hart, B.L. 1979. Problems with objectionable sociosexual behavior of dogs and cats: Therapeutic use of castration and progestins. *Compend. Contin. Educ. Pract. Vet.* 1:461–5.

21. Marder, A.R. 1991. Psychotropic drugs and behavioral therapy. *Vet. Clinics of North Amer. [Small Anim. Pract.]* 21:329–42.

22. Voith, V., DVM. Personal communication.

23. Marder, A.R., and L. Friedman. 1998. Long-term follow-up after treatment of feline elimination problems. Paper presented at annual meeting American Veterinary Society of Animal Behavior, Baltimore, July.

24. Hart, B.L. 1980. Objectionable urine spraying and urine marking in cats: Evaluation of progestin treatment in gonadectomized males and females. *JAVMA* 177:529–33.

25. Cooper, L., and B.L. Hart. 1992. Comparison of diazepam with progestins for effectiveness in suppression of urine spraying behavior in cats. *JAVMA* 200:797–801.

26. Hart, B.L., R.A. Eckstein, K.L. Powell, and N.H. Dodman. 1993. Effectiveness of buspirone on urine spraying and inappropriate urination in cats. *JAVMA* 203:254–8.

27. Marder, A.R. 1997. Clomipramine for the treatment of urine spraying and marking in cats. Paper presented at the annual meeting American Veterinary Society of Animal Behavior, Reno, July.

28. Sawyer, L.S., A.A. Moon-Fanelli, and N.H. Dodman. 1999. Psychogenic alopecia in cats: 11 cases (1993–1996). *JAVMA* 214:71–4.

29. Dodman, N.H., and L. Shuster, eds. 1998. *Psychopharmacology of animal behavior disorders*. Boston: Blackwell Scientific.

30. Hart, B.L., and L.A. Hart. 1985. *Canine and feline behavioral therapy*. Philadelphia: Lea and Febiger.

31. Overall, K.L. 1997. *Clinical behavioral medicine for small animals*. St. Louis: Mosby.

32. Plumb, D.C. 1995. *Veterinary drug handbook*. 2nd edition. Ames: Iowa State University Press.

33. Simpson, B.S. 1996. Psychopharmacology for pets: Indications and side effects. Presented at American Veterinary Medical Association (AVMA) annual convention, Pittsburgh, July.

34. Voith, V.L., and P.L. Borchelt, eds. 1996. *Readings in companion animal behavior*. Trenton, N.J.: Veterinary Learning Systems.

APPENDIX

Product List

Educational Videotapes

Dogs, Cats, and Kids. Pet Love Partnership, LP, PO Box 11331, Chicago, IL 60611, phone: 800-784-0979.

Pet Loss and Bereavement. American Animal Hospital Association, Lakewood, CO, 80228, phone: 303-986-2800.

Head Halters

Gentle Leader, Premier Pet Products, Inc., 527 Branchway Road, Richmond, VA 23236, phone: 800-933-5595.

Snoot Loop, Peter Borchelt, Ph.D., Animal Behavior Consultants, Inc., 2465 Stuart Street, Brooklyn, NY 11229, phone: 800-339-9505.

Booby Traps and Remote Punishers

Critter Gitter, Amtek, Inc., 11025 Sorrento Valley Court, San Diego, CA 92121, phone: 800-762-7613. A motion detector that, when activated, has a pulsing red light and loud squealing sound.

Grannick's Bitter Apple, Doctors Foster & Smith, PO Box 100, Rhinelander, WI 54501, phone: 800-826-7206. Comes in cream, liquid spray, and a spray plant and leaf protector to discourage cats from chewing on leaves.

Pet Agree, K-II Enterprises, PO Box 306, Camillus, NY 13031, phone: 800-262-3963. A handheld device that emits a loud, ultrasonic noise when activated; it has a belt clip for convenience.

Safety-Sport Air Horn, L.P.I. Consumer Products, Inc., 2745 East Atlantic Blvd., #300, Pompano Beach, FL 33062, phone: 954-783-5858. Small enough to hold in hand and comes in two sizes, with either an 80- or a 200-blast capacity.

Scarecrow, The Dog's Outfitter, 1 Maplewood Drive, Hazleton, PA 18201, phone: 800-367-3647. A motion detector that attaches to a garden hose and turns on the hose when activated; it can be useful in discouraging stray cats or squirrels.

Scraminal, Amtek, Inc., 11025 Sorrento Valley Court, San Diego, CA 92121, phone: 800-762-7613. A motion detector that is similar to the Critter Gitter but does not have lights.

Scat Mat, Contech Electronics, PO Box 115, Saanichton, BC, Canada, V8M 2C3, phone: 800-767-8658. A vinyl mat that delivers a mild static shock when touched; it has three settings and comes in four shapes—small and large rectangles, window strips, and quarter circles that can be used to encircle a Christmas tree, for example.

Snappy Trainer, Interplanetary Pet Products, Inc., 12441 West 49th Avenue, Suite 8, Wheat Ridge, CO 80033, phone: 888-477-4738. A harmless, modified mouse trap that is attached to a plastic paddle; when activated, the paddle snaps into the air.

Sofa Scram, R.C. Steele Wholesale Pet Supplies, PO Box 910, Brockport, NY 14420, phone: 800-872-3773. Similar to the Scat Mat.

PetMat, Radio Systems Corporation, 5008 National Drive, Knoxville, TN 37914, phone: 800-675-8360. Similar to the Scat Mat.

Sticky Paws, Fe Lines, Inc., Rt. 1, Box 438, Burleson, TX 76028. Double-sided tape that discourages the use of a particular location.

Tattle Tale, K-II Enterprises, PO Box 306, Camillus, NY 13031, phone: 800-262-3963. A handheld device, similar to the Pet Agree, that makes an audible squeal when activated.

Direct Stop, Animal Behavior Systems, Inc., 5909-G Breckenridge Parkway, Tampa, FL 33610, phone: 800-627-9447. A spray can of citronella that can be used to interrupt behavior, including dog fights.

Antibark Products

ABS Anti-barking System, Animal Behavior Systems, Inc., 5909-G Breckenridge Parkway, Tampa, FL 33610, phone: 800-627-9447. Device that delivers a spray of citronella when the dog barks.

Barker Breaker and Super Barker Breaker, Amtek, Inc., 11025 Sorrento Valley Court, San Diego, CA 92121, phone: 800-762-7613. Handheld and remote devices, respectively, that emit a squeal when activated; sensitivity is adjustable in the remote device.

Bark Inhibitor, Innotek, Inc., 9025 Coldwater Road, Bldg. 100A, Fort Wayne, IN 46825, phone: 800-826-5527. Product delivers a shock when the dog barks; it has a variable intensity.

Bark Limiter, Tri-Tronics, Inc., PO Box 17660, Tucson, AZ 85731, phone: 800-456-4343. Product delivers a shock when the dog barks; it has a variable intensity.

Behave Bark Control Collar, Elixis Corporation, 7000 NW 46th Street, Miami, FL 33166, phone: 305-592-6069. Collar that emits an ultrasonic sound in response to barking.

Bark Control Collar, Radio Systems Corporation, 5008 National Drive, Knoxville, TN 37914, phone: 800-675-8360. Collar that delivers a shock when the dog barks; it has a variable intensity.

Spray Control Anti-Bark System, Radio Systems Corporation, 5008 National Drive, Knoxville, TN 37914, phone: 800-675-8360. Product delivers a spray of citronella when the dog barks.

Remote-Training Collars

Innotek, Inc., 9025 Coldwater Road, Bldg. 100A, Fort Wayne, IN 46825, phone: 800-826-5527. A remote-controlled shock collar that has a variable intensity.

Master Plus, Animal Behavior Systems, Inc., 5909-G Breckenridge Parkway, Tampa, FL 33610, phone: 800-627-9447. A remote-controlled citronella collar.

Tri-Tronics, Inc., PO Box 17660, Tucson, AZ 85731, phone: 800-456-4343. A remote-controlled shock collar that has a variable intensity.

Ultrasonic Trainer, Radio Systems Corporation, 5008 National Drive, Knoxville, TN 37914, phone: 800-675-8360. A remote-controlled device that uses a high-decibel ultrasonic sound.

Spray Control Trainer, Radio Systems Corporation, 5008 National Drive, Knoxville, TN 37914, phone: 800-675-8360. A remote-controlled citronella collar.

Pet Containment Systems

Home Free System, Innotek, Inc., 9025 Coldwater Road, Bldg. 100A, Fort Wayne, IN 46825, phone: 800-826-5527. System delivers a shock when the dog crosses the buried wire.

Invisible Fence Company, 355 Phoenixville Pike, Malvern, PA 19355, phone: 610-651-0986. System delivers a shock when the dog crosses the buried wire; it also can deliver a warning tone.

Room Free Indoor Containment System, Innotek, Inc., 9025 Coldwater Road, Bldg. 100A, Fort Wayne, IN 46825, phone: 800-826-5527. System delivers a shock when animal crosses a boundary established by two receiver disks.

Spray Barrier Indoor System, Animal Behavior Systems, Inc., 5909-G Breckenridge Parkway, Tampa, FL 33610, phone: 800-627-9447. System delivers a spray of citronella when an animal crosses the boundary established by two receiver disks.

Radio and Deluxe Radio Fence, Radio Systems Corporation, 5008 National Drive, Knoxville, TN 37914, phone: 800-675-8360. Systems deliver a shock when an animal crosses a buried boundary wire; they are designed for small and large yards, respectively.

Spray Control Radio Fence, Radio Systems Corporation, 5008 National Drive, Knoxville, TN 37914, phone: 800-675-8360. System delivers a spray of citronella when an animal crosses the buried boundary wire; it is designed for small yards.

Indoor and Outdoor Radio Fence, Radio Systems Corporation, 5008 National Drive, Knoxville, TN 37914, phone: 800-675-8360. System delivers a shock when the dog crosses a boundary; combines features of both indoor and outdoor systems.

Indoor Radio Fence, Radio Systems Corporation, 5008 National Drive, Knoxville, TN 37914, phone: 800-675-8360. System delivers a shock when the dog crosses an indoor boundary wire; it can be used with more than one pet simultaneously.

Virtual Fence, Animal Behavior Systems, Inc., 5909-G Breckenridge Parkway, Tampa, FL 33610, phone: 800-627-9447. An outdoor system that delivers a spray of citronella when an animal crosses the buried wire.

Cat Enclosures

Cat Fence-In, P.O. Box 795, Department 117, Sparks, NV 89432, phone: 702-359-4575. Kits to attach barricades of different designs to the top of a fence to prevent a cat from climbing out.

Kritter Keepers, Intermountain Enterprise, P.O. Box 311, Bailey, CO 80421, phone: 303-838-2632. Free-standing outdoor enclosures and model designs to adjoin the house over a window or pet door—can be customized.

Katz Purr-Fect Enclosures, P.O. Box 41, Department F.D., Crescent MLS., CA 95934. Plans for a variety of models of outdoor enclosures.

Cat Litterboxes

Litter Maid Self-Scooping Litter Box, Doctors Foster & Smith, PO Box 100, Rhinelander, WI 54501, phone: 800-826-7206. Distributed by Innovative Pet Products, Inc., 5980 Miami Lakes Drive, Miami Lakes, FL 33014.

Cat Nail Caps

Soft Paws, Smart Practice, 3400 East McDowell, Phoenix, AZ 85008, phone: 800-762-7879.

Pheromone Sprays

Feliway, distributed by The Butler Company, phone: 800-551-3861.

Muzzles

Plastic-coated wire muzzles (basket type), available from The Dog's Outfitter, 1 Maplewood Drive, Hazleton, PA 18201, phone: 800-367-3647.

Wire basket muzzles, available from Doctors Foster & Smith, P.O. Box 100, Rhinelander, WI 54501, phone: 800-826-7206.

Deodorizers

Anti-Icky-Poo, Mister Max, 13256 Idyl Drive, Lakeside, CA 92040, phone: 800-745-1671.

Nature's Miracle. Pets 'N People, Inc., 930 Indian Peak Road, Suite 215, Rolling Hills Estates, CA 90274. Product also available at most major pet stores.

Oxyfresh Pet Deodorizer, Oxyfresh USA, Inc., P.O. Box 3723, Spokane, WA 99220, phone: 509-924-4999.

Toys

Booda Velvets, R.C. Steele Wholesale Pet Supplies, PO Box 910, Brockport, NY 14420, phone: 800-872-3773. Chewbones made of compressed cornstarch.

Buster Cube, Doctors Foster & Smith, PO Box 100, Rhinelander, WI 54501, phone: 800-826-7206. Also available from Legacy by Mail, PO Box 697, Carlsburg, WA 98324, phone: 800-876-9364. A hollow plastic cube with loading hole from which food falls out as dog pushes and turns the cube.

Activity Ball, imported and distributed solely by Hightower Positive Dog Training, 1630 Micheltorena, Los Angeles, CA 90026, phone: 323-667-1112. A hollow ball that can hold several cups of dry food or tidbits; food is loaded through two holes and subsequently falls out as the dog rolls the ball.

Combones, available from The Dog's Outfitters, 1 Maplewood Drive, Hazleton, PA 18201, phone: 800-367-3647. A sterilized beef bone the marrow cavity of which is filled with beef-, cheese-, or liver-flavored rawhide pieces.

Da Bird Cat , Doctors Foster & Smith, PO Box 100, Rhinelander, WI 54501, phone: 800-826-7206. One of the many cat toys that dangle from a flexible rod; owners entice cats to chase the toy by waving the rod.

Fur Mice, R.C. Steele Wholesale Pet Supplies, PO Box 910, Brockport, NY 14420, phone: 800-872-3773.

Goodie Ship and Space Ball, Planet Pet, PO Box 11778, Naples, FL 34101, phone: 800-811-8673. Durable rubber shapes with cutouts in which soft food can be stuffed; dog must chew, lick, and manipulate toy to get the food out.

Indestructible Balls, The Dog's Outfitter, 1 Maplewood Drive, Hazleton, PA 18201, phone: 800-367-3647. Hard plastic balls come in three sizes; choose a size too large for dog to pick up and carry; dog pushes and paws ball attempting to pick it up, which holds his interest without requiring owner involvement in playing fetch.

Kong Toys, The Kong Company, 11111 D West 8th Avenue, Lakewood, CO 80215, phone: 303-233-9262. Similar to the Goodie Ship; resembles the shape of a hollow beehive; food and treats can be stuffed inside.

Nylabones, R.C. Steele Wholesale Pet Supplies, PO Box 910, Brockport, NY 14420, phone: 800-872-3773. Hard plastic chewbones that now come in flavors; to make more appealing, they can be rubbed with cheese or meat.

Roll-A-Treat Ball, Ethical Products, Spot Pet Division, Newark, NJ. Available from The Dog's Outfitter, 1 Maplewood Drive, Hazleton, PA 18201, phone: 800-367-3647. A round, hollow ball with a loading hole from which food treats intermittently fall out as the ball rolls.

Roll'Em Food Ball. Imported from Japan. Available from Legacy by Mail, PO Box 697, Carlsburg, WA 98324, phone: 800-876-9364. Similar to Roll-a-Treat; reported to be more durable.

Smoked/Plain Sterilized Bones, available from The Dog's Outfitters, 1 Maplewood Drive, Hazleton, PA 18201, phone: 800-367-3647. A beef bone processed in the United States and USDA inspected.

Additional Readings

CHAPTER 3

Domjan, M. 1993. *Domjan's and Burkhard's The principles of learning and behavior*. Pacific Grove, Calif.: Brooks/Cole Publishing.

———. 1996. *The essentials of conditioning and learning*. Pacific Grove, Calif.: Brooks/Cole Publishing.

Kalish, H.L. 1981. *From behavioral science to behavior modification*. New York: McGraw-Hill.

Kazdin, A.E. 1994. *Behavior modification in applied settings*. Pacific Grove, Calif.: Brooks/Cole Publishing.

Reid, P.J. 1996. *Excel-erated learning: Explaining in plain English how dogs learn and how best to teach them*. Oakland, Calif.: James and Kenneth Publishers.

CHAPTER 4

Dunbar, I. 1987. *Sirius puppy training*. Berkeley, Calif.: James and Kenneth Publishers.

Lane, M.S. 1998. *The Humane Society of the United States complete guide to dog care*. Boston: Little, Brown.

Rutherford, C., and D.H. Neil. 1992. *How to raise a puppy you can live with*. Second ed. Loveland, Colo.: Alpine Publishing.

CHAPTER 18

Dodman, N.H., and L. Shuster, eds. 1998. *Psychopharmacology of animal behavior disorders*. Boston: Blackwell Scientific.

Overall, K.L. 1997. Pharmacologic treatment for behavior problems. *Vet. Clinics of North Amer. [Small Anim. Pract.]* 21: 637–66.

ETHOLOGY AND PSYCHOLOGY

Alcock, J.A. 1989. *Animal behavior*. Fourth edition. Sunderland, Mass.: Sinaver Associates, Inc.

Drickamer, L.C., and S.H. Vessey. 1986. *Animal behavior*. Second edition. Boston: Prindle, Weber, and Schmidt Publishers.

Hinde, R.A. 1982. *Ethology: Its nature and relations to other sciences*. New York: Oxford University Press.

Stanevich, K.E. 1992. *How to think straight about psychology*. New York: Harper Collins Publishers.

GENERAL REFERENCES ON COMPANION ANIMAL BEHAVIOR

Fox, M.W. 1965. *Canine behavior*. Springfield, Ill.: Charles C. Thomas.

Fox, M.W. 1978. *The dog: Its domestication and behavior*. Malabar, Fla.: Krieger Publishing Co.

Houpt, K.A. 1998. *Domestic animal behavior for veterinarians and animal scientists*. Third edition. Ames, Iowa: Iowa State University Press.

Thorne, C., ed. 1992. *The Waltham book of cat and dog behavior*. New York: Pergamon Press.

ANIMAL BEHAVIOR PROBLEMS

Neville, P. 1991. *Do cats need shrinks?* Chicago: Contemporary Books, Inc.

O'Farrell, V. 1992. *Manual of canine behaviour*. Second edition. Gloucestershire: British Small Animal Veterinarian Association.

Wright, J.C. 1999. *The dog who would be king*. Emmaus, Pa.: Rodale Press.

Index

counterconditioning for, 100
destructive behaviors and, 107
educating owners about, 90-91
elimination problems and, 90
euthanasia and, 287, 288
as frustration behavior, 225
managing, 220
medical causes of, 89-90
medication for, 97, 219, 220, 307, 308
misinterpretations of, 206
protocol for, 89-101
summary form for, 222
territorial aggression and, 111, 250
treating, 225
See also Spraying

Vicious behavior
defined, 173, 176
play-motivated behavior and, 243
Vicious dogs
euthanasia and, 288
labeling, 173, 176-77
VNO. *See* Vomeronasal organ

Vocalizations, 134, 137, 233
anxiety, 141, 144, 149
attention-getting, 136, 141, 144, 149
care-seeking, 136, 141, 144, 149
defensive, 142, 144, 149-50
distress, 136, 141, 144, 149
excitement, 136, 140, 144, 148
fear-based, 136, 141, 144, 149, 155, 266
frustration, 136, 142, 144, 150
greeting, 140, 148
group-motivated, 136, 142, 144, 150
pain, 136, 141-42, 144, 149
playful, 140-41
protective, 139-40, 144, 147-48
separation anxiety and, 139
territorial, 139-40, 159
See also Barking
Vomeronasal organ (VNO), 206

Water pistols, 58, 199, 261
White, S.D., 306
Wild animals, defined, 271
Wrestling, 137, 194, 199
Wright, J.C., 245, 270